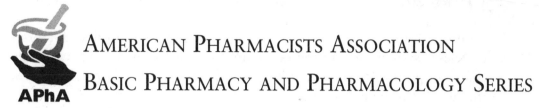
AMERICAN PHARMACISTS ASSOCIATION

BASIC PHARMACY AND PHARMACOLOGY SERIES

The Pharmacy Technician

WORKBOOK AND CERTIFICATION REVIEW

-FIFTH EDITION-

PERSPECTIVE PRESS
MORTON PUBLISHING COMPANY
www.morton-pub.com

Morton Publishing

Printed in the United States of America.

Morton Publishing Company
925 West Kenyon Avenue, Unit 12
Englewood, CO 80110
phone: 1-303-761-4805
fax: 1-303-762-9923
www.morton-pub.com

International Standard Book Number

ISBN 13: 978-1-61731-072-0

10 9 8 7 6 5 4 3 2 1

Cover design by Hannah Hogan; cover image by Elisanth_/iStockphoto®

NOTICE

To the best of the Publisher's knowledge, the information presented in this book follows general practice as well as federal and state regulations and guidelines. However, please note that you are responsible for following your employer's and your state's policies and guidelines.

The job description for pharmacy technicians varies by institution and state. Your employer and state can provide you with the most recent regulations, guidelines, and practices that apply to your work.

The Publisher of this book disclaims any responsibility whatsoever for any injuries, damages, or other conditions that result from your practice of the skills described in this book for any reason whatsoever.

THE PHARMACY TECHNICIAN

WORKBOOK AND

CERTIFICATION REVIEW

FIFTH EDITION

TABLE OF CONTENTS

1- PHARMACY & HEALTH CARE

Key Concepts	2
Fill in the Key Term	4
True/False	5
Explain Why	5
Choose the Best Answer	6

2- THE PHARMACY TECHNICIAN

Key Concepts	8
In the Workplace	10
Fill in the Key Term	15
True/False	16
Explain Why	16
Choose the Best Answer	17

3- DRUG REGULATION & CONTROL

Key Concepts	18
Controlled Substance Schedules	21
The "Orange Book"	22
Fill in the Key Term	23
True/False	24
Explain Why	24
Match the Term	25
Identify	26
Choose the Best Answer	27

4- TERMINOLOGY

Key Concepts	28
Organ System Roots	30
Common Prefixes	32
Common Suffixes	33
Common Medical Abbreviations	34
Fill in the Key Term	35
Choose the Best Answer	36

5- PRESCRIPTIONS

Key Concepts	38
Common Pharmacy Abbreviations	40
Fill in the Blank	41
The Prescription	42
Prescription Labels	43
Auxiliary Labels	43
Practice Prescriptions	44
Practice Medication Orders	50
Fill in the Key Term	54
True/False	55
Explain Why	55
Choose the Best Answer	56

6- CALCULATIONS

Ratio and Proportion	58
Conversions	59
Roman Numerals	60
Conversion Exercises	60
Problems	61
Pediatric Doses	62
Percents & Solutions	62
A Percent Solution Formula	62
Flow Rate	63
Milliequivalents—mEq	63
Problems	64
Total Parenteral Nutrition	66
Retail Math	67

TABLE OF CONTENTS

7- ROUTES & FORMULATIONS
Key Concepts   68
True/False   71
Explain Why   71
Fill in the Key Term   72
Identify   74
Choose the Best Answer   76

8- COMPOUNDING
Key Concepts   78
Using A Balance   81
Measuring   82
True/False   83
Explain Why   83
In the Workplace   84
Fill in the Key Term   88
Choose the Best Answer   90

9- PARENTERALS: COMPOUNDING STERILE FORMULATIONS
Key Concepts   92
Laminar Flow Hoods & Biological
    Safety Cabinets   94
Aseptic Techniques   95
True/False   95
Explain Why   95
In the Workplace   96
Fill in the Key Term   102
Choose the Best Answer   104

10- BASIC BIOPHARMACEUTICS
Key Concepts   106
Dose Response Curve   109
Blood Concentration—Time Profiles   109
Oral Absorption   110
Passive Diffusion   110
Protein Binding   110
Pharmacokinetics (Half-Life)   111
Fill in the Key Term   112
True/False   114
Explain Why   114
Choose the Best Answer   114

11- FACTORS AFFECTING DRUG ACTIVITY
Key Concepts   116
Fill in the Key Term   118
True/False   119

Explain Why   119
Choose the Best Answer   120

12- INFORMATION
Key Concepts   122
Fill in the Key Term   124
True/False   125
Explain Why   125
Choose the Best Answer   126

13- INVENTORY MANAGEMENT
Key Concepts   128
Fill in the Key Term   130
True/False   131
Explain Why   131
Choose the Best Answer   132

14- FINANCIAL ISSUES
Key Concepts   134
Fill in the Key Term   136
True/False   137
Explain Why   137
Choose the Best Answer   138

15- COMMUNITY PHARMACY
Key Concepts   140
In the Workplace   143
Fill in the Key Term   145
True/False   146
Explain Why   146
Choose the Best Answer   147

16- HOSPITAL PHARMACY
Key Concepts   148
Unit Dose Medications/Patient Trays   151
Medication Orders   152
Medication Administration Record   152
In the Workplace   153
Fill in the Key Term   157
True/False   158
Explain Why   158
Choose the Best Answer   159

17- OTHER ENVIRONMENTS
Key Concepts   160
True/False   161
Explain Why   162
Choose the Best Answer   162

18- COMMON DRUGS & THEIR USES

Classification of Drugs	164
Study Tip—Drug Cards	165
Key Concepts	166
Fill in the Blanks	172
Match the Brand and Generic Names	174
True/False	178
Explain Why	178
Choose the Best Answer	178

APPENDICES

A—Top 200 Brand Name Drugs	180
B—Top 200 Brand Name Drugs by Classification	186
C—Common Generic Drugs by Classification	192
D—Top 50 Canadian Drugs	196
E—Commonly Refrigerated Drugs	198
F—Labs	200

PRACTICE EXAMS

Pharmacy Technician Certification Exam (PTCE) Practice Exam	236
Exam for the Certification of Pharmacy Technicians (ExCPT) Practice Exam	246
Calculations Practice Exam	258

ANSWER KEYS	264

KEY CONCEPTS INDEX	274

PREFACE

THIS WORKBOOK

This workbook was developed to correspond with the textbook, *The Pharmacy Technician* by Perspective Press. For pharmacy technician students, it is a valuable tool for success in your training course. It provides a useful format for memorizing important information and for checking your knowledge of it. Key concepts and terms are carefully explained, and there are over 1000 exercises and problems to test your knowledge. Working out these exercises successfully will help you to succeed in your training.

It is important you follow through the workbook chapter by chapter and try answering the questions before looking up the answers. Once you have completed a chapter, review it and try to memorize the answers to the questions you missed.

New to the fifth edition is a section of 15 labs with hands-on exercises to enhance learning.

A REVIEW GUIDE

The workbook can also be used as a review guide in preparing for the national Pharmacy Technician Certification Examination (PTCE) given by the Pharmacy Technician Certification Board (PTCB) or the Exam for the Certification of Pharmacy Technicians (ExCPT) given by the National Healthcareer Association (NHA). All its chapters are important in the taking either certification exam. However, special attention should be placed on Chapter 6—Calculations, as the exam will have calculation type problem solving that is often challenging for technicians taking the exam. The method used (ratio and proportion) in this section will solve any calculation problem you come across on the certification exams as well as most problems in the pharmacy setting. A careful review of this workbook will prepare you for much of either certification exam. However, some questions on the exams require knowledge gained from practice as a technician. Pharmacy technicians who have work experience in a pharmacy setting will therefore have an advantage in taking a certification exam. As an additional study tool, we have included two practice exams at the back of this book, one in the format of the PTCE and one in the format of ExCPT.

OVERVIEW: PHARMACY TECHNICIAN CERTIFICATION EXAM (PTCE)

The national Pharmacy Technician Certification Examination was established to allow the certification of technicians. The need for highly qualified pharmacy technicians is increasingly important as pharmacists are relinquishing many dispensing duties for more clinical ones, and the technician is playing a greater role.

Currently the national examination is given by the Pharmacy Technician Certification Board (PTCB) and applications are accepted continuously throughout the year. Applications are submitted online and applicants must take the exam within 90 days of submitting their application. The cost of taking this examination is, at the time of this, writing $129.

THE PTCE EXAM

The PTCE contains 10 multiple choice pre-test questions and 80 multiple choice exam questions. The multiple choice format has four possible answers with only one answer being the best or most correct. The time limit for taking this examination is two hours: One hour and 50 minutes are for answering test questions and 10 minutes are for survey questions and a tutorial. Exams are given in a Computer-Based Testing (CBT) format and each candidate is presented with different items.

SCORING OF THE PTCE EXAM

The PTCB is planning to use a new exam starting in the latter half of 2013. The scoring of the examination will be based on the combined average of scores in nine Knowledge Domains:

1. Pharmacology for Technicians (13.75%)
2. Pharmacy Law and Regulations (12.5%)
3. Sterile and Non-Sterile Compounding (8.75%)
4. Medication Safety (12.5%)
5. Pharmacy Quality Assurance (7.5%)
6. Medication Order Entry and Fill Process (17.5%)
7. Pharmacy Inventory Management (8.75%)
8. Pharmacy Billing and Reimbursement (8.75%)
9. Pharmacy Information Systems Usage and Application (10%)

The combined score range of the exam is 300 to 900 points with 650 points required to pass.

WHAT YOU NEED TO KNOW FOR THE PTCE EXAM

Specific information on examination content is provided in the PTCB's **Guidebook to Certification,** which can be downloaded from their website: www.ptcb.org.

For additional information, contact the PTCB at:

Pharmacy Technician Certification Board
2215 Constitution Avenue, NW
Washington, DC 20037-2985
800-363-8012 (phone)
202-429-7596 (fax)
e-mail: contact@ptcb.org
www.ptcb.org

OVERVIEW: EXAM FOR THE CERTIFICATION OF PHARMACY TECHNICIANS (ExCPT)

The ExCPT is sponsored by the National Healthcareer Association. The mission of the ExCPT program is "to recognize pharmacy technicians who are proficient in the knowledge and skills needed to assist pharmacists to safely, accurately and efficiently prepare and dispense prescriptions and to promote high standards of practice for pharmacy technicians."

The exam is offered continuously, throughout the year at psi/LaserGrade testing centers. Candidates may register online at http://www.nhanow.com. The cost of taking this examination is, at the time of this writing, $125.

PREFACE

THE ExCPT EXAM

The ExCPT exam blueprint specifies that the exam contains 10 pre-test multiple choice pre-test questions and 100 scored multiple choice questions. The multiple choice format involves four possible answers with only one answer being the best or most correct. The time limit for taking this examination is two hours. Exams are given in a CBT format and each candidate is presented with different items.

SCORING OF THE ExCPT EXAM

ExCPT exam questions fall in three main areas:

1. Regulations and Technician Duties (~25% of exam)

2. Drugs and Drug Therapy (~23% of exam)

3. Dispensing Process (~52% of Exam)

Scoring for the ExCPT exam is established by the NHA ExCPT Expert Panel. The passing score is a scaled score of 390 out of 500.

WHAT YOU NEED TO KNOW FOR THE ExCPT EXAM

Specific information on examination content is provided in the ExCPT Candidate's Guide which is available from www.nhanow.com.

For additional information, contact the NHA at:

National Healthcareer Association
11161 Overbrook Road
Leawood KS 66211
800-499-9092 (phone)
913-661-6291 (fax)
e-mail: info@nhanow.com
http://www.nhanow.com

ACKNOWLEDGEMENTS

Mary F. Powers, Ph.D., R.Ph.

Mary Powers has been a key contributor on *The Pharmacy Technician*, on which this workbook is based, since the first edition. She was a key contributor to the first edition of *The Pharmacy Technician Workbook and Certification Review* and has been its sole author since the second edition. For the fifth edition of the workbook Mary collaborated with the publisher on a plan for the new edition, updated existing content to reflect changes made in the corresponding text, updated the PTCE and ExCPT Practice Exams to reflect changes in each test's "blueprint," provided the appendices of drug lists, and developed 15 new labs. A Professor of Pharmacy Practice at the University of Toledo College of Pharmacy and Pharmaceutical Sciences, Mary's input has always been enormously helpful, and we cannot thank her enough.

Others We'd Like To Thank

We would also like to acknowledge Joe Medina, CPhT, B.S. Pharmacy for his contribution to the first edition of the workbook by writing many of the exam review questions and other exercises. Joe has served as the Chairperson/Program Director for the Pharmacy Technician Programs at Front Range Community College and Arapahoe Community College.

In addition, this workbook would not have been possible without the efforts of a large number of people who worked on the corresponding text, *The Pharmacy Technician, Fifth Edition*. We would like to thank them again for their contributions: Robert P. Shrewsbury, Ph.D., R.Ph., Associate Professor of Pharmaceutics, University of North Carolina-Chapel Hill; Brenda Vonderau, B.Sc. (Pharm.), Director, Clinical Product Development, Catamaran; Cindy B. Johnson, R.Ph., L.C.S.W., RxMentor Pharmacist, Humana; Steve Johnson, B.S., R.Ph., Meditech Lead Analyst, Catholic Health Initiatives; Ruth Gilman-Duke, Pharm.D., Pharmacist, CVS Pharmacy; Pamela Nicoski-Lenaghan, Pharm.D., BCPS, Clinical Pharmacist, Loyola University Medical Center; and Britta Young, Pharm.D., Clinical Pharmacist, Ann & Robert H. Lurie Children's Hospital of Chicago.

We are also grateful to several reviewers whose insights and feedback on previous editions helped shape the fifth edition: James Austin, R.N., B.S.N., CPhT, Program Chair, Pharmacy Technology Program, Weatherford College; Ashley Bures, CVS; CVS Pharmacy; Marisa Fetzer, Institute of Technology; Claudia Johnson, M.S.N., R.N.C., A.P.N., Allied Health Instructor, Pharmacy Technician Program, Polytech Adult Education; Mary Anna Marshall, CPhT, Instructor for PTCB Examination Review, CVS/Pharmacy Regional Intern Coordinator, Pharmacy Technician Program, Hanover High School; Russell C. McGuire, Ph.D., Vice President of Allied Health Programs, Education Corporation of America; Tony David Ornelas, CPhT; Alexandria Zarrina Ostowari, Course Developer, Allied Business School; Becky Schonscheck, Director of Curriculum Development, Anthem Education Group; Jacqueline T. Smith R.N., CPhT, Department Chair-Pharmacy Technician, National College; Peter E. Vonderau, Sr., R.Ph., Pharmacy Manager, Scolari's Food & Drug, Inc.; Walgreen Co.; and Deborah Zenzal , R.N. M.S. CPC CCS-P RMA, Department Chair, Allied Health, Penn Foster Schools.

Finally, we would like to thank Ned Richardson for preparing the art; Hannah Hogan for designing and preparing the cover; Rayna Bailey, Dona Mendoza, Jes Hagerty, and Chrissy Morton of Morton Publishers for their help with the fifth edition; and Doug Morton, whose sponsorship makes this book possible.

Perspective Press

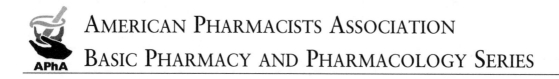

AMERICAN PHARMACISTS ASSOCIATION
BASIC PHARMACY AND PHARMACOLOGY SERIES

Dear Student or Instructor,

The American Pharmacists Association (APhA), the national professional society of pharmacists in the United States, and Morton Publishing Company, a publisher of educational texts and training materials in health care, are pleased to present this outstanding workbook, *The Pharmacy Technician Workbook and Certification Review, Fifth Edition*. It is one of a series of distinctive texts and training materials for basic pharmacy and pharmacology training that is published under this banner: *American Pharmacists Association Basic Pharmacy and Pharmacology Series*.

Each book in the series is oriented toward developing an understanding of fundamental concepts. In addition, each text presents applied and practical information on the skills necessary to function effectively in positions such as technicians and medical assistants who work with medications and whose role in health care is increasingly important. Each of the books in the series uses a visual design to enhance understanding and ease of use. We think you will find them valuable training tools.

The American Pharmacists Association and Morton Publishing thank you for using this book and invite you to look at other titles in this series, which are listed below.

Thomas E. Menighan, BSPharm, MBA
Executive Vice President
Chief Executive Officer
American Pharmacists Association

Douglas N. Morton
President
Morton Publishing Company

TITLES IN THIS SERIES:

The Pharmacy Technician, Fifth Edition
The Pharmacy Technician Workbook and Certification Review, Fifth Edition
Medication Workbook for Pharmacy Technicians: A Pharmacology Primer

The Pharmacy Technician

Workbook and Certification Review

– 1 –

PHARMACY & HEALTH CARE

KEY CONCEPTS

Test your knowledge by covering the information in the right-hand column.

pharmacology	The study of drugs, their properties, uses, application, and effects.
herbal medicine	People have used drugs derived from plants to treat illnesses and other physical conditions for thousands of years. The ancient Greeks used the bark of a white willow tree to relieve pain. The bark contained salicylic acid, the natural forerunner of the active ingredient in aspirin.
quinine	The first useful drug in the treatment of malaria, one of mankind's most deadly diseases. It was extracted from the bark of a Peruvian tree, the Cinchona.
cocaine	The first effective local anesthetic.
digitalis	The drug of the foxglove plant, which has been widely used in treating heart disease.
synthetic drugs	Drugs created by reformulating simpler chemicals into more complex ones, creating a new chemical not found in nature.
average life span	This measure of health has increased by almost 40 years in between 1900 and 2012.
germ theory	The theory that microorganisms cause food spoilage.
polio vaccine	The use of an injectable vaccine made from killed polio virus and an oral polio vaccine made from a weakened form of live polio virus was important to prevent the spread of this crippling and often fatal disease.

insulin	The hormone that lowers blood sugar in the treatment of diabetes—one of the great discoveries in medicine in the twentieth century.
penicillin	The first antibiotic.
Human Genome Project	An attempt to map the entire DNA sequence in the human genome. This information will provide a better understanding of hereditary diseases and how to treat them.
pharmacist education and training	To become a pharmacist in the United States, an individual must have earned a Doctor of Pharmacy degree from an accredited college of pharmacy (of which there are about 115 in the United States), pass a state licensing exam (in some states), and perform experiential training under a licensed pharmacist. Once licensed, the pharmacist must receive continuing education to maintain their license.
cost control	A significant trend in recent health care has been the effort to control the cost of prescription drugs, one aspect of which is the use of closed "formularies" that rely substantially on substituting generic drugs in place of more expensive brands.
computerization	Pharmacy computer systems put customer profiles, product, inventory, pricing, and other essential information within easy access. One result has been that pharmacies and pharmacists dispense more prescriptions and information than ever before.

STUDY NOTES

Use this area to write important points you'd like to remember.

FILL IN THE KEY TERM

Use these key terms to fill in the correct blank. Answers are at the end of the book.

antibiotic	human genome	pharmacognosy
antitoxin	Medicare Modernization Act	pharmacology
cocaine	MTM services	quinine
formularies	panacea	salicylic acid
hormones	penicillin	synthetic

1. _____ : A local anesthetic found in coca leaves.

2. _____ : The natural drug derived from the bark of a white willow tree, used by the Ancient Greeks to relieve pain, and the natural forerunner to the active ingredient in aspirin.

3. _____ : A drug for malaria found in cinchona bark.

4. _____ : The complete set of genetic information in the human cell.

5. _____ : A cure-all.

6. _____ : The study of drugs—their properties, uses, application, and effects.

7. _____ : A drug produced by a fungus that kills bacteria.

8. _____ : Services provided by a pharmacist that look at all the medications a patient is taking.

9. _____ : A substance that acts against a toxin in the body.

10. _____ : A substance that harms or kills microorganisms like bacteria and fungi.

11. _____ : Chemicals produced by the body that regulate body functions and processes.

12. _____ : The study of physical, chemical, biochemical, and biological properties of drugs.

13. _____ : Expanded the role of the pharmacist to provide MTM services to some Medicare patients.

14. _____ : Lists of drugs that are approved for use by patients.

15. _____ : Combining simpler chemicals into more complex compounds not found in nature.

TRUE/FALSE

Indicate whether the statement is true or false in the blank. Answers are at the end of the book.

_____ 1. The natural drug that is the forerunner to aspirin comes from the cinchona tree.

_____ 2. Most drugs used today are made synthetically.

_____ 3. Digitalis comes from the foxglove plant.

_____ 4. Cocaine was the first general anesthetic.

_____ 5. In 1900 the average American lived only until their 40s.

_____ 6. More pharmacists and technicians are employed in community pharmacies than in any other setting.

_____ 7. The second largest area of employment for pharmacists and technicians is home care.

_____ 8. The field of biotechnology has become the least dynamic area of pharmaceutical research and development.

_____ 9. According to Gallup Polls, pharmacists consistently rank as one of the most highly trusted and ethical professions in the United States.

_____ 10. iPads are not currently used to access drug information.

EXPLAIN WHY

Explain why these statements are true or important. Check your answers in the text. Discuss any questions you may have with your instructor.

1. Give at least three reasons why synthetic drugs are important.

2. Why was the use of anesthesia revolutionary?

3. Why was Paracelsus's work important?

4. Why was penicillin a major benefit in wartime?

5. Why is the Human Genome Project important to pharmacology?

6. Why are drug patents important?

7. Why are pharmacists among the most trusted professionals?

CHOOSE THE BEST ANSWER

Answers are at the end of the book.

1. The drug digitalis comes from the fox-glove plant and is used to treat some _____ conditions.
   a. liver
   b. kidney
   c. heart
   d. lung

2. The first publicized operation using general anesthesia was performed using _____ as the anesthetic.
   a. cocaine
   b. foxglove
   c. quinine
   d. ether

3. The field of _____ has resulted from the study of the human genome.
   a. pharmacology
   b. biotechnology
   c. natural medicine
   d. discovery

4. The drug form of cocoa leaves is used for
   a. local anesthesia.
   b. diabetes.
   c. heart disease.
   d. hypertension.

5. The first cloned mammal was a
   a. rat.
   b. rabbit.
   c. sheep.
   d. monkey.

6. _____ advocated "bleeding" to maintain balance of the "humours."
   a. Charaka
   b. Shen Nung
   c. Pontos
   d. Galen

7. _____ developed an oral polio vaccine.
   a. Watson and Crick
   b. Sabin
   c. Fleming
   d. Hippocrates

8. An authoritative listing of drugs and issues related to their use is a (an)
   a. pharmacopeia.
   b. materia medica.
   c. panacea.
   d. Sumerian.

9. Care that is managed by an insurer is
   a. home care.
   b. managed care.
   c. short-term care.
   d. long-term care.

10. A substance that harms or kills microorganisms is called a(an)
    a. antitoxin.
    b. anesthetic.
    c. antibiotic.
    d. vaccine.

STUDY NOTES

Use this area to write important points you'd like to remember.

— 2 —

THE PHARMACY TECHNICIAN

KEY CONCEPTS

Test your knowledge by covering the information in the right-hand column.

job responsibilities
Pharmacy technicians perform essential tasks that do not require the pharmacist's skill or expertise. Specific responsibilities and tasks differ by setting and are described in writing by each employer through job descriptions, policy and procedure manuals, and other documents.

supervision
Pharmacy technicians work under the direct supervision of a licensed pharmacist who is legally responsible for their performance.

pharmacist counseling
Having technicians assist the pharmacist frees the pharmacist for activities that require a greater level of expertise, such as counseling with patients.

scope of practice
What individuals may and may not do in their jobs is often referred to as their "scope of practice."

employment opportunities
Like pharmacists, most pharmacy technicians are employed in community pharmacies and hospitals. However, they are also employed in clinics, home care, long-term care, mail order prescription pharmacies, and various other settings.

specialized jobs
In various hospital and other environments, there are specialized technician jobs, which require more advanced skills developed from additional education, training, and experience.

trustworthiness
Pharmacy technicians are entrusted with confidential patient information, dangerous substances, and perishable products.

errors
Drugs, whether prescription or over the counter, can be dangerous if misused, and mistakes by pharmacy technicians can be life threatening.

Health Insurance Portability and Accountability Act (HIPAA)	Pharmacy technicians are legally responsible for the privacy and security of protected health information (PHI).
math skills	Pharmacy technicians routinely perform mathematical calculations in filling prescriptions and other activities.
terminology	Pharmacy technicians must learn the specific pharmaceutical terminology that will be used on the job.
teamwork	Pharmacy technicians must be able to communicate, cooperate, and work effectively with others.
standards	There is no federal standard for pharmacy technician training or competency. However there are state and employer standards that must be met.
certification	A valuable career step for pharmacy technicians is getting certification by an appropriate organization or body. It verifies an individual's competence as a technician, and indicates a high level of knowledge and skill. In the United States, the Pharmacy Technician Certification Exam (PTCE) and the Exam for the Certification of Pharmacy Technicians (ExCPT) are national exams that lead to technician certification.

STUDY NOTES

Use this area to write important points you'd like to remember.

IN THE WORKPLACE

These sample job descriptions may help you in your career choice.

Sample Pharmacy Technician Job Description—Community Pharmacy

General Definition

The purpose of the pharmacy technician is to assist the pharmacist with the day-do-day activities in the pharmacy.

Responsibilities

- Help patients who are dropping off or picking up prescription orders
- Enter prescription orders into the computer
- Create a profile of the patient's health and insurance information in the computer or update the patient's profile
- Communicate with insurance carriers to obtain payment for prescription claims
- Complete weekly distribution center medication orders, place orders on shelves, and verify all associated paperwork
- Assist the pharmacist with filling and labeling prescriptions
- Prepare the pharmacy for inventory
- Screen telephone calls for the pharmacist
- Communicate with prescribers and their agents to obtain refill authorization
- Compound oral solutions, ointments, and creams
- Prepackage bulk medications

Qualifications

- Professional demeanor
- Ability to respect confidentiality of patient data
- Strong communication skills
- Courteous attitude
- Understanding of medical terminology and calculations
- Ability to type at least 35 words per minute
- Knowledge of computer operations
- Knowledge of medication brand and generic names
- Knowledge of insurance and third-party payment systems
- High school diploma or graduate equivalent degree
- National certification desirable

Sample Pharmacy Technician Job Description—Hospital Pharmacy

General Definition

Under the direction of a pharmacist, the pharmacy technician performs pharmacy-related functions, in compliance with department policies and procedures, that provide optimal pharmaceutical care.

Responsibilities

- Rotate through all work areas of the pharmacy
- Transport medications, drug-delivery devices, and other pharmacy equipment from the pharmacy to nursing units and clinics
- Pick up copies of physician orders, automated medication administration records, and unused medications from the nursing units and return them to the pharmacy
- Fill patient medication cassettes
- Prepare medications and supplies for dispensing, including:
  —prepackaging bulk medications
  —compounding ointments, creams, oral solutions, and other medications
  —preparing chemotherapeutic agents
  —compounding total parenteral nutrition solutions
  —compounding large-volume intravenous mixtures
  —packaging and preparing drugs being used in clinical investigations
  —preparing prescriptions for outpatients
- Assist pharmacists in entering medication orders into the computer system
- Prepare inventories, order drugs and supplies from the storeroom, receive drugs, and stock shelves in various pharmacy locations
- Screen telephone calls
- Perform monthly nursing unit inspections, maintain workload records, and collect quality-assurance data
- Assist in training new employees
- Assist other pharmacy technicians

Qualifications

- Valid state pharmacy technician registration (required in some states)
- High school diploma or graduate equivalent degree
- National certification desirable

Training and Experience

Must have one year of hospital pharmacy experience, have completed a pharmacy technician vocational course, or be a pharmacy student

Knowledge and Skills

- Ability to work as a team member
- Good communication skills
- Knowledge of basic pharmacy practices and procedures
- Knowledge of medications and medical supplies
- Strong mathematical computation skills
- Knowledge of record-keeping techniques
- Attention to detail
- Accurate typing skills (minimum 35 words per minute)
- Basic understanding of computer technology

Source: Reproduced by permission from *The Pharmacy Technician Companion: Your Road Map to Technician Training and Careers* (Washington, D.C.: American Pharmaceutical Association, 1998), pp. 9–10. © 1998 by the American Pharmaceutical Association.

IN THE WORKPLACE

This sample resume may help you when applying for a position as a pharmacy technician.

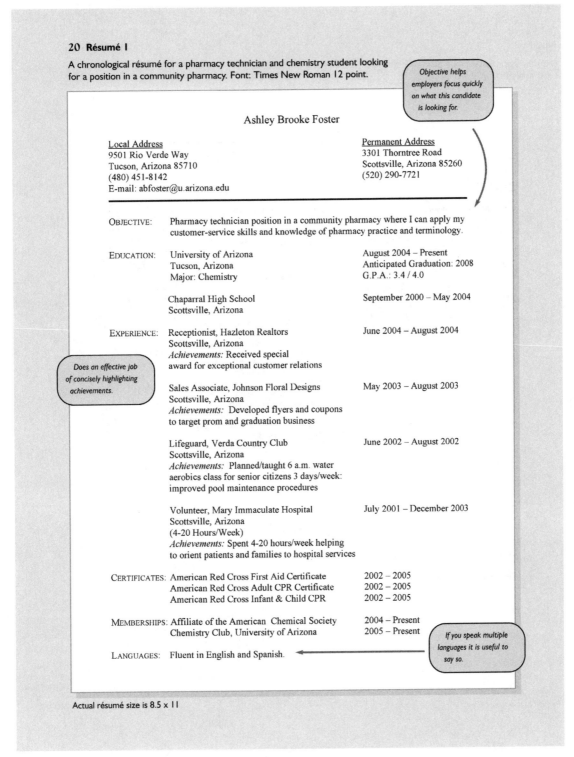

20 Résumé 1

A chronological résumé for a pharmacy technician and chemistry student looking for a position in a community pharmacy. Font: Times New Roman 12 point.

Objective helps employers focus quickly on what this candidate is looking for.

Ashley Brooke Foster

<u>Local Address</u>	<u>Permanent Address</u>
9501 Rio Verde Way	3301 Thorntree Road
Tucson, Arizona 85710	Scottsville, Arizona 85260
(480) 451-8142	(520) 290-7721
E-mail: abfoster@u.arizona.edu	

OBJECTIVE: Pharmacy technician position in a community pharmacy where I can apply my customer-service skills and knowledge of pharmacy practice and terminology.

EDUCATION:
University of Arizona — August 2004 – Present
Tucson, Arizona — Anticipated Graduation: 2008
Major: Chemistry — G.P.A.: 3.4 / 4.0

Chaparral High School — September 2000 – May 2004
Scottsville, Arizona

EXPERIENCE:
Receptionist, Hazleton Realtors — June 2004 – August 2004
Scottsville, Arizona
Achievements: Received special award for exceptional customer relations

Sales Associate, Johnson Floral Designs — May 2003 – August 2003
Scottsville, Arizona
Achievements: Developed flyers and coupons to target prom and graduation business

Lifeguard, Verda Country Club — June 2002 – August 2002
Scottsville, Arizona
Achievements: Planned/taught 6 a.m. water aerobics class for senior citizens 3 days/week: improved pool maintenance procedures

Volunteer, Mary Immaculate Hospital — July 2001 – December 2003
Scottsville, Arizona
(4-20 Hours/Week)
Achievements: Spent 4-20 hours/week helping to orient patients and families to hospital services

Does an effective job of concisely highlighting achievements.

CERTIFICATES:
American Red Cross First Aid Certificate — 2002 – 2005
American Red Cross Adult CPR Certificate — 2002 – 2005
American Red Cross Infant & Child CPR — 2002 – 2005

MEMBERSHIPS:
Affiliate of the American Chemical Society — 2004 – Present
Chemistry Club, University of Arizona — 2005 – Present

LANGUAGES: Fluent in English and Spanish.

If you speak multiple languages it is useful to say so.

Actual résumé size is 8.5 x 11

Source: Reproduced by permission from *The Pharmacy Professional's Guide to Résumés, CV's & Interviewing* (Washington, D.C.: American Pharmacists Association, 2006), pp. 20–23. © Copyright 2006 by the American Pharmacists Association.

IN THE WORKPLACE

These sample resumes may help you when applying for a position as a pharmacy technician.

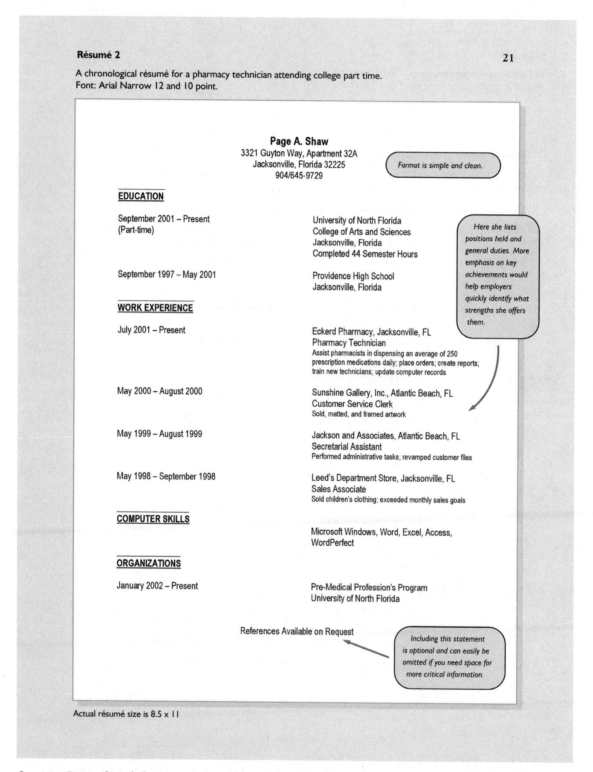

Résumé 2   21

A chronological résumé for a pharmacy technician attending college part time.
Font: Arial Narrow 12 and 10 point.

Page A. Shaw
3321 Guyton Way, Apartment 32A
Jacksonville, Florida 32225
904/645-9729

Format is simple and clean.

EDUCATION

September 2001 – Present
(Part-time)

University of North Florida
College of Arts and Sciences
Jacksonville, Florida
Completed 44 Semester Hours

September 1997 – May 2001

Providence High School
Jacksonville, Florida

Here she lists positions held and general duties. More emphasis on key achievements would help employers quickly identify what strengths she offers them.

WORK EXPERIENCE

July 2001 – Present

Eckerd Pharmacy, Jacksonville, FL
Pharmacy Technician
Assist pharmacists in dispensing an average of 250 prescription medications daily; place orders; create reports; train new technicians; update computer records

May 2000 – August 2000

Sunshine Gallery, Inc., Atlantic Beach, FL
Customer Service Clerk
Sold, matted, and framed artwork

May 1999 – August 1999

Jackson and Associates, Atlantic Beach, FL
Secretarial Assistant
Performed administrative tasks; revamped customer files

May 1998 – September 1998

Leed's Department Store, Jacksonville, FL
Sales Associate
Sold children's clothing; exceeded monthly sales goals

COMPUTER SKILLS

Microsoft Windows, Word, Excel, Access, WordPerfect

ORGANIZATIONS

January 2002 – Present

Pre-Medical Profession's Program
University of North Florida

References Available on Request

Including this statement is optional and can easily be omitted if you need space for more critical information.

Actual résumé size is 8.5 x 11

Source: Reproduced by permission from *The Pharmacy Professional's Guide to Résumés, CV's & Interviewing* (Washington, D.C.: American Pharmacists Association, 2006), pp. 20–23. © Copyright 2006 by the American Pharmacists Association.

22 Résumé 3

Chronological résumé of a certified pharmacy technician enrolled in a pre-pharmacy course of study.
Font: Arial 12 point.

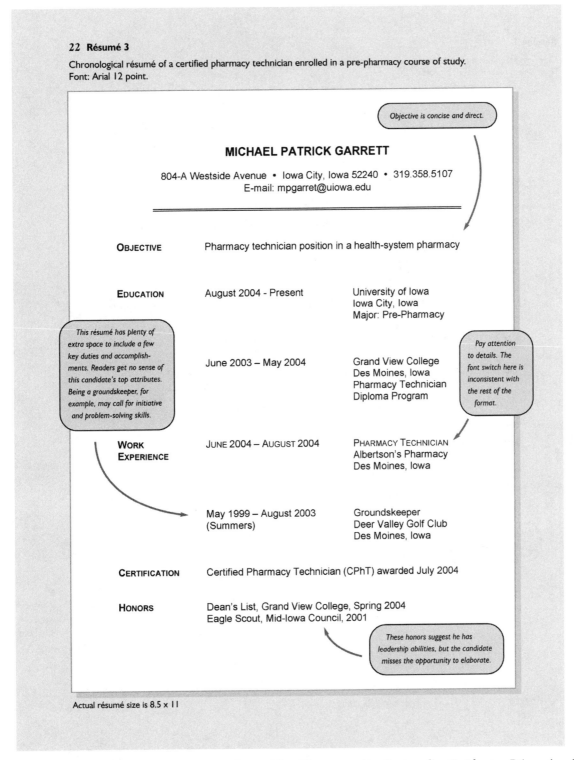

Actual résumé size is 8.5 x 11

Source: Reproduced by permission from *The Pharmacy Professional's Guide to Résumés, CV's & Interviewing* (Washington, D.C.: American Pharmacists Association, 2006), pp. 20–23. © Copyright 2006 by the American Pharmacists Association.

IN THE WORKPLACE

This sample resume may help you when applying for admission to pharmacy school.

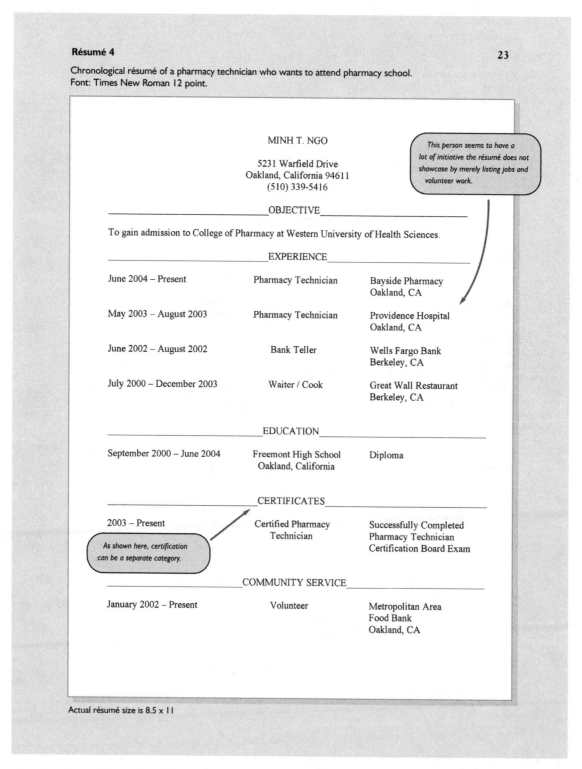

Résumé 4 23

Chronological résumé of a pharmacy technician who wants to attend pharmacy school.
Font: Times New Roman 12 point.

MINH T. NGO

5231 Warfield Drive
Oakland, California 94611
(510) 339-5416

This person seems to have a lot of initiative the résumé does not showcase by merely listing jobs and volunteer work.

————————————————OBJECTIVE————————————————

To gain admission to College of Pharmacy at Western University of Health Sciences.

————————————————EXPERIENCE————————————————

June 2004 – Present	Pharmacy Technician	Bayside Pharmacy Oakland, CA
May 2003 – August 2003	Pharmacy Technician	Providence Hospital Oakland, CA
June 2002 – August 2002	Bank Teller	Wells Fargo Bank Berkeley, CA
July 2000 – December 2003	Waiter / Cook	Great Wall Restaurant Berkeley, CA

————————————————EDUCATION————————————————

| September 2000 – June 2004 | Freemont High School Oakland, California | Diploma |

————————————————CERTIFICATES————————————————

| 2003 – Present | Certified Pharmacy Technician | Successfully Completed Pharmacy Technician Certification Board Exam |

As shown here, certification can be a separate category.

————————————————COMMUNITY SERVICE————————————————

| January 2002 – Present | Volunteer | Metropolitan Area Food Bank Oakland, CA |

Actual résumé size is 8.5 x 11

Source: Reproduced by permission from *The Pharmacy Professional's Guide to Résumés, CV's & Interviewing* (Washington, D.C.: American Pharmacists Association, 2006), pp. 20–23. © Copyright 2006 by the American Pharmacists Association.

FILL IN THE KEY TERM

Use these key terms to fill in the correct blank. Answers are at the end of the book.

ASHP
certification
confidentiality
continuing education
ExCPT

HIPAA
patient welfare
performance review
personal inventory
pharmacist

professionals
PTCE
scope of practice
technicians

1. _____ : What individuals may and may not do in their jobs.

2. _____ : To assess characteristics, skills, qualities, etc.

3. _____ : The requirement of health-care providers to keep all patient information private among the patient, the patient's insurer, and the providers directly involved in the patient's care.

4. _____ : The most important consideration in health care.

5. _____ : Exam offered by the Pharmacy Technician Certification Board.

6. _____ : A legal proof or document that an individual meets certain objective standards, usually provided by a neutral professional organization.

7. _____ : Individuals who are given a basic level of training designed to help them perform specific tasks.

8. _____ : Individuals who receive extensive and advanced levels of education before being allowed to practice, such as physicians and pharmacists.

9. _____ : Technicians always work under their direct supervision.

10. _____ : Employer documents employee's job competency.

11. _____ : Has model curriculum for technician training.

12. _____ : Exam given by the National Healthcareer Association.

13. _____ : A critical element in maintaining competency for pharmacy technicians.

14. _____ : Law that makes health-care providers responsible for the privacy and security of a patient's health information.

True/False

Indicate whether the statement is true or false in the blank. Answers are at the end of the book.

_____ 1. Specific technician responsibilities differ by setting and job description.

_____ 2. Technicians may sometimes provide counseling services to patients.

_____ 3. Most pharmacy technicians are employed in hospitals.

_____ 4. Mathematics skills are very important to the pharmacy technician.

_____ 5. It is essential for technicians to have good interpersonal skills.

_____ 6. The U.S. government sets standards for technician training.

_____ 7. PHI is considered public information.

_____ 8. As a technician, your employer is legally responsible for your performance.

_____ 9. Studies have shown that certified technicians have lower turnover.

_____ 10. Every two years a CPhT must complete 40 contact hours of continuing education.

Explain Why

Explain why these statements are true or important. Check your answers in the text. Discuss any questions you may have with your instructor.

1. Give at least two reasons technicians must work under the supervision of a pharmacist.

2. Why is knowing your "scope of practice" important?

3. Why is dependability important?

4. Why is it important that pharmacy technicians understand their responsibilities under the 1996 Health Insurance Portability and Accountability Act (HIPAA)?

5. Why should technicians have math skills?

6. Why are interpersonal skills important?

7. Why is certification a good idea for technicians?

8. Why is continuing education valuable for technicians?

Choose the Best Answer

Answers are at the end of the book.

1. When technicians perform appropriate essential tasks, this allows the pharmacist time for tasks requiring more advanced professional expertise such as
   a. telephoning insurance companies.
   b. consulting with patients.
   c. counting tablets.
   d. ringing the cash register.

2. Taking routine patient information is a duty of the
   a. consultant.
   b. cashier.
   c. pharmacist.
   d. pharmacy technician.

3. Pharmacy technicians should be detail-oriented. This means
   a. technicians' work can always be done by pharmacists.
   b. technicians are not as important as pharmacists.
   c. patients must receive medications exactly as they are prescribed.
   d. tardiness is acceptable.

4. Do pharmacy technicians need to maintain good physical and mental health?
   a. Yes, to decrease the chance of making serious mistakes.
   b. Yes, because some belong to labor unions.
   c. No. Pharmacists are always responsible for the technician, so technicians don't have to worry about getting enough sleep.
   d. No. Pharmacists have more education and so will catch all errors made.

5. According to HIPAA, it is okay to
   a. discuss patient information within earshot of other patients.
   b. bill insurance using HIPAA-compliant EDI.
   c. bill insurance using nonsecure EDI.
   d. casually discuss a patient's condition with a patient's spouse.

6. _____ refers to being qualified for or capable of performing a task or job.
   a. Scope of practice
   b. Compounding
   c. Dependability
   d. Competent

7. _____ are regularly scheduled events to monitor and document technician competency.
   a. PTCE
   b. PTCB
   c. Performance reviews
   d. TJC

8. _____ is a legal proof or document that an individual meets certain objective standards, usually provided by a neutral professional organization.
   a. Registration
   b. Certification
   c. Documentation
   d. Prior authorization

9. CPhT stands for
   a. Certified Pharmacy Trainer.
   b. Complete Pharmacy Technician.
   c. Certified Pharmacy Technician.
   d. Certified Pharmacist Technician.

10. To pass the ExCPT, candidates must score at least
    a. 550.
    b. 600.
    c. 390.
    d. 750.

— 3 —

DRUG REGULATION & CONTROL

KEY CONCEPTS

Test your knowledge by covering the information in the right-hand column.

Food and Drug Administration
The leading enforcement agency at the federal level for regulations concerning drug products.

Drug Enforcement Administration
The agency that controls the distribution of drugs that may be easily abused.

Food and Drug Act of 1906
Prohibited interstate commerce in adulterated or misbranded food, drinks, and drugs. Government preapproval of drugs is required.

1938 Food, Drug and Cosmetic (FDC) Act
In response to the fatal poisoning of 107 people, primarily children, by an untested sulfanilamide concoction, this comprehensive law requires new drugs be shown to be safe before marketing.

1951 Durham-Humphrey Amendment
This law defines what drugs require a prescription by a licensed practitioner and requires them to include this legend on the label: "Caution: Federal Law prohibits dispensing without a prescription."

1962 Kefauver-Harris Amendments
Requires drug manufacturers to provide proof of both safety and effectiveness before marketing the drug.

1970 Poison Prevention Packaging Act
Requires childproof packaging on all controlled and most prescription drugs dispensed by pharmacies.

1970 Controlled Substances Act (CSA)
The CSA classifies drugs that may be easily abused and restricts their distribution. It is enforced by the Drug Enforcement Administration (DEA) within the Justice Department.

1990 Omnibus Budget Reconciliation Act (OBRA)
Among other things, this act required pharmacists to offer counseling to Medicaid patients regarding medications, effectively putting the common practice into law.

1996 Health Insurance Portability and Accountability Act (HIPAA)	Provided broad and stringent regulations to protect patients' privacy.
placebos	Inactive substances, not real medications, that are used to test the effectiveness of drugs.
new drugs	All new drugs, whether made domestically or imported, require FDA approval before they can be marketed in the United States.
clinical tests	Tests on proposed new drugs (investigational drugs) are "controlled" by comparing the effect of a proposed drug on one group of patients with the effect of a different treatment on other patients.
blind tests	Patients in a trial are always "blind" to the treatment, i.e., they are not told which control group they are in. In a "double-blind" test, neither the patients nor the physicians know what the medication is.
patent protection	A patent for a new drug gives its manufacturer an exclusive right to market the drug for a specific period of time under a brand name. A drug patent is in effect for 17 years from the date of the drug's discovery. The Hatch-Waxman Act of 1984 provided for up to five-year extensions of patent protection to the patent holders to make up for time lost while products went through the FDA approval process.
generics	Once a patent for a brand drug expires, other manufacturers may copy the drug and release it under its pharmaceutical or "generic" name.
labels and product labeling	All drugs are required to have clear and accurate information for all labels, inserts, packaging, and so on, but there are different information requirements for various categories of drugs.
prescription drug labels	The minimum requirements on prescription labels for most drugs are as follows: name and address of dispenser, prescription serial number, date of prescription or filling, name of prescriber, name of patient, directions for use, and cautionary statements.
NDC (National Drug Code) number	The number assigned by the manufacturer. Each NDC number has three parts, or sets, of numbers: The first set indicates the manufacturer; the next set indicates the medication, its strength, and dosage form; the last set indicates the package size.

KEY CONCEPTS

Test your knowledge by covering the information in the right-hand column.

controlled substances

A drug which has the potential to be abused and for which distribution is controlled by one of five "schedules."

control classifications

Manufacturers must clearly label controlled drugs with their control classification.

DEA number/formula

The **number** all prescribers of controlled substances are assigned and which must be used on all controlled drug prescriptions. It has two letters followed by seven single-digit numbers, e.g., AB1234563. The **formula** for checking a DEA number on a prescription form is: if the sum of the first, third and fifth digits is added to twice the sum of the second, fourth, and sixth digits, the total should be a number whose last digit is the same as the last digit of the DEA number.

risks of approved drugs

There is always the risk that an approved drug may produce adverse side effects when used on a larger population.

recalls

Recalls are, with a few exceptions, voluntary on the part of the manufacturer. There are three classes of recalls: I. where there is a strong likelihood that the product will cause serious adverse effects or death; II. where a product may cause temporary but reversible adverse effects, or in which there is little likelihood of serious adverse effects; III. where a product is not likely to cause adverse effects.

MedWatch

FDA reporting program for health-care professionals to report adverse effects that occur from the use of an approved drug or other medical product. The MedWatch Online Voluntary Reporting Form 3500 is used for FDA-regulated drugs, biologics, medical devices, and special nutritional products and cosmetics.

state regulations

State boards of pharmacy are responsible for licensing all prescribers and dispensers and administering regulations for the practice of pharmacy in the state.

liability

Legal liability means you can be prosecuted for misconduct.

negligence

Failing to do something that should or must be done.

Controlled Substance Schedules

The five control schedules are as follows*:

Schedule I:

➡ Each drug has a high potential for abuse and no accepted medical use in the United States. It may not be prescribed. Heroin, various opium derivatives, and hallucinogenic substances are included on this schedule.

Schedule II:

➡ Each drug has a high potential for abuse and may lead to physical or psychological dependence, but also has a currently accepted medical use in the United States. Amphetamines, opium, cocaine, methadone, and various opiates are included on this schedule.

Schedule III:

➡ Each drug's potential for abuse is less than those in Schedules I and II and there is a currently accepted medical use in the United States, but abuse may lead to moderate or low physical dependence or high psychological dependence. Anabolic steroids and various compounds containing limited quantities of narcotic substances such as codeine are included on this schedule.

Schedule IV:

➡ Each drug has a low potential for abuse relative to Schedule III drugs and there is a current accepted medical use in the United States, but abuse may lead to limited physical dependence or psychological dependence. Phenobarbital, the sedative chloral hydrate, and the anesthetic methohexital are included in this group.

Schedule V:

➡ Each drug has a low potential for abuse relative to Schedule IV drugs and there is a current accepted medical use in the United States, but abuse may lead to limited physical dependence or psychological dependence. Compounds containing limited amounts of a narcotic such as codeine are included in this group.

*21 USC Sec. 812. Source: http://www.deadiversion.usdoj.gov/21cfr/21usc/812.htm. Note: These schedules are revised periodically. It is important to refer to the most current schedule.

Controlled-Substance Prescriptions

Controlled-substance prescriptions have greater requirements at both federal and state levels than other prescriptions, particularly Schedule II drugs. On controlled-substance prescriptions, the DEA number must appear on the form and the patient's full street address must be entered.

On Schedule II prescriptions, the form must be signed by the prescriber. In many states, there are specific time limits that require Schedule II prescriptions be promptly filled. Generally, quantities are limited and no refills are allowed.

Federal requirements for Schedules III–V are less stringent than for Schedule II. *For example, Schedules III–V prescriptions may be refilled up to five times within six months.* However, state and other regulations may be stricter than federal requirements, so it is necessary to know the requirements for your specific job setting.

APPROVED DRUG PRODUCTS WITH THERAPEUTIC EQUIVALENCE EVALUATIONS (THE "ORANGE BOOK")

The FDA annually publishes *Approved Drug Products With Therapeutic Equivalence Evaluations* (the "Orange Book"), and updates it throughout the year online at http://www.accessdata.fda.gov/scripts/cder/ob/default.cfm. The "Orange Book" provides a two-letter evaluation code to allow users to determine whether the FDA has evaluated a particular product as therapeutically equivalent to other pharmaceutically equivalent products (first letter) and to provide additional information on the basis of FDA's evaluations (second letter).

"**A**" drug products are those the FDA considers to be therapeutically equivalent to other pharmaceutically equivalent products. There are (1) no known or suspected bioequivalence problems or (2) the actual or potential bioequivalence problems have been resolved with adequate in vivo and/or in vitro evidence supporting bioequivalence.

"**B**" drug products are those the FDA considers not to be therapeutically equivalent to other pharmaceutically equivalent products. Often, the problem is with specific dosage forms rather than with the active ingredient.

A listing of the codes is below:

AA   Products in conventional dosage forms not presenting bioequivalence problems
AB   Products meeting bioequivalence requirements
AN   Solutions and powders for aerosolization
AO   Injectable oil solutions
AP   Injectable aqueous solutions
AT   Topical products

BC   Extended-release tablets, extended-release capsules, and extended-release injectables
BD   Active ingredients and dosage forms with documented bioequivalence problems
BE   Delayed-release oral dosage forms
BN   Products in aerosol-nebulizer drug delivery systems
BP   Active ingredients and dosage forms with potential bioequivalence problems
BR   Suppositories or enemas for systemic use
BS   Products with drug standard deficiencies
BT   Topical products with bioequivalence issues
BX   Insufficient data

There are some products that cannot be described with just the two letter code, i.e., a more complete explanation is needed. These products often have problems with identity, analytical methodology, or bioequivalence standards. For some of these products, bioequivalence has not been established or no generic product is currently available.

FILL IN THE KEY TERM

Use these key terms to fill in the correct blank. Answers are at the end of the book.

adverse effect   legend drug   pediatric
Controlled Substances Act   liability   placebo
DEA number   NDC (national drug ode)   product labeling
dual marketing status   negligence   recall
injunction   OTC drugs

1. _____ : The number all prescribers of controlled substances are assigned and which must be used on all controlled drug prescriptions.

2. _____ : A court order preventing a specific action, such as the distribution of a potentially dangerous drug.

3. _____ : An inactive substance given in place of a medication.

4. _____ : An unintended side affect of a medication that is negative or in some way injurious to a patient's health.

5. _____ : Any drug which requires a prescription and this "legend" on the label: Rx only.

6. _____ : Failing to do something you should have done.

7. _____ : Having to do with the treatment of children.

8. _____ : Important associated information that is not on the label of a drug product itself.

9. _____ : A drug that has prescription and OTC status.

10. _____ : Means you can be prosecuted for misconduct.

11. _____ : The action taken to remove a drug from the market and have it returned to the manufacturer.

12. _____ : 1970 law that established schedules of controlled substances.

13. _____ : The number on a manufacturer's label indicating the manufacturer and product information.

14. _____ : Drugs that do not require a prescription.

TRUE/FALSE

Indicate whether the statement is true or false in the blank. Answers are at the end of the book.

_____ 1. Childproof packaging was required by the Fair Packaging and Labeling Act.

_____ 2. The CMEA sets daily and monthly restrictions on the sale of pseudoephedrine.

_____ 3. Only about 25% of drugs tested on humans are approved for use by the FDA.

_____ 4. Over-the-counter medications do not require a prescription but sometimes prescriptions are written for them.

_____ 5. The name of the prescriber must appear on the label of a dispensed prescription container.

_____ 6. A Class III recall is most likely to cause harm or death.

_____ 7. Negligence is the most common form of misconduct.

_____ 8. Schedule III, IV, and V drugs may be stored openly on shelves in retail and hospital settings.

_____ 9. All controlled substances must be ordered using a DEA controlled substance order form.

_____ 10. Beneficence means the actions should be in the best interests of the patient.

EXPLAIN WHY

Explain why these statements are true or important. Check your answers in the text. Discuss any questions you may have with your instructor.

1. Why is blind testing used in the drug approval process?

2. Give three reasons why OTC labels should be clear and understandable.

3. Why are some drugs "controlled" by the DEA?

4. Why are some drug patents extended past the original 17-year period?

5. Why would a manufacturer want to recall a drug product?

6. Give three reasons why failing to do something could result in a criminal charge of negligence.

MATCH THE TERM — CONTROLLED SUBSTANCES AND RECALLS

Use these key terms to fill in the correct blank. Answers are at the end of the book.

Schedule I Drugs   **Schedule V Drugs**
Schedule II Drugs   **Class I Recall**
Schedule III Drugs   **Class II Recall**
Schedule IV Drugs   **Class III Recall**

1. _____ :   Amphetamines, opium, cocaine, methadone, and various opiates are included on this schedule.

2. _____ :   Anabolic steroids and various compounds containing limited quantities of narcotic substances such as codeine are included on this schedule.

3. _____ :   When a product is not likely to cause adverse effects.

4. _____ :   Compounds containing limited amounts of a narcotic such as codeine are included in this group.

5. _____ :   When a product may cause temporary but reversible adverse effects, or in which there is little likelihood of serious adverse effects.

6. _____ :   Heroin, various opium derivatives, and hallucinogenic substances are included on this schedule.

7. _____ :   Phenobarbital, the sedative chloral hydrate, and the anesthetic methohexital are included in this group.

8. _____ :   When there is a strong likelihood that the product will cause serious adverse effects or death.

IDENTIFY

Identify the required elements on this manufacturer's bottle label by answering in the space beneath the question.

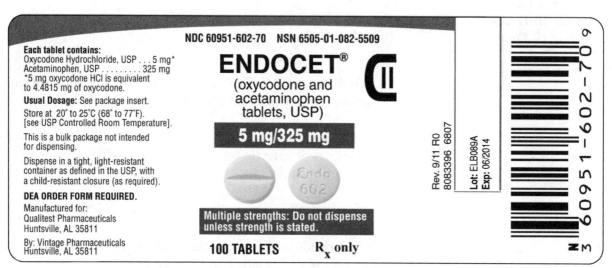

Endocet® label courtesy Endo Pharmaceuticals, Inc.

1. In what kind of container should this medication be dispensed?

2. Who is the manufacturer of this drug product?

3. What is the product's brand name?

4. What is the product's generic name?

5. What is the drug form?

6. What are the active ingredients?

7. What control level is the drug product?

8. What are the storage requirements?

9. What is the expiration date?

CHOOSE THE BEST ANSWER

Answers are at the end of the book.

1. The _____ defined what drugs require a prescription.
   a. 1970 Poison Prevention Packaging Act
   b. 1962 Kefauver-Harris Amendment
   c. Sherley Amendment
   d. 1951 Durham-Humphrey Amendment

2. A need for tighter drug regulations from the thalidomide lesson led to the
   a. Kefauver-Harris Amendment.
   b. Durham-Humphrey Amendment.
   c. Food and Drug Act of 1906.
   d. Food Drug and Cosmetic Act.

3. Legend drugs should have the legend _____ on the manufacturer's label.
   a. "Federal law prohibits transfer of this prescription"
   b. "Store at room temperature"
   c. "For external use only"
   d. "RX only"

4. In clinical trials, the testing is done
   a. on mice.
   b. on people.
   c. in vitro.
   d. on dogs.

5. The main purpose of phase II clinical trials is
   a. efficacy.
   b. dosage.
   c. safety.
   d. economics.

6. The monthly sales limit of pseudoephedrine base is
   a. 7.5 g per household.
   b. 7.5 g per purchaser.
   c. 7.5 g per transaction.

7. The national drug code (NDC) is assigned by the
   a. FDA.
   b. DEA.
   c. CDER.
   d. manufacturer.

8. DEA form _____ is used to order Schedule II controlled substances.
   a. 41
   b. 106
   c. 222
   d. 224

9. In each state, pharmacists are licensed by the
   a. DEA.
   b. FDA.
   c. federal government.
   d. state board of pharmacy.

10. Ethical value that patients have the right to choose their treatment:
    a. autonomy.
    b. beneficence.
    c. non-maleficence.
    d. justice.

— 4 —

TERMINOLOGY

KEY CONCEPTS

Test your knowledge by covering the information in the right-hand column.

terminology	Much of medical science is made up of a small number of root words, suffixes, and prefixes that originated from either Greek or Latin words.
root word	The base component of a term that gives it a meaning that may be modified by other components.
prefix	A modifying component of a term located before the other components of the term.
suffix	A modifying component of a term located after the other components of the term.
combining vowel	Combining vowels are used to connect the prefix, root, or suffix parts of the term.
cardiovascular system	Distributes blood throughout the body using blood vessels called arteries, capillaries, and veins.
endocrine system	Consists of the glands that secrete hormones (chemicals that assist in regulating body functions).
gastrointestinal (GI) tract	Contains the organs that are involved in the digestion of foods and the absorption of nutrients.
integumentary system	The body's first line of defense, acting as a barrier against disease and other hazards.
lymphatic system	The center of the body's immune system. Lymphocytes are white blood cells that helps the body defend itself against bacteria and diseased cells.
muscular system	The body contains more than 600 muscles, which give shape and movement to it.

nervous system	The body's system of communication. The neuron (nerve cell) is its basic functional unit.
skeletal system	Protects soft organs and provides structure and support for the body's organ systems.
female reproductive system	Produces hormones (estrogen, progesterone), controls menstruation, and provides for childbearing.
male reproductive system	Produces sperm and secretes the hormone testosterone.
respiratory system	Brings oxygen into the body through inhalation and expels carbon dioxide gas through exhalation.
urinary tract	The primary organ is the kidney, which filters the blood for unwanted material and makes urine.
ear	The sense of hearing, as well as the maintenance of body equilibrium, is performed by the ear.
eyes	The eyelids protect the eye and assist in its lubrication. The conjunctiva is the blood-rich membrane between the eye and the eyelid.
drug classifications	A grouping of a number of drugs that have some properties in common. The same steps in interpreting other medical science terminology can be used to interpret drug classification names.

STUDY NOTES

Use this area to write important points you'd like to remember.

ORGAN SYSTEM ROOTS

CARDIOVASCULAR SYSTEM

aneur	widening
angi	vessel
aort	aorta
arter	artery
ather	plaque
card	heart
cyte	cell
embol	embolus
oxy	oxygen
pector	chest
phleb	vein
stenosis	narrowing
thromb	clot
vas(cu)	blood vessel
ven	vein

ENDOCRINE SYSTEM

aden	gland
adrena	adrenal
crine	to secrete
glyc	sugar
lipid	fat
myx	mucos
nephr	kidney
pancreat	pancreas
plas	development
somat	body
tetan	tetanus
thym	thymus
thyroid	thyroid

GASTROINTESTINAL SYSTEM

chol	bile
col	colon
duoden	duodenum
enter	intestine
esophag	esophagus
gastr	stomach
hemat	blood
hepat	liver
herni	hernai
lapar	abdomen
orexia	appetitie
pancreat	pancreas
pepsia	digestion
phag	swallow

INTEGUMENTARY SYSTEM

adip	fat
cutane	skin
derm(at)	skin
hist	tissue
kerat	hard
mast	breast
melan	black
necr	death (of cells, etc.)
onych	nail

LYMPHATIC SYSTEM

aden	gland
bacter	bacteria
cyt	cell
hemo, hemat	blood
leuk	white
lymph	lymph
phleb	vein
sepsis	to putrify
splen	spleen
thromb	clot
thym	thymus

MUSCULAR SYSTEM

burs	bursa
chondr	cartilage
fibr	fiber
my	muscle
rhabdo	rod
tendin	tendon

NERVOUS SYSTEM

alges	pain
cerebr	cerebrum
encephal	brain
esthes	sensation
mening	meninges
ment	mind
myel	spinal cord
neur	nerve
phas	speech
psycho	mind
somat	body

SKELETAL SYSTEM

arthr	joint
carp	wrist

crani	cranium
dactyl	finger or toe
femor	thigh bone
fibul	small, lower leg bone
humer	upper arm bone
lord	curve
oste	bone
patell	kneecap
ped, pod	foot
pelv	pelvis
phalang	bones of fingers and toes
rachi	vertebrae
scoli	crooked, bent
spondyl	vertebrae
stern	sternum, breastbone
tibi	large, lower leg bone

FEMALE REPRODUCTIVE SYSTEM

cervic	cervix
condyle	knob, knuckle
eclamps	shining forth
gynec	woman
hyster	uterus
lact	milk
mamm	breast
mast	breast
men	menstruation
metr	uterus
ovari	ovary
salping	fallopian tube
toc	birth
uter	uterine
vagin	vagina

MALE REPRODUCTIVE SYSTEM

andr	male
balan	glans penis
crypt	hidden
orch, orchid	testis
prostat	prostate gland
semin	semen
sperm	sperm
varic	varicose veins
vas	vessel, duct
test	testicle

RESPIRATORY SYSTEM

aer	air
aero	gas
bronch	bronchus
capn	carbon dioxide

cyan	blue
laryng	larynx
nas	nose
ox	oxygen
pector	chest
pneumon	lung, air
pulmon	lung
respir	breath
rhin	nose
sinus	sinus

URINARY TRACT

albumin	protein
cyst	bladder
glycos	glucose
keto	ketones
lith	stone
nephr	kidney
ren	kidney
ur	kidney
uresis	urination
ureter	ureter
urethr	urethra
uria	urine, urination
vesic	bladder

HEARING

acous	hearing
acusis	hearing condition
audi	hearing
cerumin	waxy
labyrinth	inner ear
myring	eardrum
ot	ear
salping	eustachian tube
tympan	eardrum

SIGHT

ambly	dim, dull
blephar	eyelid
conjuctiv	conjunctiva
corne	cornea
glauc	gray
irid, ir	iris
lacrim	tear duct
ocul	eye
ophthalm	eye
opia	vision
opt	eye
retin	retina
stigmat	point(ed)

COMMON PREFIXES

a	without		melan	black
ambi	both		meso	middle
an	without		meta	beyond, after, changing
ante	before		micro	small
anti	against		mid	middle
bi	two or both		mono	one
brady	slow		multi	many
chlor	green		neo	new
circum	around		pan	all
cirrh	yellow		para	alongside or abnormal
con	with		peri	around
contra	against		polio	gray
cyan	blue		poly	many
dia	across or through		post	after
dis	separate from or apart		pre	before
dys	painful, difficult		pro	before
ec	away or out		pseudo	false
ecto	outside		purpur	purple
endo	within		quadri	four
epi	upon		re	again or back
erythr	red		retro	after
eu	good or normal		rube	red
exo	outside		semi	half
hemi	half		sub	below or under
hyper	above or excessive		super	above or excessive
hypo	below or deficient		supra	above or excessive
im	not		sym	with
immun	safe, protected		syn	with
in	not		tachy	fast
infra	below or under		trans	across, through
inter	between		tri	three
intra	within		ultra	beyond or excessive
iso	equal		uni	one
leuk	white		xanth	yellow
macro	large		xer	dry
medi	middle			

COMMON SUFFIXES

ac	pertaining to	ole	small
al	pertaining to	oma	tumor
algia	pain	opia	vision
ar	pertaining to	opsia	vision
ary	pertaining to	osis	abnormal condition
asthenia	without strength	osmia	smell
cele	pouching or hernia	ous	pertaining to
cyesis	pregnancy	paresis	partial paralysis
cynia	pain	pathy	disease
eal	pertaining to	penia	decrease
ectasis	expansion or dilation	phagia	swallowing
ectomy	removal	phasia	speech
emia	blood condition	philia	attraction for
genic	origin or production	phobia	fear
gram	record	plasia	formation
graph	recording instrument	plasty	surgical reconstruction
graphy	recording process	plegia	paralysis, stroke
ia	condition of	rrhage	to burst forth
iasis	condition, formation of	rrhea	discharge
iatry	treatment	sclerosis	narrowing, constriction
ic	pertaining to	scope	examination instrument
icle	small	scopy	examination
ism	condition of	spasm	involuntary contraction
itis	inflammation	stasis	stop or stand
ium	tissue	tic	pertaining to
lith	stone, calculus	tocia	childbirth, labor
logy	study of	tomy	incision
malacia	softening	toxic	poison
megaly	enlargement	tropic	stimulate
meter	measuring instrument	ula	small
metry	measuring process	ule	small
mycosis	fungal infection	y	condition, process of
oi	resembling		

COMMON MEDICAL ABBREVIATIONS

ABG	arterial blood gases		IO, I/O	fluid intake and output
ADD	attention deficit disorder		IOP	intraocular pressure
AIDS	acquired immune deficiency syndrome		IV	intravenous
ASAP	as soon as possible		KVO	keep vein open
AV	atrial-ventricular		LBW	low birth weight
AMI	acute myocardial infarction		LDL	low density lipoprotein
ANS	autonomic nervous system		LOC	loss of consciousness
BM	bowel movement		MI	myocardial infarction
BP	blood pressure		MICU	medical intensive care unit
BPH	benign prostatic hyperplasia		MRI	magnetic resonance imaging
BS	blood sugar		NKA	no known allergies
BSA	body surface area		NPO	nothing by mouth
CA	cancer		NVD	nausea, vomiting, diarrhea
CABG	coronary artery bypass graft		OR	operating room
CAD	coronary artery disease		PAP	pulmonary artery pressure
CF	cardiac failure		PMH	past medical history
CHF	congestive heart failure		PUD	peptic ulcer disease
CMV	cytomegalovirus		PVD	peripheral vascular disease
CNS	central nervous system		RA	rheumatoid arthritis
COPD	chronic obstructive pulmonary disease		RBC	red blood count or red blood cell
CV	cardiovascular		ROM	range of motion
CVA	cerebrovascular accident (stroke)		SBP	systolic blood pressure
DI	diabetes insipidus		SOB	short of breath
DM	diabetes melitus		STD	sexually transmitted diseases
DOB	date of birth		T	temperature
Dx	diagnosis		T&C	type and cross-match
ECG/EKG	electrocardiogram		TB	tuberculosis
ENT	ears, nose, throat		TEDS	thrombo-embolic disease stockings
ER	emergency room		TPN	total parenteral nutrition
FH	family history		Tx	treatment
GERD	gastroesophageal reflux disease		U	units
GI	gastrointestinal		U/A	urinalysis
HA	headache		UCHD	usual childhood diseases
HBP	high blood pressure		URD	upper respiratory diseases
HDL	high density lipoprotein		UTI	urinary tract infection
HIV	human immunodeficiency virus		VD	venereal disease
HR	heart rate		VS	vital signs
ID	infectious diseases		WBC	white blood count/cell
IH	infectious hepatitis		WT	weight

FILL IN THE KEY TERM

Use these key terms to fill in the correct blank. Answers are at the end of the book.

aphagia	dysuria	hepatitis	patchyderm
arthritis	encephalitis	hernia	prostatolith
blepharitis	endometriosis	hyperglycemia	pulmonary
bronchitis	epidermis	hypertension	subcutaneous
cardiomyopathy	euthyroid	lordosis	tendinitis
colitis	fibromalgia	lymphoma	transdermal
cystitis	hematoma	neuralgia	vasectomy
dyspepsia	hemophilia	parathyroid	

1. _____ : High blood pressure.
2. _____ : Chronic pain in the muscles.
3. _____ : Inflammation of the brain.
4. _____ : Normal thyroid.
5. _____ : Disease of the heart muscle.
6. _____ : Next to the thyroid gland.
7. _____ : Inflammation of the joint.
8. _____ : High blood sugar.
9. _____ : Inability to swallow.
10. _____ : Condition of indigestion.
11. _____ : Inflamed or irritable colon.
12. _____ : Inflammation of the liver from various causes.
13. _____ : Protrusion of organ or tissue.
14. _____ : Painful urination.
15. _____ : Beneath the skin.
16. _____ : Through the skin.
17. _____ : A collection of blood, often clotted.
18. _____ : A disease in which the blood does not clot normally.
19. _____ : Lymphatic system tumor.
20. _____ : Top layer of skin.
21. _____ : Inflammation of a tendon.
22. _____ : Severe pain in a nerve.
23. _____ : Abnormal thickness of skin.
24. _____ : Abnormal growth of uteral tissue within the pelvis.
25. _____ : Removal of a section of the vas deferens.
26. _____ : A prostate stone.
27. _____ : Inflammation of bronchial membranes.
28. _____ : Pertaining to the lungs.
29. _____ : Inflammation of the bladder.
30. _____ : Forward curve of spine.
31. _____ : Inflammation of the eyelids.

CHOOSE THE BEST ANSWER

Answers are at the end of the book.

1. The system of medical and pharmaceutical nomenclature is made of these four elements:
   a. prefixes, suffixes, root words, and combining vowels.
   b. prefixes, suffixes, key words, and combining vowels.
   c. prefixes, suffixes, key words, and combining consonants.
   d. prefixes, suffixes, root words, and combining consonants.

2. The root word "plas" means
   a. skin.
   b. development.
   c. chest.
   d. lung.

3. Hematemesis is the vomiting of
   a. partially digested food.
   b. clear colorless liquid.
   c. blood.
   d. kidney.

4. The suffix "paresis" means
   a. treatment.
   b. tissue or structure.
   c. formation.
   d. partial paralysis.

5. Sublingual means
   a. narrowing of the tongue.
   b. inflammation of the tongue.
   c. under the tongue.
   d. without strength.

6. Prostatitis means
   a. a prostate stone.
   b. inability to produce semen.
   c. inflammation of the testes.
   d. inflammation of the prostate.

7. The primary organ of the urinary tract is the
   a. liver.
   b. kidney.
   c. bladder.
   d. intestine.

8. A keratosis is
   a. a skin inflammation.
   b. a fungal infection of the nails.
   c. an area of increased hardness.
   d. softening of the skin.

9. The suffix "emia" means
   a. tissue.
   b. pain.
   c. blood condition.
   d. recording process.

10. The suffix "tocia" means
    a. condition of.
    b. childbirth, labor.
    c. fear of.
    d. pain.

11. Arteriosclerosis means
    a. disease of the heart.
    b. concerning heart muscle.
    c. hardening of the arteries.
    d. clotting of blood.

12. The suffix "rrhage" means
    a. to burst forth.
    b. to discharge.
    c. around.
    d. origin or production.

13. The prefix "pseudo" means
    a. halt.
    b. false.
    c. around.
    d. with.

STUDY NOTES

Use this area to write important points you'd like to remember.

— 5 —

PRESCRIPTIONS

KEY CONCEPTS

Test your knowledge by covering the information in the right-hand column.

prescription	An instruction from a medical practitioner that authorizes a patient to be issued a drug or device.
prescription verification	It is necessary to check with the pharmacist on potential forgeries, on prescriptions that are more than a few days old, or on prescriptions that in any way appear questionable.
online billing	A prescription is interpreted and confirmed by the prescription system. If third-party billing is involved, this is done online simultaneously.
preparation	Once the prescription and third-party billing is confirmed, the label and receipt are printed and the prescription is prepared.
label	The general purpose of the prescription label is to provide information to the patient regarding the dispensed medication and how to take it. Additionally, the label includes information about the pharmacy, the patient, the prescriber, and the prescription or transaction number assigned to the prescription. Computer-generated prescription labels must be placed on containers so they are easy to locate and easy to read.
directions for use	Also known as Signa. Since the patient is expected to self-administer the medication, these must be clear and easily understood by the patient.
pharmacist check	If a prescription has been prepared by a technician, there is a final check by the pharmacist to make sure that it is correct.
judgment questions	Technicians must request the advice of the pharmacist whenever judgment is required.
prescription origin code	Additional prescription information a technician adds into the computer system (e.g., written, electronic, etc.).

| auxiliary labels | Many computerized prescription systems will automatically indicate which auxiliary labels to use with each drug. |

auxiliary labels

Many computerized prescription systems will automatically indicate which auxiliary labels to use with each drug.

controlled substance labels

Schedules II, III, and IV substances must carry an auxiliary label stating: "Caution: Federal law prohibits the transfer of this drug to any person other than the patient for whom it was prescribed."

institutional settings

There are different requirements for institutional prescriptions since nursing staff generally administer medications to patients. Rules for institutional pharmacy prescription labels vary by institution but often do not contain much more than the name, strength, manufacturer, expiration date, and dosage form of the medication.

medication orders

Used in institutional settings instead of a prescription form.

Health Insurance Portability and Accountability Act (HIPAA)

The Health Insurance Portability and Accountability Act. A federal law that protects patient privacy and regulates the sharing of protected health information.

protected health information (PHI)

Any personal information that could be used to identify an individual or their health history.

STUDY NOTES

Use this area to write important points you'd like to remember.

COMMON PHARMACY ABBREVIATIONS

Here are the most common pharmacy abbreviations.

ROUTE

a.d.	right ear
a.s., a.l.	left ear
a.u.	each ear
i.m., IM	intramuscular
inj.	injection
i.v., IV	intravenous
i.v.p., IVP	intravenous push
IVPB	intravenous piggyback
o.d.	right eye
o.s., o.l.	left eye
o.u.	each eye
per neb	by nebulizer
p.o.	by mouth
p.r.	rectally, into the rectum
p.v.	vaginally, into the vagina
SC, subc, subq	subcutaneously
S.L.	sublingually, under the tongue
top.	topically, locally

FORM

aq, aqua	water
caps	capsules
cm	cream
elix.	elixir
liq.	liquid
supp.	suppository
SR, XR, XL	slow/extended release
syr.	syrup
tab.	tablet
ung., oint.	ointment

TIME

a.c.	before food, before meals
a.m.	morning
b.i.d., bid	twice a day
h	hour, at the hour of
h.s.	at bedtime
p.c.	after food, after meals
p.m.	afternoon or evening
p.r.n., prn	as needed
q.i.d., qid	four times a day
q	each, every
q_h	every hour
stat.	immediately
t.i.d., tid	three times a day

MEASUREMENT

$\bar{\text{i}}$	one
a.a. or aa	of each
ad	to, up to
aq. ad	add water up to
dil.	dilute
div.	divide
f, fl.	fluid
fl. oz.	fluid ounce
g., G., gm	gram
gtt	drop
l, L	liter/Litre
mcg.	microgram
mEq	milliequivalent
mg	milligram
ml, mL	milliliter/millilitre
q.s.	a sufficient quantity
q.s. ad	add sufficient quantity to make
$\overline{\overline{\text{ss}}}$ or ss	one-half
tbsp.	tablespoon
tsp.	teaspoon

OTHER

c	with
disp.	dispense
f, ft.	make, let it be made
NR	no refill
$\bar{\text{s}}$	without
ut dict., u.d.	as directed
sig.	write, label
DAW	dispense as written

Note that the use of periods in abbreviations varies greatly. It is important to be able to recognize abbreviations with or without periods.

FILL IN THE BLANK

Answers are at the end of the book.

a.a. or aa	1. _____		mg	33. _____
a.c.	2. _____		ml	34. _____
a.d.	3. _____		NR	35. _____
a.m.	4. _____		NS	36. _____
a.s.	5. _____		o.d.	37. _____
a.u.	6. _____		o.s.	38. _____
aq	7. _____		o.u.	39. _____
BSA	8. _____		p.c.	40. _____
bid	9. _____		per neb	41. _____
c	10. _____		p.o.	42. _____
caps	11. _____		prn	43. _____
per g	12. _____		q	44. _____
dil.	13. _____		q4h	45. _____
disp.	14. _____		q6h	46. _____
per ngt	15. _____		qid	47. _____
D5W	16. _____		q.s.	48. _____
elix.	17. _____		qsad	49. _____
f, fl.	18. _____		s̄	50. _____
g., G., gm.	19. _____		SC	51. _____
gtt	20. _____		s̈s or ss	52. _____
h	21. _____		sig.	53. _____
h.s.	22. _____		stat.	54. _____
i.m., IM	23. _____		supp.	55. _____
i.v., IV	24. _____		syr.	56. _____
i.v.p., IVP	25. _____		tid	57. _____
NR	26. _____		tab.	58. _____
IVPB	27. _____		tbsp.	59. _____
L	28. _____		top.	60. _____
l	29. _____		tsp.	61. _____
liq.	30. _____		ung.	62. _____
mcg	31. _____		u.d.	63. _____
mEq	32. _____			

THE PRESCRIPTION

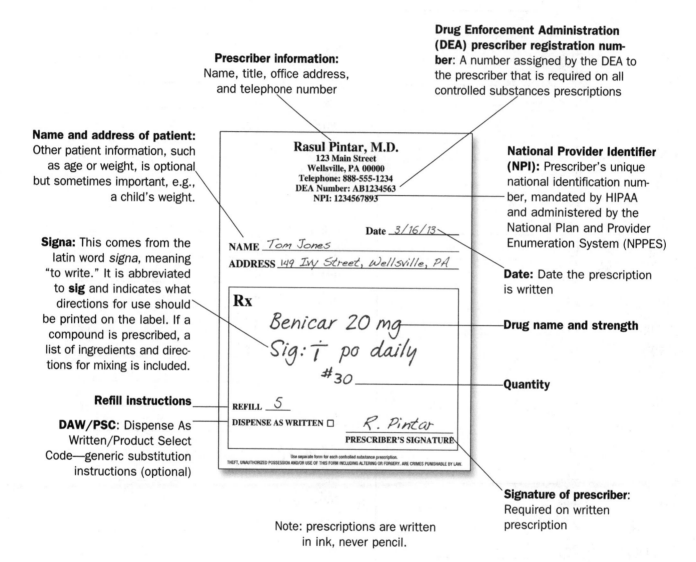

Prescriber information: Name, title, office address, and telephone number

Drug Enforcement Administration (DEA) prescriber registration number: A number assigned by the DEA to the prescriber that is required on all controlled substances prescriptions

Name and address of patient: Other patient information, such as age or weight, is optional but sometimes important, e.g., a child's weight.

National Provider Identifier (NPI): Prescriber's unique national identification number, mandated by HIPAA and administered by the National Plan and Provider Enumeration System (NPPES)

Signa: This comes from the latin word *signa*, meaning "to write." It is abbreviated to **sig** and indicates what directions for use should be printed on the label. If a compound is prescribed, a list of ingredients and directions for mixing is included.

Date: Date the prescription is written

Drug name and strength

Quantity

Refill instructions

DAW/PSC: Dispense As Written/Product Select Code—generic substitution instructions (optional)

Signature of prescriber: Required on written prescription

Rasul Pintar, M.D.
123 Main Street
Wellsville, PA 00000
Telephone: 888-555-1234
DEA Number: AB1234563
NPI: 1234567893

Date _3/16/13_

NAME _Tom Jones_
ADDRESS _149 Ivy Street, Wellsville, PA_

Rx

Benicar 20 mg
Sig: Ī po daily
#30

REFILL _5_
DISPENSE AS WRITTEN ☐

R. Pintar
PRESCRIBER'S SIGNATURE

Use separate form for each controlled substance prescription.
THEFT, UNAUTHORIZED POSSESSION AND/OR USE OF THIS FORM INCLUDING ALTERING OR FORGERY, ARE CRIMES PUNISHABLE BY LAW.

Note: prescriptions are written in ink, never pencil.

PRESCRIPTION LABELS

the name, address, and telephone number of the pharmacy

the date dispensed

the prescription and/or transaction number

the name of the patient for whom the medication is dispensed

directions for use that are clear and accurate

the name, quantity, strength, manufacturer (name or NDC number), and dosage form of the medication dispensed

expiration date of the medication

the name of the prescriber

refill information.

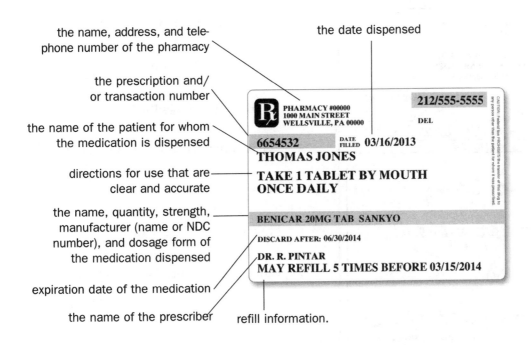

```
℞ PHARMACY #00000          212/555-5555
  1000 MAIN STREET
  WELLSVILLE, PA 00000      DEL

6654532         DATE FILLED 03/16/2013
THOMAS JONES
TAKE 1 TABLET BY MOUTH
ONCE DAILY

BENICAR 20MG TAB  SANKYO

DISCARD AFTER: 06/30/2014

DR. R. PINTAR
MAY REFILL 5 TIMES BEFORE 03/15/2014
```

AUXILIARY LABELS

Additional, often colored auxiliary labels may also be applied to the prescription container in order to provide additional information to the patient (e.g., Shake Well, Keep Refrigerated, Take with Food or Milk). Many computerized prescription systems will automatically indicate which auxiliary labels to use.

Controlled substances from Schedules II, III, and IV must carry an auxiliary label stating:

Caution: Federal law prohibits the transfer of this drug to any person other than the patient for whom it was prescribed.

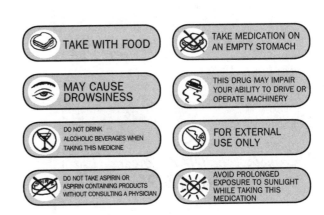

TAKE WITH FOOD

TAKE MEDICATION ON AN EMPTY STOMACH

MAY CAUSE DROWSINESS

THIS DRUG MAY IMPAIR YOUR ABILITY TO DRIVE OR OPERATE MACHINERY

DO NOT DRINK ALCOHOLIC BEVERAGES WHEN TAKING THIS MEDICINE

FOR EXTERNAL USE ONLY

DO NOT TAKE ASPIRIN OR ASPIRIN CONTAINING PRODUCTS WITHOUT CONSULTING A PHYSICIAN

AVOID PROLONGED EXPOSURE TO SUNLIGHT WHILE TAKING THIS MEDICATION

PRACTICE PRESCRIPTIONS

Identify the elements on these prescriptions by answering in the space beneath the question.

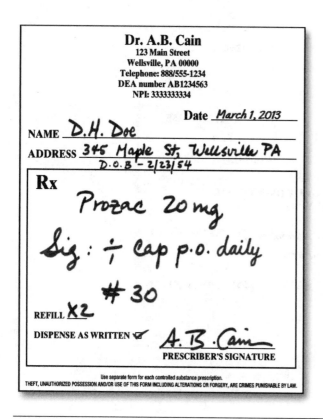

Dr. A.B. Cain
123 Main Street
Wellsville, PA 00000
Telephone: 888/555-1234
DEA number AB1234563
NPI: 3333333334

Date *March 1, 2013*

NAME *D.H. Doe*

ADDRESS *345 Maple St, Wellsville PA*
D.O.B – 2/23/54

Rx

Prozac 20 mg

Sig : ÷ cap p.o. daily

 # 30

REFILL *X2*

DISPENSE AS WRITTEN ☑ *A. B. Cain*

PRESCRIBER'S SIGNATURE

Use separate form for each controlled substance prescription.
THEFT, UNAUTHORIZED POSSESSION AND/OR USE OF THIS FORM INCLUDING ALTERATIONS OR FORGERY, ARE CRIMES PUNISHABLE BY LAW.

1. What is the name of the drug?

2. What is the strength?

3. What is the dosage form?

4. What is the route of administration?

5. What is the dosage?

6. How many refills are there?

7. Can there be generic substitution?

JANE T. DOE, MD
1002 Main Street
WELLSVILLE, PA, 00000
(212) 555-5555
NPI: 2222222228

Date *6/5/2013*

NAME *John Jones*

ADDRESS

Rx

Triamcinolone 0.1% Cream 15g
Apply BID

REFILL *1*

Doe

DEA No.

PRESCRIBER'S SIGNATURE

Use separate form for each controlled substance prescription.
THEFT, UNAUTHORIZED POSSESSION AND/OR USE OF THIS FORM INCLUDING ALTERATIONS OR FORGERY, ARE CRIMES PUNISHABLE BY LAW.

1. What is the strength of triamcinolone cream ordered by Dr. Doe?

2. How often should the medication be applied?

PRACTICE PRESCRIPTIONS

Identify the elements on these prescriptions by answering in the space beneath the question.

JANE T. DOE, MD
1002 Main Street
WELLSVILLE, PA, 00000
(212) 555-5555
NPI: 2222222228

Date __6/5/2013__

NAME __Andrew Jones__

ADDRESS _____

Rx

Protonix 40 mg #60
T BID x 8 weeks

REFILL __1__

Doe

DEA No. _____

PRESCRIBER'S SIGNATURE

Use separate form for each controlled substance perscription
THEFT, UNAUTHORIZED POSSESSION AND/OR USE OF THIS FORM INCLUDING ALTERATIONS OR FORGERY, ARE CRIMES PUNISHABLE BY LAW.

1. This prescription is written for Protonix®. If the medication is taken as prescribed, every day, how many days will this prescription last?

2. How many refills have been ordered for this prescription?

JANE T. DOE, MD
1002 Main Street
WELLSVILLE, PA, 00000
(212) 555-5555
NPI: 2222222228

Date __6/5/2013__

NAME __Steve Jones__

ADDRESS _____

Rx

Atrovent HFA #1 2-3 puff TID
Flovent HFA 110 mcg #1 2 puff BID

REFILL __5__

Doe

DEA No. _____

PRESCRIBER'S SIGNATURE

Use separate form for each controlled substance perscription
THEFT, UNAUTHORIZED POSSESSION AND/OR USE OF THIS FORM INCLUDING ALTERATIONS OR FORGERY, ARE CRIMES PUNISHABLE BY LAW.

1. By reading the box for the Atrovent® HFA you find that each inhaler contains 200 inhalations. What is the days supply that should be entered in the computer for the Atrovent prescription?

2. Flovent® HFA 110 mcg is dispensed in a 12 g canister that contains 120 metered doses. What is the days supply that should be entered in the computer for the Flovent® prescription?

PRACTICE PRESCRIPTIONS

Identify the elements on these prescriptions by answering in the space beneath the question.

JANE T. DOE, MD
1002 Main Street
WELLSVILLE, PA, 00000
(212) 555-5555
NPI: 2222222228

Date 6/5/2013

NAME *Samuel Jones*

ADDRESS

Rx

Synthroid 0.05 mg DAW #30
Ⅰ po daily

REFILL 5

Doe

DEA No.

PRESCRIBER'S SIGNATURE

Use separate form for each controlled substance perscription
THEFT, UNAUTHORIZED POSSESSION AND/OR USE OF THIS FORM INCLUDING ALTERATIONS OR FORGERY, ARE CRIMES PUNISHABLE BY LAW.

1. This patient has a dual co-pay of $15 for brand and $5 for generic. The patient has requested the generic for this prescription. What is written on the prescription that does not allow the generic to be dispensed?

JANE T. DOE, MD
1002 Main Street
WELLSVILLE, PA, 00000
(212) 555-5555
NPI: 2222222228

Date 6/5/2013

NAME *Francis Jones*

ADDRESS

Rx

Miacalcin 200 IU /nasal
Ⅰ inh daily (alt. nostrils)

REFILL 1

Doe

DEA No.

PRESCRIBER'S SIGNATURE

Use separate form for each controlled substance perscription
THEFT, UNAUTHORIZED POSSESSION AND/OR USE OF THIS FORM INCLUDING ALTERATIONS OR FORGERY, ARE CRIMES PUNISHABLE BY LAW.

1. How should the patient use this medication?

PRACTICE PRESCRIPTIONS

Identify the elements on these prescriptions by answering in the space beneath the question.

JANE T. DOE, MD
1002 Main Street
WELLSVILLE, PA, 00000
(212) 555-5555
NPI: 2222222228

Date 6/5/2013

NAME *Sandra Jones*

ADDRESS _____

Rx

Metrogel Vaginal 70 g
T applic PV qhs x 5D

REFILL *nr*

Doe

DEA No._____

PRESCRIBER'S SIGNATURE

Use separate form for each controlled substance perscription
THEFT, UNAUTHORIZED POSSESSION AND/OR USE OF THIS FORM INCLUDIND ALTERATIONS OR FORGERY, ARE CRIMES PUNISHABLE BY LAW.

1. What does 70 g mean for this prescription?

2. What does PV mean?

JANE T. DOE, MD
1002 Main Street
WELLSVILLE, PA, 00000
(212) 555-5555
NPI: 2222222228

Date 6/5/2013

NAME *Joyce Jones*

ADDRESS _____

Rx

Premarin 1.25 mg #21
T daily x 21, off 7

Provera 10 mg #5
1 daily days 10-14

REFILL 5

Doe

DEA No._____

PRESCRIBER'S SIGNATURE

Use separate form for each controlled substance perscription
THEFT, UNAUTHORIZED POSSESSION AND/OR USE OF THIS FORM INCLUDIND ALTERATIONS OR FORGERY, ARE CRIMES PUNISHABLE BY LAW.

1. How many days will the Premarin® prescription last?

2. How many days will the Provera® prescription last?

PRACTICE PRESCRIPTIONS

Identify the elements on these prescriptions by answering in the space beneath the question.

JANE T. DOE, MD
1002 Main Street
WELLSVILLE, PA, 00000
(212) 555-5555
NPI: 2222222228

Date **6/5/2013**

NAME **Cindy Jones**

ADDRESS _____

Rx

Ortho-Novum 777 28 day
T daily

REFILL **6**

DEA No. _____

Doe

PRESCRIBER'S SIGNATURE

Use separate form for each controlled substance perscription
THEFT, UNAUTHORIZED POSSESSION AND/OR USE OF THIS FORM INCLUDIND ALTERATIONS OR FORGERY, ARE CRIMES PUNISHABLE BY LAW.

1. What is the total number of compacts indicated by this prescription (including the original fill plus refills)?

JANE T. DOE, MD
1002 Main Street
WELLSVILLE, PA, 00000
(212) 555-5555
NPI: 2222222228

Date **6/5/2013**

NAME **Jane Jones**

ADDRESS _____

Rx

Bactrim DS 20
T po BID

REFILL **nr**

DEA No. _____

Doe

PRESCRIBER'S SIGNATURE

Use separate form for each controlled substance perscription
THEFT, UNAUTHORIZED POSSESSION AND/OR USE OF THIS FORM INCLUDIND ALTERATIONS OR FORGERY, ARE CRIMES PUNISHABLE BY LAW.

1. As you are entering this prescription in the computer, an allergy warning is displayed on the computer screen. What type of allergy does Jane Jones have?

PRACTICE PRESCRIPTIONS

Identify the elements on these prescriptions by answering in the space beneath the question.

JANE T. DOE, MD
1002 Main Street
WELLSVILLE, PA, 00000
(212) 555-5555
NPI: 2222222228
Date _6/5/2013_

NAME _Ann Jones_

ADDRESS _____

Rx

Cefadroxil 500mg/5ml
iȝ po BID x 10

REFILL _ur_

DEA No. _____

Doe

PRESCRIBER'S SIGNATURE

Use separate form for each controlled substance persoription
THEFT, UNAUTHORIZED POSSESSION AND/OR USE OF THIS FORM INCLUDIND ALTERATIONS OR FORGERY, ARE CRIMES PUNISHABLE BY LAW.

1. What directions should be placed on the label for this prescription?

JANE T. DOE, MD
1002 Main Street
WELLSVILLE, PA, 00000
(212) 555-5555
NPI: 2222222228
Date _6/5/2013_

NAME _Tom Jones_

ADDRESS _____

Rx

Amoxicillin 500 mg 2 po BID x 7
Biaxin 500 mg po BID x 7
Aciphex 20 mg po BID x 7

REFILL _ur_

DEA No. _____

Doe

PRESCRIBER'S SIGNATURE

Use separate form for each controlled substance persoription
THEFT, UNAUTHORIZED POSSESSION AND/OR USE OF THIS FORM INCLUDIND ALTERATIONS OR FORGERY, ARE CRIMES PUNISHABLE BY LAW.

1. How many capsules should be dispensed for the amoxicillin?

2. How many tablets should be dispensed for the Biaxin®?

3. How many tablets should be dispensed for the Aciphex®?

PRACTICE MEDICATION ORDERS

Identify the elements on this medication order by answering in the space beneath the question.

<table>
<tr><td colspan="4" rowspan="2">DOCTOR'S ORDERS</td><td colspan="2">PATIENT IDENTIFICATION</td></tr>
<tr><td>099999999
SMITH, JOHN
12/06/1950

DR. P. JOHNSON</td><td>675-01</td></tr>
</table>

DATE	TIME	DOCTOR'S ORDERS ①	DATE/TIME INITIALS	DATE/TIME INITIALS
1/3/13	22⁰⁰	Admit patient to 6th floor		
		Pneumonia, Dehydration		
		All: PCN- Rash		
		Order CBC, chem-7, blood cultures stat		
		NS @ 125ml/hr IV		
		—Dr Johnson X2222		

DATE	TIME	DOCTOR'S ORDERS ②	DATE/TIME INITIALS	DATE/TIME INITIALS
2/01/13	3⁰⁰	Tylenol 650mg po q4-6 hrs PRN for Temp > 38°C		
		Verbal Order Dr Johnson/Jane Doe, RN		

DATE	TIME	DOCTOR'S ORDERS ③	DATE/TIME INITIALS	DATE/TIME INITIALS
2/01/13	6⁰⁰	Start Clarithromycin 500mg po q 12°		
		Multivitamin po daily		
		Order CXR for this a.m.		
		—Dr Johnson X2222		

1. What is the patient's disorder/condition?

2. Does the patient have allergies?

3. What route and dosage is ordered for the Tylenol® 650 mg?

4. What orders did the physician sign for?

5. What route and dosage are prescribed for the Clarithromycin?

6. What route and dosage are prescribed for the multivitamin?

PRACTICE MEDICATION ORDERS

Identify the elements on this medication order by answering in the space beneath the question.

PATIENT: John Smith AGE: 35 SEX: m CHART #: #123555	CITY HOSPITAL PHYSICIAN'S ORDERS			

ALLERGIES:	DIAGNOSIS:		COMPLETED OR DISCONTINUED	

DATE	TIME	ORDERS	SIGNATURE	NAME	DATE	TIME
		Meds:				
5/13	12:34 pm	① Lopressor 50 mg po daily				
		② HCTZ 25 mg po daily				
		③ Sonata 5 mg po hs prn				
		Doe				

PHARMACY COPY

1. What three medications have been ordered?

2. How often should the Sonata® be taken?

PRACTICE MEDICATION ORDERS

Identify the elements on these medication orders by answering in the space beneath the question.

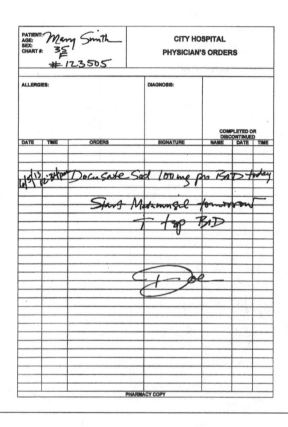

1. What medication has been ordered for today?

2. What medication should be started tomorrow?

1. What does STAT mean in the order for Vitamin B-12?

2. What is the route of administration for Vitamin B-12?

PRACTICE MEDICATION ORDERS

Identify the elements on these medication orders by answering in the space beneath the question.

PATIENT: Steve Smith	CITY HOSPITAL
AGE: 45 SEX: m CHART #: 123777	PHYSICIAN'S ORDERS

ALLERGIES: Penicillin

DIAGNOSIS:

DATE	TIME	ORDERS	SIGNATURE	COMPLETED OR DISCONTINUED NAME	DATE	TIME
6/5/13	10:15ᵃᵐ	IVF NS @ 100 cc/hr for 2 days				
		HCTZ 25 mg po daily				
		Diovan 80 mg po daily				
		Doe				

PHARMACY COPY

1. What is the rate for the IV in this medication order?

2. What medications are to be given orally?

PATIENT: Barbara Smith	CITY HOSPITAL
AGE: 45 SEX: F CHART #: 123718	PHYSICIAN'S ORDERS

ALLERGIES: Codeine

DIAGNOSIS:

DATE	TIME	ORDERS	SIGNATURE	COMPLETED OR DISCONTINUED NAME	DATE	TIME
6/5/13	10:00ᵃᵐ	FS AC & HS				
		Glyburide 5mg po daily				
		Ambien 5mg po hs prn				
		Doe				

PHARMACY COPY

1. What medications have been ordered?

2. Which medication would be administered at bedtime, as needed?

FILL IN THE KEY TERM

Use these key terms to fill in the correct blank. Answers are at the end of the book.

auxiliary label	HIPAA	prescription origin code
DAW	look-alikes	Rx
DEA number	medication order	Schedule II drugs
DUR	NPI	unit dose labels
extemporaneous compounding	PHI	

1. _____ :   Drugs that have a high abuse potential and require special handling.

2. _____ :   The pharmaceutical preparation of a medication from ingredients.

3. _____ :   Health Insurance Portability and Accountability Act that requires pharmacies to provide written notice of their privacy practices.

4. _____ :   Information added in the computer system about a prescription's source (e.g., written, electronic, etc.).

5. _____ :   The additional warning labels that are placed on filled prescription containers.

6. _____ :   The form used to prescribe medications for patients in institutional settings.

7. _____ :   Drug names that have similar appearance, particularly when written.

8. _____ :   Abbreviation for the Latin word "recipe."

9. _____ :   Dispense As Written, meaning generic substitution not allowed.

10. _____ :   Protected health information defined under HIPAA.

11. _____ :   Often do not contain much more than the name, strength, manufacturer, expiration date, and dosage form of the medication.

12. _____ :   Drug utilization review.

13. _____ :   Prescriber's unique national identification number.

14. _____ :   Required on all controlled substance prescriptions.

TRUE/FALSE

Indicate whether the statement is true or false in the blank. Answers are at the end of the book.

_____ 1. In addition to the primary prescribers, nurse practitioners, pharmacists, and physician assistants are allowed to write prescriptions in some states.

_____ 2. Prescriptions may be handwritten or electronically produced.

_____ 3. Rules and regulations for dispensing prescriptions for hospital inpatients are the same as for community pharmacies.

_____ 4. If DAW is indicated, generic substitution may not be used.

_____ 5. A prescription has no time limit.

_____ 6. Counseling patients on the use of OTC medications should be done by the pharmacist.

_____ 7. One of the primary purposes of the prescription label is to provide the patient with clear instructions on how to take the medication.

_____ 8. Unit dose labels must have the same information as in the community setting.

_____ 9. Pharmacy clerks are not required to have formal HIPAA training.

_____ 10. A DEA number is required on all prescriptions.

EXPLAIN WHY

Explain why these statements are true or important. Check your answers in the text. Discuss any questions you may have with your instructor.

1. Why must the pharmacist always check the filled prescription before it is dispensed to the patient?

2. Why must the directions for use be clear and understandable to the patient in the community setting?

3. What are the differences between the prescription and the medication order? Why?

4. Why must prescriptions be written in ink?

5. Why are auxiliary labels important?

CHOOSE THE BEST ANSWER

Answers are at the end of the book.

1. A prescription was written for Zocor® and simvastatin was dispensed in accordance with insurance plan guidelines. This is an example of
   a. D.A.W.
   b. look-alike.
   c. generic substitution.
   d. prior authorization.

2. In community pharmacies, _____ generally receive the prescription and collect patient data and enter this information into the computer.
   a. pharmacists
   b. pharmacy technicians

3. In institutional settings, _____ generally administer medications to patients.
   a. nursing staff
   b. pharmacy staff

4. When a prescription is written for a medication that is not commercially available, the medication can be prepared by mixing the ingredients required and this is called
   a. alligation.
   b. extemporaneous compounding.
   c. trituration.
   d. admixture.

5. If a new prescription has been prepared by a pharmacy technician, the final check is done by the
   a. lead pharmacy technician.
   b. pharmacist.
   c. patient.
   d. physician.

6. Prescriptions are written in
   a. ink.
   b. either ink or pencil.
   c. pencil.

7. The DEA Number is required on prescriptions for
   a. legend drugs.
   b. medical devices.
   c. controlled substances.
   d. OTCs.

8. An excellent resource for drug safety information:
   a. OTC.
   b. NDC.
   c. ISMP.
   d. PSC.

9. The NPI was mandated by
   a. the APhA.
   b. the ASHP.
   c. HIPAA.
   d. the ISMP.

10. The route of administration should be indicated on the prescription if it is different from
    a. injectable.
    b. rectal.
    c. oral.
    d. topical.

11. When the Sig contains t.i.d., the medication should be taken _____ times a day.
    a. one
    b. two
    c. three
    d. four

12. Labels from _____ pharmacies contain more information than labels from _____ pharmacies.
    a. community, institutional
    b. institutional, hospital
    c. institutional, community
    d. hospital, institutional

CHOOSE THE BEST ANSWER

Answers are at the end of the book.

13. If a prescription requires extemporaneous compounding, the technician should inform the patient that
    a. the medication may be obtained without a prescription.
    b. there may be a delay in filling the prescription.
    c. a DEA number is required.
    d. any refills cannot be honored.

14. Directions should start with a
    a. verb.
    b. noun.
    c. adjective.
    d. pronoun.

15. For the prescription: Bactrim® DS #20 ī b.i.d. nr, how many days should the prescription last?
    a. 2
    b. 5
    c. 10
    d. 20

STUDY NOTES

Use this area to write important points you'd like to remember.

— 6 —

Calculations

RATIO AND PROPORTION

Most of the calculations pharmacy technicians will face on the job or in the certification exam can be performed using the ratio and proportion method.

A ratio states a relationship between two quantities. ➡ $\dfrac{a}{b}$

A proportion contains two equal ratios. ➡ $\dfrac{a}{b} = \dfrac{c}{d}$

When three of the four quantities in a proportion are known, the value of the fourth (x) can be easily solved. ➡ $\dfrac{x}{b} = \dfrac{c}{d}$

CONDITIONS FOR USING RATIO AND PROPORTION

1. Three of the four values must be known.

2. Numerators must have the same units.

3. Denominators must have the same units.

STEPS FOR SOLVING PROPORTION PROBLEMS

1. Define the variable and correct ratios.

2. Set up the proportion equation.

3. Establish the x equation.

4. Solve for x.

5. Express the solution in correct units.

Example

If there are 125 mg of a substance in a 500 ml solution, and 50 mg is desired, the amount of solution needed can be determined with this equation:

$$\frac{x \text{ ml}}{50 \text{ mg}} = \frac{500 \text{ ml}}{125 \text{ mg}}$$

multiplying both sides by 50 mg gives:

x ml = 2,500 ml/125

solving for x gives:

x = 200

answer: 200 ml of solution are needed.

CONVERSIONS

Many proportion problems involve the use of conversions from one unit of measure to another. Here is a list of the most common.

Liquid Metric

1 l	=	10 dl	= 1,000 ml
1 dl	=	0.1 l	= 100 ml
1 ml	=	0.001 l	= 0.01 dl

Solid Metric

1 kg	=	1,000 g	
1 g	=	0.001 kg	= 1,000 mg
1 mg	=	0.001 g	= 1,000 mcg
1 mcg	=	0.001 mg	

Avoirdupois

1 lb	=	16 oz
1 oz	=	437.5 gr
1 gr	=	64.8 mg (.0648 g)

Apothecary

1 gal	=	4 qt
1 qt	=	2 pt
1 pt	=	16 fl oz
1 fl oz	=	8 fl dr
1 fl dr	=	60 m

Household

1 tsp	=	5 ml	
1 tbs	=	3 tsp	= 15 ml
1 cup	=	8 fl oz	

Temperature

F temperature = (1 ⅘ times number of degrees C) + 32

C temperature = ⁵⁄₉ x (number of degrees F - 32)

$9C = 5F - 16$

Conversions Between Systems

1 l	=	33.8 fl oz		1 lb	=	453.59 g
1 pt	=	473.167 ml		1 oz	=	28.35 g
1 fl oz	=	29.57ml		1 g	=	15.43 gr
1 kg	=	2.2 lb		1 gr	=	64.8 mg

ROMAN NUMERALS

Roman numerals can be capital or lower case letters, and are:

ss = 1/2	L or l = 50
I or i = 1	C or c = 100
V or v = 5	D or d = 500
X or x = 10	M or m = 1,000

RULES:

➡ When the second of two letters has a value equal to or smaller than that of the first, their values are to be added.

➡ When the second of two letters has a value greater than that of the first, the smaller is to be subtracted from the larger.

CONVERSION EXERCISES

Convert these numbers to decimals:

1. 5/8 _____
2. 0.2% _____
3. 1/5 _____
4. 2/3 _____
5. 12% _____
6. 38.5% _____
7. 1.5% _____

Convert these numbers to percents:

8. 0.7 _____
9. 75/100 _____
10. 1.5 _____
11. 1/4 _____
12. 0.04 _____
13. 4/5 _____
14. 0.025 _____

Write the following in Roman numerals:

15. 67 _____
16. 29 _____
17. 41 _____
18. 108 _____
19. 6 _____
20. 98 _____
21. 9 _____

Write the following in arabic numbers:

22. XIX _____
23. CIII _____
24. CMM _____
25. iss _____
26. XX _____
27. LIV _____

PROBLEMS

1. You have a prescription that calls for 1 cap po tid x 10 days. How many capsules are needed?

2. You have a prescription that calls for 1 cap po tid x 7 days. How many capsules are needed?

3. If a compounding order calls for Flagyl® 125 mg bid x 7 days, and only 500 mg tablets are available, how many tablets will it take to fill the order?

4. How much talc is needed for an order for 30 g of the following compound: Nupercainal® ointment 4%, zinc oxide 20%, talc 2%?

5. A prescription calls for 200 mg of a drug that you have in a 10 mg/15 ml concentration. How many ml of the liquid do you need?

PEDIATRIC DOSES

Because of the many variables, conversion formulas for pediatric doses are rarely used in the pharmacy. Doses are generally given by the physician. **Children's doses are stated by kg of body weight (dose/ kg).** Since 1 kg = 2.2 lb, you can solve for the prescribed dose by using a proportion equation if you know the child's body weight. See the following example.

> An antibiotic IV is prescribed for an infant. The dose is to be 15 mg/kg twice a day. The baby weighs 12 lbs. How much drug is to be given for one dose? First the infant's weight in kilograms should be calculated.

> x kg / 12 lb = 1 kg / 2.2 lb

> x kg = 12 lb times $\dfrac{1 \text{ kg}}{2.2 \text{ lb}} = \dfrac{12 \text{ kg}}{2.2} = 5.45$ kg

The next part of this problem can be solved with a simple equation.

> one dose = 15 mg times 5.45 = 81.75 mg

PERCENTS & SOLUTIONS

Percents are used to indicate the amount or **concentration** of something in a solution. Concentrations are indicated in terms of weight to volume or volume to volume. The standard units are:

> **Weight to Volume: grams per 100 milliliters** ➡ **g/100 ml**

> **Volume to Volume: milliliters per 100 milliliters** ➡ **ml/100 ml**

A PERCENT SOLUTION FORMULA

Technicians find that they often have to convert a solution at one concentration to a solution having a different concentration, especially during the preparation of hyperalimentation or TPNs. It is possible to make such conversions using a simple proportion equation with these elements:

$$\frac{x \text{ volume wanted}}{\text{want \%}} = \frac{\text{volume prescribed}}{\text{have \%}}$$

FLOW RATE

In some settings, the flow rate or rate of administration for an IV solution needs to be calculated. This is done using a ratio and proportion equation. Rates are generally calculated in ml/hour, but for pumps used to dispense IV fluids to a patient, the calculation may need to be done in ml/min or gtt/min.

For example, if you have an order for KCl 10 mEq and K Acetate 15 mEq in D5W 1,000 ml to run at 80 ml/hour, you would determine the administration rate in ml/minute as follows:

x ml/1 min = 80 ml/60 min

x = 80/60 = 1.33

To get **drops per minute (gtt/min)**, you must have a conversion rate of drops per ml. For example, if the administration set for the above order delivered 30 drops per ml, you would find the drops per minute as follows:

$$\frac{80 \text{ ml}}{60 \text{ min}} \text{ x } \frac{30 \text{ gtt}}{1 \text{ ml}} = \frac{2400 \text{ gtt}}{60 \text{ min}} = 40 \text{ gtt/min}$$

MILLIEQUIVALENTS—MEQ

Electrolytes are substances that conduct an electrical current and are found in the body's blood, tissue fluids, and cells. Salts are electrolytes and saline solutions are a commonly used electrolyte solution. The concentration of electrolytes in a volume of solution is measured in units called milliequivalents (mEq). They are expressed as milliequivalents per milliliter or equivalents per liter.

Milliequivalents are a unit of measurement specific to each electrolyte. For example, a 0.9% solution of one electrolyte will have a different mEq value than a 0.9% solution of another because mEq values are based on each electrolyte's atomic weight and electron properties, each of which is different.

If the mEq value of a solution is known, it is relatively easy to mix it with other solutions to get a different mEq volume ratio by using proportions.

EXAMPLE

A solution calls for 5 mEq of an electrolyte that you have in a 1.04 mEq/ml solution. How many ml of it do you need?

x ml/5 mEq = 1 ml/1.04 mEq

$$\text{x ml } = 5 \text{ mEq times } \frac{1 \text{ ml}}{1.04 \text{ mEq}} = \frac{5 \text{ ml}}{1.04} = 4.8 \text{ ml}$$

Answer: 4.8 ml of the solution is needed.

PROBLEMS

6. An IV requires the addition of 40 mEq potassium chloride (KCl). You have a vial of KCl at a concentration of 20 mEq per 10 ml. How many ml should be added?

7. If 100 grams of dextrose is ordered using a 50% dextrose solution, how many ml are needed?

8. A prescription calls for 0.36 mg of a drug that you have in 50 mcg/ml concentration. How many ml do you need?

9. The infusion rate of an IV is 300 ml over 5 hours. What is the ml/minute rate?

10. The infusion rate of an IV is 1,000 ml over 12 hours. What is the rate in ml per minute?

11. An IV order calls for administration of 1.5 ml/minute of a solution for two hours. How much solution will be needed.

12. If a physician orders 25% dextrose ,1000 ml and all you have is 70% dextrose 1,000 ml, how much 70% dextrose and how much sterile water will be used?

13. If a physician orders 20% dextrose 1,000 ml and all you have is 70% dextrose 1,000 ml, how much 70% dextrose and how much sterile water will be used?

14. If a physician orders 25% dextrose 500 ml and you have 50% dextrose 1,000 ml, how much 50% dextrose and how much sterile water do you need?

Total Parenteral Nutrition

A TPN order calls for the amounts on the left (including additives) to be made from the items on the right. The total volume is to be 1,000 ml. How much of each ingredient and how much sterile water do you need to prepare this TPN?

TPN Order	On Hand	
Aminosyn® 4.25%	Aminosyn® 8.5%	1,000 ml
dextrose 20%	dextrose 50%	500 ml

Additives:

KCl	24 mEq	KCl 2 mEq/ml	20 ml
MVI	5 ml	MVI	10 ml
NaCl	24 mEq	NaCl 4.4 mEq/ml	20 ml

Figure out the amounts and enter the answer on the blank line.

1. Aminosyn®   _____

2. dextrose   _____

3. KCl   _____

4. MVI   _____

5. NaCl   _____

6. sterile water   _____

RETAIL MATH

Technicians in community pharmacies must know how to perform common retail calculations. Besides simple addition and subtraction, the most important calculations involve using percentages, especially in doing markups or discounts. A markup is the amount of the retailer's selling price minus their purchase cost. It is calculated by multiplying the retailer's purchase cost by the markup percentage and adding the amount to the cost.

For example, a 30% markup on an item purchased for $2.30 is $0.69 (Note that 30% equals 0.3, and that $2.30 x 0.3 = $0.69), so the selling price would be $2.99 ($2.30 + $0.69).

Conversely, if you knew a $2.99 sale item was marked up $0.69 and were asked to figure out the percent markup, you would subtract the $0.69 from $2.99 to get the cost of the item ($2.30), and then divide the markup by the cost: $0.69 ÷ $2.30 = 0.3 = 30%.

Discounts involve subtracting a percentage amount from the marked up price of an item. A 30% discount on the $2.99 item is $0.90, so $2.09 would be the discounted price ($2.99-$0.90). Note that this is different than the cost of the item, because you deducted the percentage from the marked up price.

— 7 —

ROUTES & FORMULATIONS

KEY CONCEPTS

Test your knowledge by covering the information in the right-hand column.

formulations

Drugs are contained in products called formulations. There are many drug formulations and many different routes to administer them.

route of administration

Routes are classified as enteral or parenteral. Enteral refers to anything involving the tract from the mouth to the rectum. There are three enteral routes: oral, sublingual, and rectal. Any route other than oral, sublingual, and rectal is considered a parenteral administration route. Oral administration is the most frequently used route of administration.

local and systemic effects

A local effect occurs when the drug activity is at the site of administration (e.g., eyes, ears, nose, skin). A systemic effect occurs when the drug is introduced into the circulatory system.

oral administration

The stomach has a pH around 1–2. Certain drugs cannot be taken orally because they are degraded or destroyed by stomach acid and intestinal enzymes. Drugs administered by liquid dosage forms generally reach the circulatory system faster than drugs formulated in solid dosage forms.

oral formulations

Oral formulations contain various ingredients besides the active drug. These inactive ingredients include binders, lubricants, fillers, diluents, and disintegrants.

gastrointestinal action

The disintegration and dissolution of tablets, capsules, and powders generally begins in the stomach, but will continue to occur when the stomach empties into the intestine. Modified-release formulations extend dissolution over a period of hours and provide a longer duration of effect compared to plain tablets. Enteric coated tablets prevent the tablet from disintegrating until it reaches the higher pHs of the intestine.

sublingual administration	These tablets are placed under the tongue. They are generally fast-dissolving, uncoated tablets that contain highly water-soluble drugs. When the drug is released from the tablet, it is quickly absorbed into the circulatory system since the membranes lining the mouth are very thin and there is a rich blood supply to the mouth.
rectal administration	Rectal administration may be used to achieve a variety of systemic effects, including: asthma control, antinausea, anti-motion sickness, and anti-infective. However, absorption from rectal administration is erratic and unpredictable. The most common rectal administration forms are suppositories, solutions, and ointments.
parenteral administration	Parenteral routes are often preferred when oral administration causes drug degradation or when a rapid drug response is desired, as in an emergency situation. The parenteral routes requiring a needle are intravenous, intramuscular, intradermal, and subcutaneous. These solutions must be sterile (bacteria-free), have an appropriate pH, and be limited in volume.
intravenous formulations	Intravenous dosage forms are administered directly into a vein (and the blood supply). Most solutions are aqueous (water based), but they may also have glycols, alcohols, or other nonaqueous solvents in them.
IV emulsions	Fat emulsions and TPN emulsions are used to provide triglycerides, fatty acids, and calories for patients who cannot absorb them from the gastrointestinal tract.
infusion	Infusion is the gradual intravenous injection of a volume of fluid into a patient.
intravenous sites	Several sites on the body are used to intravenously administer drugs: the veins of the antecubital area (in front of the elbow), the back of the hand, and some of the larger veins in the foot. On some occasions, a vein must be exposed by a surgical cut.
intramuscular injections	The principal sites of injection are the gluteal maximus (buttocks), deltoid (upper arm), and vastus lateralis (thigh) muscles. Intramuscular injections generally result in lower but longer lasting blood concentrations than with intravenous administration.
subcutaneous injections	Injection sites include the back of the upper arm, the front of the thigh, the lower portion of the abdomen and the upper back. The subcutaneous (SC, SQ) route can be used for both short-term and very long-term therapies. Insulin is the most important drug routinely administered by this route.

KEY CONCEPTS

Test your knowledge by covering the information in the right hand column.

intradermal injections

Intradermal injections involve small volumes that are injected into the top layer of skin. The usual site for intradermal injections is the anterior surface of the forearm.

ophthalmic formulations

Every ophthalmic product must be manufactured to be sterile in its final container. A major problem of ophthalmic administration is the immediate loss of a dose by natural spillage from the eye.

intranasal formulations

Intranasal formulations are primarily used for their decongestant activity on the nasal mucosa, the cellular lining of the nose. The drugs that are typically used are decongestants, antihistamines, and corticosteroids. Nasal administration often causes amounts of the drug to be swallowed, in some cases this may lead to a systemic effect.

inhalation formulations

Inhalation dosage forms are intended to deliver drugs to the pulmonary system (lungs). Most of the inhalation dosage forms are aerosols that depend on the power of compressed or liquefied gas to expel the drug from the container. Gaseous or volatile anesthetics are the most important drugs administered via this route. Other drugs administered affect lung function, act as bronchodilators, or treat allergic symptoms. Examples of drugs administered by this route are adrenocorticoid steroids (beclomethasone), bronchodilators (epinephrine, isoproterenol, metaproterenol, albuterol), and antiallergics (cromolyn sodium).

dermal formulations

Most dermal dosage forms are used for local (topical) effects on or within the skin. Dermal formulations are used to treat minor skin infections, itching, burns, diaper rash, insect stings and bites, athlete's foot, corns, calluses, warts, dandruff, acne, psoriasis, and eczema. The major disadvantage of this route of administration is that the amount of drug that can be absorbed will be limited to about 2 mg/hour.

vaginal administration

Formulations for this route of administration are: solutions, powders for solutions, ointments, creams, aerosol foams, suppositories, tablets, and IUDs. Vaginal administration leads to variable absorption since the vagina is a physiologically and anatomically dynamic organ with pH and absorption characteristics changing over time. Another disadvantage of this route is that administration of a formulation during menstruation could predispose the patient to toxic shock syndrome.

True/False

Indicate whether the statement is true or false in the blank. Answers are at the end of the book.

_____ 1. Buccal administration is a parenteral route of administration.

_____ 2. Oral administration is the most frequently used route of administration.

_____ 3. With oral formulations, drugs administered by solid dosage forms generally reach the systemic circulation faster than liquid dosage forms.

_____ 4. A low pH value such as 1 or 2 indicates a high acidity.

_____ 5. In an emulsion, if the oleaginous component is present as droplets, the emulsion is called water-in-oil.

_____ 6. Phlebitis can be a complication of intravenous administration.

_____ 7. The needle length for a subcutaneous injection is generally shorter than the needle length for an intramuscular injection.

_____ 8. It takes about 20 seconds for an intravenously administered drug to circulate throughout the body.

_____ 9. Ophthalmic ointment tubes typically hold about 3.5 g of ointment.

_____ 10. Toxic shock syndrome is a disease caused by a bacterial infection.

Explain Why

Explain why these statements are true or important. Check your answers in the text. Discuss any questions you may have with your instructor.

1. Give three reasons why a drug might not be used for oral administration.

2. Give three reasons why a drug might not be used for parenteral administration.

3. Why do most parenterals require skilled personnel to administer them?

4. Why is the pH of intravenous solutions important?

5. Why is the development of infusion pumps important?

6. Why is a spacer sometimes used with a metered dose inhaler?

FILL IN THE KEY TERM

Answers are at the end of the book.

aqueous	intradermal injections	pH
atomizer	intramuscular injection sites	suspensions
buccal	intravenous sites	sterile
buffer system	IUD	sublingual
bulk powders	lacrimal canalicula	syringeability
colloids	lacrimal gland	syrups
diluent	local effect	systemic effect
disintegration	metered dose inhalers	toxic shock syndrome
dissolution	nasal inhaler	transcorneal transport
emulsions	nasal mucosa	viscosity
enteric coated	necrosis	water soluble
hemorrhoid	ophthalmic	wheal
hydrates	parenteral	Z-tract injection
injectability	percutaneous absorption	

1. _____ : When the drug activity is at the site of administration (e.g., eyes, ears, nose, skin).

2. _____ : When a drug is introduced into the circulatory system by any route of administration and carried to the site of activity.

3. _____ : Ingredients designed to control the pH of a product.

4. _____ : Solid formulations to be mixed with water or juice.

5. _____ : The pouch between the cheeks and teeth in the mouth.

6. _____ : Absorbs water.

7. _____ : Coating that will not let the tablet disintegrate until it reaches the higher pHs of the intestine.

8. _____ : The property of a substance being able to dissolve in water.

9. _____ : Under the tongue.

10. _____ : Measure of acidity or alkalinity of a substance.

11. _____ : Any route that does not involve the alimentary tract.

12. _____ : Increase in cell death.

13. _____ : Related to the eye.

14. _____ : Injections administered into the top layer of the skin using short needles.

15. _____ : The veins of the antecubital area (in front of the elbow), the back of the hand, and some of the larger veins in the foot.

16. _____ : Painful/swollen veins in the anal/rectal area.

17. _____ : Liquid formulations in which the drug does not completely dissolve in the solvent.

18. _____ : Tear ducts.

19. _____ : Drug transfer into the eye.

20. _____ : A mixture of two liquids that do not mix with each other in which one liquid is spread through the other by mixing and use of a stabilizer.

21. _____ : Gluteal (buttocks), deltoid (upper arm), and vastus lateralis (thigh) muscles.

22. _____ : Ease with which a suspension can be drawn into a syringe.

23. _____ : The thickness of a liquid.

24. _____ : Water-based.

25. _____ : A raised blister-like area on the skin, as caused by an intradermal injection.

26. _____ : The gland that produces tears for the eye.

27. _____ : Breaking a part of a tablet into smaller pieces.

28. _____ : Suspended formulation with particle size up to a hundred times smaller than a suspension.

29. _____ : Injection technique for medications that stain the skin.

30. _____ : The cellular lining of the nose.

31. _____ : Device used to convert liquid to a spray.

32. _____ : A device that contains a drug that is vaporized by inhalation.

33. _____ : Ease of flow when a suspension is injected into a patient.

34. _____ : Aerosols that use special metering valves to deliver a fixed dose when the aerosol is actuated.

35. _____ : The absorption of drugs through the skin, often for a systemic effect.

36. _____ : When the smaller pieces of a disintegrated tablet dissolve in solution.

37. _____ : Concentrated solutions of sugar in water.

38. _____ : Free of microorganisms.

39. _____ : A rare and potentially fatal disease that results from a severe bacterial infection of the blood.

40. _____ : A solvent that dissolves a freeze-dried powder or dilutes a solution.

41. _____ : An intrauterine contraceptive device that is placed in the uterus for a prolonged period of time.

IDENTIFY

Identify the route of administration.

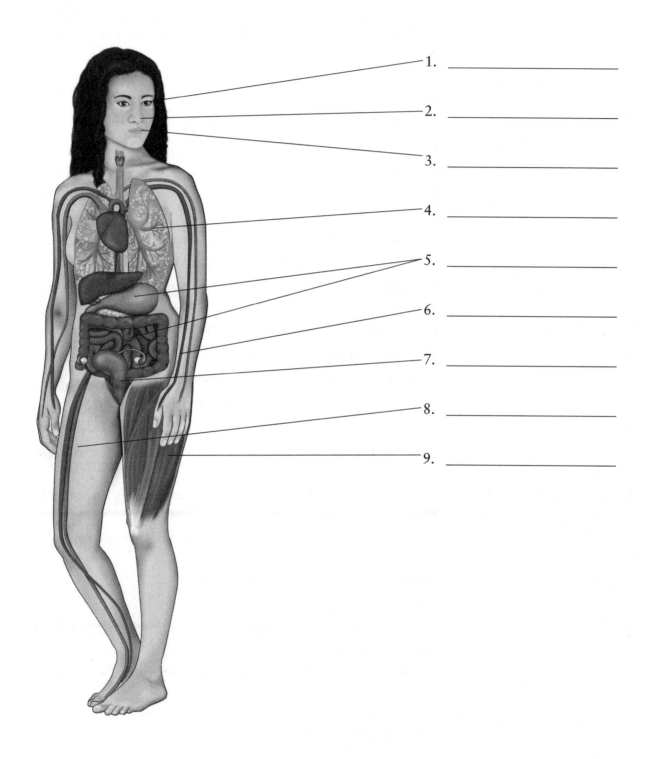

1. _____

2. _____

3. _____

4. _____

5. _____

6. _____

7. _____

8. _____

9. _____

IDENTIFY

Identify the routes of administration.

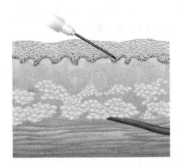

1. _____

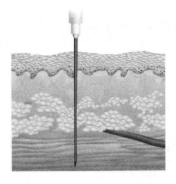

4. _____

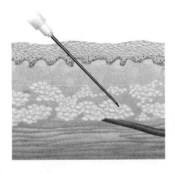

2. _____

Identify these sites of intramuscular administration on the figure at right:

1. deltoid _____

2. gluteus maximus _____

3. gluteus medius _____

4. vastus lateralis _____

5. ventrogluteal _____

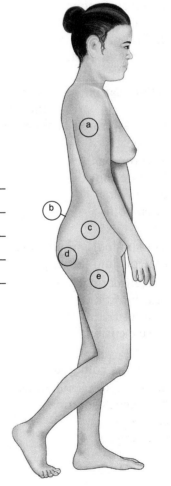

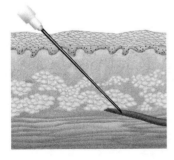

3. _____

CHOOSE THE BEST ANSWER

Answers are at the end of the book.

1. _____ tablets are placed under the tongue.
   a. Enteric coated
   b. Buccal
   c. Sublingual
   d. TSS

2. The pH of the stomach is around
   a. 1–2.
   b. 4–5.
   c. 5–6.
   d. 6–7.

3. _____ injections are administered directly into veins.
   a. Subcutaneous
   b. Intravenous
   c. Transdermal
   d. Intramuscular

4. Inflammation of a vein is also known as _____ and can be a complication associated with intravenous administration.
   a. thrombus
   b. toxic shock
   c. phlebitis
   d. embolus

5. The gradual intravenous injection of a volume of fluid into a patient is called
   a. transdermal.
   b. infiltration.
   c. infusion.
   d. suspension.

6. The most common kind of oral solution:
   a. nonaqueous solutions.
   b. aqueous solutions.
   c. elixirs.
   d. tinctures

7. _____ contain the drug and other ingredients packaged in a gelatin shell.
   a. Tablets
   b. Capsules
   c. Emulsions
   d. Gels

8. A disadvantage of solutions:
   a. may require additives or techniques to mask the objectionable taste.
   b. completely homegenous doses.
   c. immediately available for absorpton.
   d. doses can be easily adjusted.

9. Fits needle recommendations for subcutaneous injection:
   a. 27 gauge 1/2".
   b. 27 gauge 1.5".
   c. 19 gauge 3/8".
   d 20 gauge 1.5".

10. A device that goes between an aerosol's mouthpiece and the patient's mouth is a/an
   a. atomizer.
   b. nebulizer.
   c. spacer.
   d. MDI.

11. MDIs are used to deliver drugs by
   a. inhalation.
   b. infusion.
   c. injection.

12. _____ absorption is the absorption of drugs through the skin, often for systemic effect.
   a. Intravenous
   b. Intramuscular
   c. Subcutaneous
   d. Percutaneous

13. The most common injection route for insulin is
    a. subcutaneous.
    b. intramuscular.
    c. sublingual.
    d. intradermal.

14. Devices that have special metering valves to administer drugs by inhalation:
    a. spacers
    b. adapters
    c. atomizers
    d. MDI aerosols

STUDY NOTES

Use this area to write important points you'd like to remember.

— 8 —

COMPOUNDING

KEY CONCEPTS

Test your knowledge by covering the information in the right-hand column.

extemporaneous compounding	The on-demand preparation of a drug product according to a physician's prescription, formula, or recipe.
United States Pharmacopeia (USP)	Has federal authority to set standards for pharmacy compounding.
quality assurance (QA)	Program of activities to assure the compounded formulation meets specifications and satisfies standards.
quality control (QC)	A set of testing procedures that determine the quality of the compounded formulation.
class A torsion balances	Can weigh as little as 120 mg of material with a 5% error. Always use the balance on a level surface and in a draft-free area. Always arrest the balance before adding or removing weight from either pan, or storing.
sensitivity	The amount of weight that will move the balance pointer one division mark.
electronic or analytical balances	Highly sensitive balances that can weigh quantities smaller than 120 mg with acceptable accuracy.
weighing papers or boats	Should always be placed on the balance pans before any weighing is done. Balances must be readjusted after a new weighing paper or boat has been placed on each pan. Weighing papers taken from the same box can vary in weight by as much as 65 mg.
volumetric glassware	For weighing liquid drugs, solvents, or additives. Includes graduates, flasks, pipets, and syringes. Erlenmeyer flasks, beakers, and prescription bottles, regardless of markings, are not volumetric glassware.
graduated cylinders	Cylindrical graduates are preferred over cone shaped ones because they are more accurate. When selecting a graduate, always choose the smallest graduate capable of containing

the volume to be measured. Avoid measurements of volumes that are below 20 percent of the capacity of the graduate because the accuracy is unacceptable.

syringes	Used to measure small volumes. Measurements made with syringes are more accurate and precise than those made with cylindrical graduates. Measure volumes to the edge of the syringe stopper.
meniscus	The curved surface of a volume of liquid. When reading a volume of a liquid against a graduation mark, hold the graduate so the meniscus is at eye level and read the mark at the bottom of the meniscus.
droppers	Used to deliver small liquid doses, but must first be calibrated.
mortar and pestle	Made of three types of materials: glass, wedgewood, and porcelain. Wedgewood and porcelain mortars are used to grind crystals and large particles into fine powders. Glass mortars and pestles are preferable for mixing liquids and semisolid dosage forms.
trituration	The fine grinding of a powder.
levigation	The trituration of a powdered drug with a solvent in which the drug is insoluble to reduce the particle size of the drug.
geometric dilution	A technique for mixing two powders of unequal size. The smaller amount of powder is diluted in steps by additions of the larger amount of powder.
aqueous solution	Clear liquids in which the drug is completely dissolved in water.
syrup	A concentrated or nearly saturated solution of sucrose in water. Syrups containing flavoring agents are known as flavoring syrups (e.g., cherry syrup, acacia syrup, etc.).
nonaqueous solutions	Solutions that contain solvents other than water.
suspensions	A "two-phase" compound consisting of a finely divided solid dispersed in a liquid. Most solid drugs are levigated in a mortar to reduce the particle size as much as possible before adding to the vehicle. Common levigating agents are alcohol or glycerin.
flocculating agents	Electrolytes that carry an electrical charge and enhance particle "dispersibility" in a solution.
thickening agents	Reduce the settling (sedimentation rate) of a suspension.
emulsion	An unstable system consisting of at least two immiscible (unmixable) liquids, one that is dispersed as small droplets throughout the other, and a stabilizing agent.

KEY CONCEPTS

Test your knowledge by covering the information in the right hand column.

oil-in-water (o/w)	An emulsion of oils, petroleum hydrocarbons, and/or waxes with water, where the aqueous phase is generally in excess of 45% of the total weight of the emulsion.
water-in-oil (w/o)	When water or aqueous solutions are dispersed in an oleaginous (oil based) medium, with the aqueous phase constituting less than 45% of the total weight.
emulsifiers	Emulsifiers provide a protective barrier around the dispersed droplets that stabilize the emulsion. Commonly used emulsifiers include: tragacanth, sodium lauryl sulfate, sodium dioctyl sulfosuccinate, and polymers known as the Spans® and Tweens®.
ointments and creams	Ointments are simple mixtures of a drug(s) in an ointment base. A cream is a semisolid emulsion. Oleaginous (oil based) bases generally release substances slowly and unpredictably. Water miscible or aqueous bases tend to release drugs more rapidly.
suppository bases	There are three classes that are based on their composition and physical properties: oleaginous bases, water soluble or miscible bases, and hydrophilic bases.
polyethylene glycols (PEGs)	Popular water soluble bases that are chemically stable, non-irritating, miscible with water and mucous secretions, and can be formulated by molding or compression in a wide range of hardnesses and melting points.
compression molding	A method of preparing suppositories by mixing the suppository base and the drug ingredients and forcing the mixture into a special compression mold.
fusion molding	A method in which the drug is dispersed or dissolved in a melted suppository base. The fusion method can be used with all types of suppositories and must be used with most of them.
capsules	When filling, the smallest capsule capable of containing the final volume is used since patients often have difficulty swallowing large capsules.

USING A BALANCE

Class A Balance

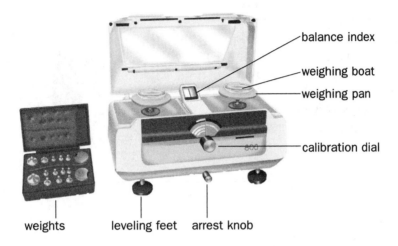

weights   leveling feet   arrest knob

BASIC GUIDELINES FOR USING BALANCES

There are some general rules about using a balance that help to maintain the balance in top condition.

✔ Always cover both pans with weighing papers or use weighing boats. These protect the pans from abrasions, eliminate the need for repeated washing, and reduce loss of drug to porous surfaces.

✔ A clean paper or boat should be used for each new ingredient to prevent cross contamination of components.

✔ The balance must be readjusted after a new weighing paper or boat has been placed on each pan. Weighing papers taken from the same box can vary in weight by as much as 30 mg. If the new zero point is not established, an error of as much as 30 mg can be made. On 200 mg of material, this is more than 15%. Weighing boats also vary in weight.

✔ Always arrest the balance before adding or removing weight from either pan. Although the balance is noted for its durability, repeated jarring of the balance will ultimately damage the working mechanism of the balance and reduce its accuracy.

✔ Always clean the balance, close the lid, and arrest the pans before storing the balance between uses.

✔ Always use the balance on a level surface and in a draft-free area.

MEASURING

MENISCUS

When reading a volume of a liquid against a graduation mark, hold the graduate so the meniscus is at eye level and read the mark at the bottom of the meniscus. Viewing the level from above will create the incorrect impression that there is more volume in the graduate. If the container is very narrow, the meniscus can be quite large.

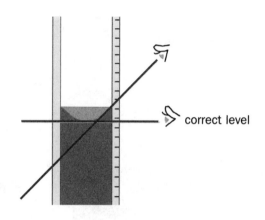

correct level

SYRINGE

When reading a volume of a liquid in a syringe, read to the edge of the stopper.

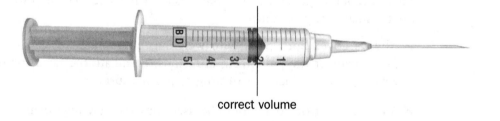

correct volume

CAPSULE SIZES

The relative sizes and fill capacities of capsules are:

Size	Volume (ml)
000	1.37
00	0.95
0	0.68
1	0.5
2	0.37
3	0.3
4	0.2
5	0.13

the punch method of filling capsules

TRUE/FALSE

Indicate whether the statement is true or false in the blank. Answers are at the end of the book.

_____ 1. Compounding must always be done upon receipt of a prescription, never in advance.

_____ 2. Protect from freezing means to store above 0°C.

_____ 3. Cylindrical graduates are more accurate than conical ones.

_____ 4. Erlenmeyer flasks are not volumetric glassware.

_____ 5. Disposable syringes are generally used for measuring small volumes.

_____ 6. When aqueous and nonaqueous solutions are mixed, the volume is always equal to the sum of the two volumes.

_____ 7. The punch method is a method to prepare suppositories.

_____ 8. Coloring agents are required in all sterile solutions.

_____ 9. Flocculating agents are used to reduce the sedimentation rate in suspensions.

_____ 10. PEGs with molecular weight over 1,000 are solids.

_____ 11. Cocoa butter is a well-known hydrophilic base.

_____ 12. Capsule size 000 can hold more ingredient than capsule size 5.

EXPLAIN WHY

Explain why these statements are true or important. Check your answers in the text. Discuss any questions you may have with your instructor.

1. Why is the stability of a compound important?

2. Why is accuracy in each step of compounding important?

3. Why is the smallest device that will accommodate a volume used to measure it?

4. Why are class A balances not used for very small amounts?

5. Why is geometric dilution used when mixing unequal amounts of powders?

Sample Formulation Record

Formulation Record

Name: _____

Strength: _____

Dosage Form: _____

Route of Administration: _____

Date of Last Review or Revision: _____

Person Completing Last Review or Revision: _____

Formula: [*The formula and all of the information about the individual ingredients are described.*]

Ingredient	Quantity	Physical Description	Solubility	Therapeutic Activity

Example Calculations: [*Examples of calculations that must be made each time the formula is compounded are shown.*]

Equipment Required:

Method of Preparation:

1.   [*The method is a step-by-step sequence in the correct order of mixing.*]

2.   [*The description of should be clear and detailed so all personnel can complete the step in exactly the same manner.*]

3.   [*The description can also consist of graphs, tables, charts, etc.*]

Description of Finished Product:

Formulation Record - Page 2

Name: _____

Strength: _____

Dosage Form: _____

Route of Administration: _____

Quality Control Procedures: [*Details of all quality assurance tests to be performed on final product.*]

Packaging Container:

Storage Requirements:

Beyond-Use Date Assignment: [*Criteria used to assign a beyond-use date.*]

Label Information: [*Auxiliary labels to include.*]

Source of Recipe:

Literature Information: [*Copies of relevant references or primary literature.*]

IN THE WORKPLACE

Sample Compounding Record

Compounding Record

Name: _____

Strength: _____

Dosage Form: _____

Route of Administration: _____

Quantity Prepared: _____

Date of Preparation: _____

Person Preparing Formulation: _____

Person Checking Formulation: _____

Formula: [*This information is completed at the time of compounding.*]

Ingredient	Manufacturer and Lot Number	Purity Grade	Description	Quantity Required	Actual Quantity Used

Calculations: [Calculations performed at the time of compounding.]

Equipment Operation: [*Equipment performance notes or alternate equipment used.*]

Method of Preparation: [*Description of any deviation from the Formulation Record method of preparation.*]

Description of Finished Product:

Quality Control Procedures: [*Details of quality assurance test results and data.*]

Beyond-Use Date Assignment: [*Assigned beyond-use date and reasons for difference from Formulation Record if applicable.*]

Sample Standard Operating Procedure Form

Standard Operating Procedure

Subject:	Policies and Procedures		
	Effective Date:	Revision Date	Revision No.
	Approved by:	Reviewed by:	
[What the SOP is concerning]	*[Additional Items]*	*[Additional Items]*	*[Additional Items]*

Purpose of the SOP: *[Describe the purpose and the desired outcome of the SOP.]*

Procedure:

1.   *[The procedure is a step-by-step sequence in the order of tasks to perform.]*

2.   *[The description of should be clear and detailed so all personnel can complete the step in exactly the same manner]*.

3.   *[The description can also consist of graphs, tables, charts, etc.]*

Documentation:

[Executing the SOP may generate data or information that needs to be documented. This information may be best reported on a form and maintained in a separate notebook or binder. The form should refer to the execution of the SOP by including the name of the procedure, date it was executed, personnel name conducting the procedure, and then the relevant data or information.]

FILL IN THE KEY TERM

Answers are at the end of the book.

aliquot	flocculating agent	nonaqueous solutions	trituration
aqueous solutions	formulation record	ointments	USP–NF Chapter
calibrate	geometric dilution	pipets	<795>
compounding record	hydrophilic emulsifier	primary emulsion	USP–NF Chapter
cream	immiscible	sensitivity	<797>
emulsifier	levigation	sieves	USP–NF grade
emulsion	lipophilic emulsifier	spatulation	volumetric
extemporaneous	meniscus	syrup	
compounding	mucilage	thickening agent	

1. _____ : The on-demand preparation of a drug product according to a physician's prescription, formula, or recipe.

2. _____ : Regulations pertaining to nonsterile compounding or formulations.

3. _____ : Regulations that pertain to sterile compounding or formulations.

4. _____ : To set, mark, or check the graduations of a measuring device.

5. _____ : Measures volume.

6. _____ : A record of what actually happened when the formulation was compounded.

7. _____ : The curved surface of a column of liquid.

8. _____ : The fine grinding of a powder.

9. _____ : Triturating a powdered drug with a solvent in which it is insoluble to reduce its particle size.

10. _____ : A technique for mixing two powders of unequal size.

11. _____ : Mesh screens.

12. _____ : Mixing powders with a spatula.

13. _____ : Formulas and procedures of what should happen when a formulation is compounded.

14. _____ : A portion of a mixture.

15. _____ : A concentrated or nearly saturated solution of sucrose in water.

16. _____ : The amount of weight that will move the balance pointer one division mark.

17. _____ : Electrolytes used in the preparation of suspensions.

18. _____ : An agent used in the preparation of suspensions to increase the viscosity of the liquid.

19. _____ : Lowest grade of purity for an ingredient in a compound.

20. _____ : Simple mixtures of drug(s) in an ointment base.

21. _____ : A stabilizing agent in emulsions.

22. _____ : An unstable system consisting of at least two immiscible liquids.

23. _____ : Solutions that contain solvents other than water.

24. _____ : A semisolid emulsion.

25. _____ : A stabilizing agent for water based dispersion mediums.

26. _____ : A stabilizing agent for oil based dispersion mediums.

27. _____ : The initial emulsion formed in a preparation to which ingredients are added to create the final volume.

28. _____ : A wet, slimy preparation formed as an initial step in a wet emulsion preparation method.

29. _____ : Clear liquids in which the drug is completely dissolved in water.

30. _____ : Cannot be mixed.

31. _____ : Thin glass tubes for volumetric measurement.

STUDY NOTES

Use this area to write important points you'd like to remember.

CHOOSE THE BEST ANSWER

Answers are at the end of the book.

1. Establishes standards of quality, strength, purity, packaging, and labeling for compounded medications:
   a. USP–NF.
   b. FDA.
   c. ASHP.
   d. DEA.

2. The storage temperature definition for a freezer is
   a. -30°C to 0°C.
   b. -20°C to -10°C.
   c. 8°C to 15°C.
   d. 30°C to 40°C.

3. The minimum weighable quantity for a class A balance is
   a. 120 mg.
   b. 500 ml.
   c. 120 ml.
   d. 500 mg.

4. Metric weights used for weighing ingredients using a class A balance should be handled with
   a. water.
   b. fingers.
   c. forceps.
   d. oil.

5. Quantities less than 120 mg
   a. may be measured using a class A balance.
   b. may be measured using electronic or analytical balances.
   c. may be measured using a class C balance.
   d. may be measured using a class B balance.

6. _____ is the term for triturating a powdered drug with a solvent in which it is insoluble to reduce its particle size.
   a. Suspension
   b. Trituration
   c. Emulsion
   d. Levigation

7. Mixing powders using a spatula is called
   a. extemporaneous compounding.
   b. spatulation.
   c. emulsification.
   d. levigation.

8. A solution that contains the maximum amount of drug it can contain at room temperature is
   a. supersaturated.
   b. saturated.
   c. unsaturated.
   d. eutectic.

9. An appropriate flavoring for a metallic tasting drug is
   a. mint.
   b. orange.
   c. cinnamon.
   d. anise.

10. _____ are electrolytes used in the preparation of suspensions.
    a. Flocculating agents
    b. Suspending agents
    c. Complex carbohydrates
    d. Simple sugars

11. A two-phase system consisting of a finely divided solid dispersed in a liquid is a/an
    a. suspension.
    b. emulsion.
    c. solution.
    d. trituration.

12. _____ are thickening agents used in the preparation of suspensions.
    a. Electrolytes
    b. Preservatives
    c. Flocculating agents
    d. Suspending agents

13. An example of a water soluble base is
    a. glycerinated gelatin.
    b. cocoa butter.
    c. synthetic triglycerides.
    d. Fattibase®.

14. The method of choice for making emulsions with the consistency of a lotion or cream is the
    a. Continental method.
    b. Beaker method.
    c. Wet Gum method.
    d. Dry Gum method.

15. Polyethylene glycol (PEG) polymers are used to make _____ suppositories.
    a. cocoa butter
    b. water soluble or miscible
    c. oleaginous
    d. hydrophilic

16. _____ are mixtures of oleaginous and water miscible bases for making suppositories.
    a. Hydrophobic bases
    b. Hydrophonic
    c. Hydrophilic bases
    d. Hydrotonic bases

STUDY NOTES

Use this area to write important points you'd like to remember.

— 9 —

PARENTERALS: COMPOUNDING STERILE FORMULATIONS

KEY CONCEPTS

Test your knowledge by covering the information in the right-hand column.

parenteral solutions

There are two types of products: large volume parenteral (LVP) solutions and small volume parenteral (SVP) solutions. LVP solutions are typically bags or bottles containing larger volumes of intravenous solutions. SVP solutions are generally contained in ampules or vials.

properties

Solutions for injection or infusion must be sterile, free of visible particulate material, pyrogen-free, stable for their intended use, have a pH around 7.4, and in most (but not all) cases isotonic.

admixtures

When a drug is added to a parenteral solution, the drug is referred to as the additive, and the final mixture is referred to as the admixture.

total parenteral nutrition solutions

These are complex admixtures composed of dextrose, fat, protein, electrolytes, vitamins, and trace elements. They are hypertonic solutions. Most of the volume of TPN solutions is made up of macronutrients: amino acid solution (a source of protein) and a dextrose solution (a source of carbohydrate calories). Several electrolytes, trace elements, and multiple vitamins (together referred to as micronutrients) may be added to the base solution to meet individual patient requirements. Common electrolyte additives include sodium chloride (or acetate), potassium chloride (or acetate), calcium gluconate, magnesium sulfate, and sodium (or potassium) phosphate. Multiple vitamin preparations containing both water-soluble and fat-soluble vitamins are usually added on a daily basis. A trace element product containing zinc, copper, manganese, selenium, and chromium may be added.

IV fat emulsions

Intravenous fat (lipid) emulsion is required as a source of essential fatty acids. It is also used as a concentrated source of calories. Fat provides nine calories per gram, compared to 3.4 calories per gram provided by dextrose. Intravenous fat emulsion may be admixed into the parenteral nutrition solution with amino acids and dextrose, or piggybacked into the administration line.

peritoneal dialysis solutions

Used by patients who do not have functioning kidneys to remove toxic substances, excess body waste, and serum electrolytes through osmosis. The solution is administered directly into the peritoneal cavity (the cavity between the abdominal lining and the internal organs) to remove toxic substances, excess body waste, and serum electrolytes through osmosis. These solutions are hypertonic to blood so the water will not move into the circulatory system.

flow rate

The rate at which the solution is administered to the patient.

pumps

Infusion pumps, syringe pumps, and ambulatory pumps are devices used to administer LVP solutions and control flow rates. Administration sets are threaded through infusion pumps, and the pumps control the gravity flow. Infusion pumps have made the infusion process much more accurate and easier to administer and have been a major factor in the growth of home infusion.

piggybacks

Small volumes of fluid (usually 50–100 ml) infused into the administration set of an LVP solution.

laminar flow hood

Establishes and maintains an ultraclean work area for the preparation of IV admixtures.

biological safety cabinets

Used in the preparation of hazardous drugs. They protect both personnel and the environment from contamination.

aseptic techniques

Maintain the sterility of all sterile items and are used in preparing IV admixtures.

syringes

Syringes come in sizes ranging from 1 to 60 ml. As a rule, a syringe size is used that is one size larger than the volume to be measured. The volume of solution in a syringe is measured to the edge of the plunger's stopper while the syringe is held upright and all air has been removed from the syringe.

needle sizes

Needle sizes are indicated by length and gauge. The higher the gauge number, the smaller is the lumen (the hollow bore of the needle shaft). Large needles may be needed with highly viscous solutions but are more likely to cause coring.

filters

Often used to remove contaminating particles from solutions. Depth filters and membrane filters are the two basic groups.

LAMINAR FLOW HOODS & BIOLOGICAL SAFETY CABINETS

HEPA filter

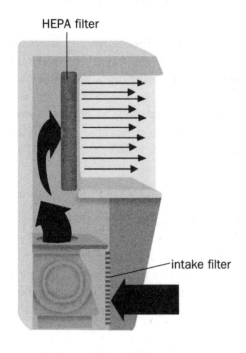

intake filter

LAMINAR FLOW HOOD

With a laminar flow hood, room air is drawn into a horizontal hood and passed through a prefilter to remove relatively large contaminants such as dust and lint. The air is then channeled through a high efficiency particulate air (HEPA) filter that removes particles larger than 0.3 μm (microns). The purified air then flows over the work surface in parallel lines at a uniform velocity (i.e., laminar flow). The constant flow of air from the hood prevents room air from entering the work area and removes contaminants introduced in the work area by material or personnel.

top down view

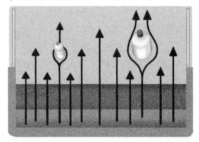

BIOLOGICAL SAFETY CABINETS

Biological safety cabinets protect both personnel and the environment from contamination. They are used in the preparation of hazardous drugs. A biological safety cabinet functions by passing air through a HEPA filter and directing it down toward the work area. As the air approaches the work surface, it is pulled through vents at the front, back, and sides of the hood. A major portion of the air is recirculated back into the cabinet and a minor portion passes through a secondary HEPA filter and is exhausted into the room.

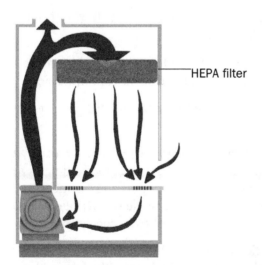

HEPA filter

RULES FOR WORKING WITH FLOW AND SAFETY HOODS

✔ **Never sneeze, cough, talk directly into a hood.**

✔ **Close doors or windows.** Breezes can disrupt the air flow sufficiently to contaminate the work area.

✔ **Perform all work at least 6 inches inside the hood** to derive the benefits of the laminar air flow. Laminar flow air begins to mix with outside air near the edge of the hood.

✔ **Maintain a direct, open path between the filter and the area inside the hood.**

✔ **Place nonsterile objects, such as solution containers or your hands, downstream from sterile ones.** Particles blown off these objects can contaminate anything downstream from them.

✔ **Do not put large objects at the back of the work area next to the filter.** They will disrupt air flow.

ASEPTIC TECHNIQUE

HAND WASHING

✔ Remove all jewelry and scrub hands and arms to the elbows with a suitable antibacterial agent.

✔ Stand far enough away from the sink so clothing does not come in contact with it.

✔ Turn on water. Wet hands and forearms thoroughly. Keep hands pointed downward.

✔ Scrub hands vigorously with an antibacterial soap.

✔ Work soap under fingernails by rubbing them against the palm of the other hand.

✔ Interlace the fingers and scrub the spaces between the fingers.

✔ Wash wrists and arms up to the elbows.

✔ Thoroughly rinse the soap from hands and arms.

✔ Dry hands and forearms thoroughly using a nonshedding paper towel.

✔ Use a dry paper towel to turn off the water faucet.

✔ After hands are washed, avoid touching clothes, face, hair, or any other potentially contaminated object in the area.

CLOTHING AND BARRIERS

✔ Wear clean lint-free garments or barrier clothing, including gowns, hair covers, and a mask.

✔ Wear sterile gloves.

✔ Follow facility or manufacturer guidelines for putting on and removing barrier clothing. Unless barriers are put on properly, they can easily become contaminated.

TRUE/FALSE

Indicate whether the statement is true or false in the blank. Answers are at the end of the book.

_____ 1. Otic dosage forms are not required to be sterile.

_____ 2. 0.9% sodium chloride is an isotonic solution.

_____ 3. Physiological pH is about 7.4.

_____ 4. Coring is more likely to occur with a 27 gauge needle than a 13 gauge needle.

_____ 5. Class 2 Type A Biological Safety Cabinets provide the minimum recommended environment for preparing chemotherapy agents.

_____ 6. Epinephrine is a "U-list" waste.

EXPLAIN WHY

Explain why these statements are true or important. Check your answers in the text. Discuss any questions you may have with your instructor.

1. Why should intravenous solutions generally be isotonic?

2. Why is the position of objects on a laminar flow hood work surface important?

3. Why is visual inspection of parenteral solutions important?

IN THE WORKPLACE

Use these tools to practice and check some of your workplace skills.

Name: _____

Pharmacy Technician Skills Checklist
ASEPTIC TECHNIQUE: HAND WASHING

Skill or Procedure	Self-Assessment		Supervisor Review		
	Needs to Improve	Meets or Exceeds	Needs to Improve*	Meets or Exceeds	*Plan of Action
1. Removes all jewelry and scrubs hands and arms to the elbows with suitable antibacterial agent.					
2. Stands far enough away from sink so clothing does not come in contact with sink.					
3. Turns on water, wets hands and forearms thoroughly, keeps hands pointed downward.					
4. Scrubs hands vigorously with antibacterial soap.					
5. Works soap under fingernails by rubbing them against the palm of the other hand.					
6. Interlaces fingers and scrubs the spaces between the fingers.					
7. Washes wrists and arms up to the elbows.					
8. Thoroughly rinses the soap from hands and arms.					
9. Dries hands and forearms thoroughly using a nonshedding paper towel.					
10. Uses a dry paper towel to turn off water faucet.					

Name: _____

Pharmacy Technician Skills Checklist
LAMINAR FLOW HOOD

Skill or Procedure	Self-Assessment		Supervisor Review		
	Needs to Improve	Meets or Exceeds	Needs to Improve*	Meets or Exceeds	*Plan of Action
1. Turns on and lets run for at least 30 minutes prior to use.					
2. Does not allow jewelry, long sleeves, or other non-sterile materials within the hood.					
3. Uses clean gauze/sponge to clean hood with 70% isopropyl alcohol.					
4. Uses long side-to-side motions on the back surface of the hood and works from top to bottom to clean hood.					
5. Uses back-to-front motions, working from the top to the bottom of each side to clean the sides of the hood.					
6. Uses back-to-front motions to clean the surface of the hood.					
7. Takes care so that cleaned surfaces do not become contaminated during cleaning.					
8. Takes care when placing items in hood so that airflow is not blocked.					
9. Takes care when preparing admixtures, that airflow is not blocked by hands or other objects.					
10. Takes care so that hands remain under the hood during admixture preparation, and does not leave the hood during admixture preparation.					
11. Does not utilize outer 6 inches of hood opening or work too closely to sides and back of hood during drug preparation and manipulations.					
12. Does not contaminate hood by coughing, sneezing, chewing gum, or excessive talking.					

IN THE WORKPLACE

Use these tools to practice and check some of your workplace skills.

Pharmacy Technician Skills Checklist
GLASS AMPULES

Name: _____

Skill or Procedure	Self-Assessment		Supervisor Review		*Plan of Action
	Needs to Improve	Meets or Exceeds	Needs to Improve*	Meets or Exceeds	
1. If ampule is not pre-scored, uses a fine file to lightly score the neck of the ampule at its narrowest point.					
2. Holds ampule upright and taps the top.					
3. Swabs neck of ampule with an alcohol swab.					
4. Wraps gauze pad around neck of ampule and quickly snaps ampule moving hands outward and away.					
5. Inspects opened ampule for glass particles.					
6. Tilts ampule (about 20 degree angle).					
7. Inserts needle into ampule, so needle point does not touch opening of ampule.					
8. Positions needle into solution placing beveled edge against side of ampule.					
9. Withdraws correct amount of the drug while keeping the needle submerged.					
10. Withdraws needle from ampule and removes air bubbles from syringe					
11. Transfers solution to final container using filter needle or membrane filter.					

Name: _____

Pharmacy Technician Skills Checklist
VIAL WITH SOLUTION

Skill or Procedure	Self-Assessment		Supervisor Review		
	Needs to Improve	Meets or Exceeds	Needs to Improve*	Meets or Exceeds	*Plan of Action
1. Takes care in removing vial cover.					
2. Uses care in cleaning top of vial with alcohol wipe.					
3. Draws into syringe a volume of air equal to the volume of drug to be withdrawn.					
4. Penetrates the vial without coring and injects air.					
5. Turns the vial upside down and withdraws correct amount of drug into syringe.					
6. Withdraws needle from vial and with needle end up, taps syringe to allow air bubbles to come to the top of the syringe. Presses plunger to remove air and excess solution.					
7. Transfers solution into the IV bag or bottle, minimizing coring.					

IN THE WORKPLACE

Use these tools to practice and check some of your workplace skills.

Pharmacy Technician Skills Checklist
VIAL WITH POWDER

Name:

Skill or Procedure	Self-Assessment		Supervisor Review		
	Needs to Improve	Meets or Exceeds	Needs to Improve*	Meets or Exceeds	*Plan of Action
1. Takes care in removing vial cover.					
2. Uses care in cleaning top of vial with alcohol wipe.					
3. Draws into syringe a volume of air equal to the volume of diluent to be withdrawn.					
4. Penetrates the diluent vial without coring and injects air.					
5. Turns the diluent vial upside down and withdraws correct amount of diluent into syringe.					
6. Injects diluent into medication vial, and then withdraws a slight amount of air.					
7. Shakes vial until drug dissolves (unless shaking is not recommended)					
8. Reinserts needle and removes proper volume of drug solution (without injecting air).					
9. Removes all bubbles from syringe and transfers reconstituted solution to final container.					

Pharmacy Technician Skills Checklist
ADDING A DRUG (SVP) TO AN LVP

Name: _____

Skill or Procedure	Self-Assessment		Supervisor Review		
	Needs to Improve	Meets or Exceeds	Needs to Improve*	Meets or Exceeds	*Plan of Action
1. Removes protective covering from LVP package.					
2. Assembles the needle and syringe.					
3. If drug is in powder form, reconstitutes drug with recommended diluent.					
4. Swabs the SVP with an alcohol swab and draws the necessary volume of drug solution.					
5. Swabs the medication port of the LVP with an alcohol swab.					
6. Inserts needle into the medication port and through the inner diaphragm (medication port is fully extended).					
7. Injects the SVP solution.					
8. Removes the needle.					
9. Shakes and inspects the admixture					

FILL IN THE KEY TERM

Answers are at the end of the book.

admixture	dialysis	irrigation solution	piggybacks
anhydrous	diluent	ions	pyrogens
aseptic techniques	final filter	isotonic	shaft
bevel	Flashball	laminar flow	sharps
biological safety	flow rate	lumen	TPN solution
cabinets	gauge	membrane filter	valence
buffer capacity	HEPA filter	osmosis	zone of turbulence
clean rooms	heparin lock	osmotic pressure	
coring	hypertonic	peritoneal dialysis	
depth filter	hypotonic	solution	

1. _____ : Techniques that maintain sterile condition.

2. _____ : Chemicals produced by microorganisms that can cause pyretic (fever) reactions in patients.

3. _____ : Flexible rubber tubing at the end of a needle on an administration set.

4. _____ : When a solution has an osmolarity equivalent to another.

5. _____ : When a solution has a greater osmolarity than another.

6. _____ : When a solution has a lesser osmolarity than another.

7. _____ : The rate (in ml/hour or ml/minute) at which the solution is administered to the patient.

8. _____ : An injection device that uses heparin to keep blood from clotting in the device.

9. _____ : Small volume solutions added to an LVP.

10. _____ : Rooms that house laminar flow hoods and biological safety cabinets.

11. _____ : The resulting solution when a drug is added to a parenteral solution.

12. _____ : Ability of a solution to resist a change in pH.

13. _____ : A liquid that dilutes a substance or solution.

14. _____ : Without water molecules.

15. _____ : An angled surface, as with the tip of a needle.

16. _____ : With needles, the higher the number, the thinner the lumen.

17. _____ : The hollow center of a needle.

PARENTERALS: COMPOUNDING STERILE FORMULATIONS — 9

18. _____ : When a needle damages the rubber closure of a parenteral container, causing fragments of the closure to fall into the container and contaminate its contents.

19. _____ : A filter that attaches to a syringe and filters solution through a membrane as the solution is expelled from the syringe.

20. _____ : A filter placed inside a needle hub that can filter solutions being drawn in or expelled, but not both.

21. _____ : A filter that filters solution immediately before it enters a patient's vein.

22. _____ : Continuous movement at a stable rate in one direction.

23. _____ : A high efficiency particulate air filter.

24. _____ : Are used in the preparation of hazardous drugs and protect both personnel and the environment from contamination.

25. _____ : Large splash solutions used during surgical or urologic procedures to bathe and moisten body tissue.

26. _____ : The stem of the needle that provides for the overall length of the needle.

27. _____ : Needles, jagged glass or metal objects, or any items that might puncture or cut the skin.

28. _____ : Molecular particles that carry electrical charges.

29. _____ : Characteristic of a solution determined by the number of particles dissolved in it.

30. _____ : The number of positive or negative charges on an ion.

31. _____ : Higher concentration passes to a lower concentration through a permeable membrane.

32. _____ : A solution placed in and emptied from the peritoneal cavity to remove toxic substances.

33. _____ : Intravenous solution with amino acids, dextrose, and additional micronutrients.

34. _____ : Area of blocked air flow in a laminar flow hood.

35. _____ : Movement of particles in a solution through permeable membranes.

CHOOSE THE BEST ANSWER

Answers are at the end of the book.

1. Pyrogens are chemicals that are produced by
   a. coring.
   b. microorganisms.
   c. precipitation.
   d. heat.

2. A(an) _____ solution has greater osmolarity than blood.
   a. hypotonic
   b. isotonic
   c. hypertonic
   d. pyrogenic

3. Piggybacks usually contain _____ of fluid and are infused over a period of 30–60 minutes.
   a. 50–100 ml
   b. 250–500 ml
   c. 5,000–1,000 ml
   d. 1,000 ml–2,000 ml

4. When a drug is added to a parenteral solution, the drug is referred to as the _____ and the final mixture is referred to as the _____.
   a. admixture, additive
   b. suspension, solution
   c. additive, admixture
   d. solution, suspension

5. Some examples of syringe tips include
   a. heparin lock and Ringer's solution.
   b. Luer-Lok® and Slip-Tip®.
   c. Add-Vantage®, Add-a-Vial®, and Mini-Bag Plus®.
   d. Ringer's solution and Lactated Ringer's solution.

6. _____ is the part of the needle that attaches to the syringe.
   a. The lumen
   b. The bevel
   c. The coring
   d. The hub

7. _____ are filters that can be placed inside of needles.
   a. Membrane filters
   b. Filter needles
   c. HEPA filters
   d. Intake filters

8. In horizontal laminar flow hoods, air blows
   a. down toward the work area.
   b. away from the operator.
   c. toward the operator.
   d. up toward the HEPA filter.

9. Biological safety cabinets have
   a. vertical air flow down toward the work.
   b. horizontal air flow away from the operator.
   c. vertical air flow up toward the HEPA filter.
   d. horizontal air flow toward the operator.

10. When positioning supplies for use in a laminar flow hood
    a. larger supplies should be placed closer to the HEPA filter.
    b. smaller supplies should be placed closer to the HEPA filter.
    c. space the supplies close together to minimize laminar flow.
    d. the spacing of supplies has no effect on laminar flow.

11. Sharps containers should be disposed of when _____ full.
    a. 1/3
    b. 1/2
    c. 2/3
    d. 3/4

12. If an ampule has not been pre-scored, the technician should
    a. score the neck of the ampule with a fine file.
    b. use sterile pliers to open the ampule.
    c. use a file to file all the way through the neck.
    d. just snap the ampule since manufacturers always pre-score when necessary.

13. If 50 mg of a drug are added to a 100 ml IV bag, what is the percent strength of the resulting solution?
    a. 0.0005%
    b. 0.005%
    c. 0.05%
    d. 0.5%

14. What is the molecular weight of $CaCl_2$ if the atomic weight of Ca is 40.08 and the atomic weight of Cl is 35.43?
    a. 70.86
    b. 110.94
    c. 75.51
    d. 106.29

15. What is the valence of KCl?
    a. 0
    b. 2
    c. 1

16. What is the weight of one osmole of KCl? (molecular weight = 74.6)
    a. 74.6 g
    b. 74.6 mg
    c. 37.3 g
    d. 37.3 mg

STUDY NOTES

Use this area to write important points you'd like to remember.

— 10 —

BASIC BIOPHARMACEUTICS

KEY CONCEPTS

Test your knowledge by covering the information in the-right hand column.

objective of drug therapy	To deliver the right drug, in the right concentration, to the right site of action at the right time to produce the desired effect.
receptors	When a drug produces an effect, it is interacting on a molecular level with cell material that is called a receptor. Receptor activation is responsible for most of the pharmacological responses in the body.
site of action	Only those drugs able to interact with the receptors in a particular site of action can produce effects in that site. This is why specific cells only respond to certain drugs.
agonists	Drugs that activate receptors and produce a response that may either accelerate or slow normal cell processes.
antagonists	Drugs that bind to receptors but do not activate them. They prevent other drugs or substances from interacting with receptors.
dose-response curve	Specific doses of a drug is given to various subjects and the effect or response is measured in terms of dose and effect.
blood concentration	The primary way to monitor a drug's concentration in the body and its related effect is to determine its blood concentration.
minimum effective concentration (MEC)	When there is enough drug at the site of action to produce a response.
minimum toxic concentration (MTC)	An upper blood concentration limit beyond which there are undesired or toxic effects.

therapeutic window	The range between the minimum effective concentration and the minimum toxic concentration is called the therapeutic window. When concentrations are in this range, most patients receive the maximum benefit from their drug therapy with a minimum of risk.
ADME	Blood concentrations are the result of four simultaneously acting processes: absorption, distribution, metabolism, and excretion.
disposition	Another term for ADME.
elimination	Metabolism and excretion combined.
half-life	The amount of time it takes for the blood concentration of a drug to decline to one-half of an initial value.
passive diffusion	Besides the four ADME processes, a critical factor of drug concentration and effect is how drugs move through biological membranes. Most drugs penetrate biological membranes by passive diffusion.
hydrophobic drugs	Lipid (fat) soluble drugs that penetrate the lipoidal (fat-like) cell membrane better than hydrophilic drugs.
hydrophilic drugs	Drugs that are attracted to water.
aqueous pores	Openings in cell membranes that allow entry of water and water-soluble drugs.
absorption	The transfer of drug into the blood from an administered drug product is called absorption.
gastric emptying	Most drugs are given orally and absorbed into the blood from the small intestine. One of the primary factors affecting oral drug absorption is the gastric emptying time.
distribution	The movement of a drug within the body once the drug has reached the blood.
selective action	Drug action that is selective to certain tissues or organs, due both to the specific nature of receptor action as well as to various factors that can affect distribution.
protein binding	Many drugs bind to proteins in blood plasma to form a complex that is too large to penetrate cell openings. So the drug remains inactive.

metabolism	The body's process of transforming drugs. The primary site of drug metabolism in the body is the liver. Enzymes produced by the liver interact with drugs and transform them into metabolites.
enzyme	A complex protein that causes chemical reactions in other substances.
metabolite	The transformed drug.
enzyme induction	The increase in enzyme activity that results in greater metabolism of drugs.
enzyme inhibition	The decrease in enzyme activity that results in reduced metabolism of drugs.
first-pass metabolism	When a drug is substantially degraded or destroyed by the liver's enzymes before it reaches the circulatory system, an important factor with orally administered drugs.
enterohepatic cycling	The transfer of drugs and their metabolites from the liver to the bile in the gall bladder and then into the intestine.
excretion	The process of excreting drugs and metabolites, primarily performed by the kidney through the urine.
glomerular filtration	The blood-filtering process of the kidneys. As plasma water moves through the nephron, waste substances (including drugs and metabolites) are secreted into the fluid, with urine as the end result.
bioavailability	The amount of a drug that is delivered to the site of action and the rate at which it is available is called the bioavailability of the drug.
bioequivalency	The comparison of bioavailability between two dosage forms.
pharmaceutical equivalents	Pharmaceutical equivalents are drug products that contain identical amounts of the same active ingredients in the same dosage form, but may contain different inactive ingredients.
pharmaceutical alternatives	Pharmaceutical alternatives are drug products that contain the identical active ingredients, but not necessarily in the same amount or dosage form.
therapeutic equivalent	Pharmaceutical equivalents that produce the same effects in patients.

DOSE RESPONSE CURVE

When a series of specific doses is given to a number of people, the results show that some people respond to low doses but others require larger doses for a response to be produced. Some differences are due to the product itself, but most are due to human variability: different people have different characteristics that affect how a drug product behaves in them. A dose-response curve shows that as doses increase, responses increase up to a point where increased dosage no longer results in increased response.

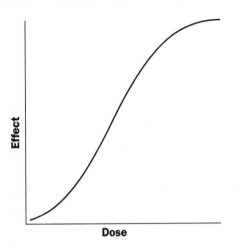

BLOOD CONCENTRATION—TIME PROFILES

Blood concentration begins at zero at the time the drug is administered (before it has been absorbed into the blood). With time, the drug leaves the formulation and enters the blood, causing concentrations to rise. Minimum effective concentration (MEC) is when there is enough drug at the site of action to produce a response. The time this occurs is called the onset of action. With most drugs, when blood concentrations increase, so does the intensity of the effect, since blood concentrations reflect the site of action concentrations that produce the response.

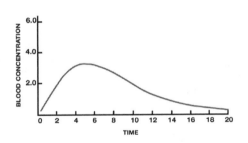

Some drugs have an upper blood concentration limit beyond which there are undesired or toxic effects. This limit is called the minimum toxic concentration (MTC). The range between the minimum effective concentration and the minimum toxic concentration is called the therapeutic window. When concentrations are in this range, most patients receive the maximum benefit from their drug therapy with a minimum of risk.

The last part of the curve shows the blood concentrations declining as absorption is complete. The time between the onset of action and the time when the minimum effective concentration is reached by the declining blood concentrations is called the duration of action. The duration of action is the time the drug should produce the desired effect.

Oral Absorption

Most drugs are given orally and absorbed into the blood from the small intestine. The small intestine's large surface area makes absorption easier. However, there are many conditions in the stomach that can affect absorption positively or negatively before the drug even reaches the small intestine. One of the primary factors affecting oral drug absorption is the gastric emptying time. This is the time a drug will stay in the stomach before it is emptied into the small intestine. Since stomach acid can degrade many drugs and since most absorption occurs in the intestine, gastric emptying time can significantly affect a drug's action. If a drug remains in the stomach too long, it can be degraded or destroyed, and its effect decreased. Gastric emptying time can be affected by a various conditions, including the amount and type of food in the stomach, the presence of other drugs, the person's body position, and their emotional condition. Some factors increase the gastric emptying time, but most slow it. The pH of the gastrointestinal organs is illustrated at right.

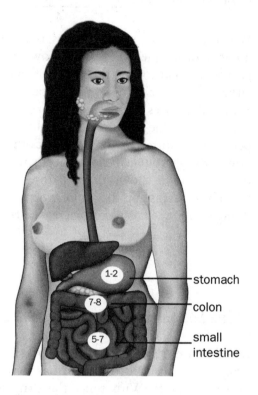

Passive Diffusion

Before an effective concentration of a drug can reach its site of action, it must overcome many barriers, most of which are biological membranes, complex structures composed of lipids (fats) and proteins. Most drugs penetrate biological membranes by passive diffusion. This occurs when drugs in the body's fluids move from an area of higher concentration to an area of lower concentration, until the concentrations in each area are in a state of equilibrium. Passive diffusion causes most orally administered drugs to move from the intestine to the blood and from the blood to the site of action.

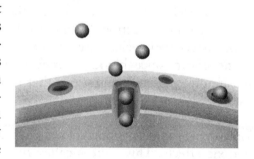

Protein Binding

Many drugs bind to proteins in blood plasma to form a complex that is too large to penetrate cell openings. So the drug remains inactive. Protein binding can be considered a type of drug storage within the body. Some drugs bind extensively to proteins in fat and muscle, and are gradually released as the blood concentration of the drug falls. These drugs remain in the body a long time, and therefore have a long duration of action.

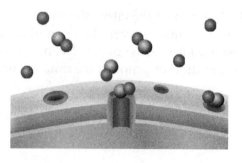

PHARMACOKINETICS (HALF-LIFE)

Besides providing correlations between a pharmacological effect and time, blood concentration-time profiles can be used to describe rate processes. The rate of transfer of an amount of drug from one location to another (e.g., drug transferred to the urine by urinary excretion) or from one chemical form to another (e.g., metabolism of active drug to inactive drug) are common examples of rate processes. Pharmacokinetics is the study of the ADME processes of the body that affect an administered drug.

The data from a blood concentration-time profile is used to determine the bioavailability and bioequivalency of drug products. The same data can be used to obtain three additional pharmacokinetic parameters: half-life of elimination, area-under-curve (AUC), and total body clearance.

HALF-LIFE OF ELIMINATION: This half-life is the amount of time it takes for a blood concentration to decline to one-half an initial value. For example, if at 6 hours, a blood concentration was 30 mcg/ml, and at 15 hours, the blood concentration was 15 mcg/ml, then the half-life would be equal to 9 hours (15 – 6 hours). For most cases, five times the half-life of elimination will estimate how long the elimination processes will be important in the disposition of the administered drug. In the example, 5 x 9 hours, or 45 hours, is low long it will take for the processes of elimination to essentially remove the drug from the body.

AREA-UNDER-CURVE: The AUC is a mathematical number expressing how much physical area is contained under the blood concentration-time profile. The units of AUC are concentration x time (mcg/ml x hours). The AUCs of formulations are used to help determine the bioequivalency of different dosage forms. It is also used to calculate another important pharmacokinetic parameter, total body clearance.

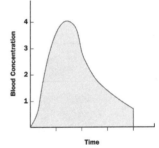

TOTAL BODY CLEARANCE: Total body clearance (Cl) reflects the combined effect of all processes eliminating the drug from the body: urinary excretion, metabolism, expiration through the lungs, and fecal excretion. The units of Cl are ml/min or ml/hour: clearance tells you the number of ml cleared of the drug per time unit. For example, if a drug's clearance is 120 ml/min, then 120 ml of volume is cleared of the drug every minute. That can be said from a conceptual point of view. But in the body, you don't just clear a portion of the volume. Distribution is an ongoing process, as is elimination, so any volume that is cleared will be "refilled" as soon as it is emptied. The overall effect is that blood concentrations continue to fall as the drug is cleared from the body.

FILL IN THE KEY TERM

Answers are at the end of the book.

absorption
active transport
agonist
antagonist
bioavailability
bioequivalency
biopharmaceutics
complexation
disposition
duration of action
elimination

enterohepatic cycling
enzyme
enzyme induction
enzyme inhibition
first pass metabolism
gastric emptying time
hydrophilic
hydrophobic
ionized
lipoidal
metabolite

nephron
passive diffusion
pharmaceutical alternative
pharmaceutical equivalent
protein binding
receptor
therapeutic equivalent
therapeutic window
unionized

1. _____ : The study of the factors associated with drug products and physiological processes, and the resulting systemic concentrations of the drugs.

2. _____ : The process of metabolism and excretion.

3. _____ : The cellular material at the site of action that interacts with the drug.

4. _____ : The movement of the drug from the dosage form to the blood.

5. _____ : Drugs that activate receptors to accelerate or slow normal cell function.

6. _____ : Drugs that bind with receptors but do not activate them. They block receptor action by preventing other drugs or substances from activating them.

7. _____ : When different molecules associate or attach to each other.

8. _____ : The time the drug concentration is above the MEC.

9. _____ : A drug's blood concentration range between its minimum effective concentration and minimum toxic concentration.

10. _____ : A term sometimes used to refer to all of the ADME processes together.

11. _____ : The movement of drugs from an area of higher concentration to lower concentration.

12. _____ : The movement of drug molecules across membranes by active means, rather than passive diffusion.

13. _____ : Water repelling; cannot associate with water.

14. _____ : Capable of associating with or absorbing water.

15. _____ : Fat-like substance.

16. _____ : The time a drug will stay in the stomach before it is emptied into the small intestine.

17. _____ : When acids dissociate.

18. _____ : The attachment of a drug molecule to a plasma or tissue protein, effectively making the drug inactive, but also keeping it within the body.

19. _____ : The substance resulting from the body's transformation of an administered drug.

20. _____ : A complex protein that causes chemical reactions in other substances.

21. _____ : The increase in enzyme activity that results in greater metabolism of drugs.

22. _____ : The decrease in enzyme activity that results in reduced metabolism of drugs.

23. _____ : The substantial degradation of a drug caused by enzyme metabolism in the liver before the drug reaches the systemic circulation.

24. _____ : The transfer of drugs and their metabolites from the liver to the bile in the gall bladder and then into the intestine.

25. _____ : The functional unit of the kidneys.

26. _____ : Drugs that are more lipid soluble.

27. _____ : The relative amount of an administered dose that reaches the general circulation and the rate at which this occurs.

28. _____ : The comparison of bioavailability between two dosage forms.

29. _____ : Drug products that contain identical amounts of the same active ingredients in the same dosage form.

30. _____ : Drug products that contain the same active ingredients, but not necessarily in the same amount or dosage form.

31. _____ : Pharmaceutical equivalents that produce the same effects in patients.

TRUE/FALSE

Indicate whether the statement is true or false in the blank. Answers are at the end of the book.

_____ 1. Receptors are located on the surfaces of cell membranes and inside cells.

_____ 2. Like a lock and key, only certain drugs are able to interact with certain receptors.

_____ 3. Antagonists bind to cell receptors but do not activate them.

_____ 4. After all receptors are occupied by a drug, its effect can still be increased by increasing the dose.

_____ 5. A drug's concentration in its blood is not related to its effect.

_____ 6. Most patients receive the maximum benefit from drug therapy when the amount of the drug in the blood is between the minimum effective and minimum toxic concentration.

_____ 7. Five times the half-life is used to estimate how long it takes for elimination from the body.

_____ 8. Concentrations decrease during absorption, before absorption reaches complexation.

_____ 9. Most orally administered drugs are absorbed from the stomach.

_____ 10. Protein binding can result in the gradual release of a drug into the bloodstream.

_____ 11. Erythromycin capsules and erythromycin tablets are pharmaceutical equivalents.

EXPLAIN WHY

Explain why these statements are true or important. Check your answers in the text. Discuss any questions you may have with your instructor.

1. Why can a drug be developed to have a specific therapeutic effect?

2. Why can the same drug have different effects in different people?

3. Why is gastric emptying time important?

4. Why does the chronic administration of some drugs require increases in dosage to achieve the same effect or decreases to avoid toxicity?

5. Why is a pharmaceutical equivalent not necessarily therapeutically equivalent?

CHOOSE THE BEST ANSWER

Answers are at the end of the book.

1. _____ are drugs that activate receptors to accelerate or slow normal cellular function.
   a. Channels
   b. Agonists
   c. Antagonists
   d. Protein binding

2. The time between the onset of action and the time when the MEC is reached by declining blood concentrations is the
   a. duration of action.
   b. MTC.
   c. therapeutic window.
   d. dose-response curve.

3. When studying concentration and effect, _____ is the time MEC is reached and the response occurs.
   a. therapeutic window
   b. MTC
   c. onset of action
   d. blood concentration

4. Most absorption of oral drugs occurs in the
   a. stomach.
   b. small intestine.
   c. large intestine.

5. Complex proteins in the liver that catalyze chemical reactions are
   a. enzymes.
   b. metabolites.
   c. antagonists.
   d. nephrons.

6. _____ refers to the transfer of drug into the blood from an administered drug product.
   a. Absorption
   b. Excretion
   c. Distribution
   d. Metabolism

7. "First-pass metabolism" occurs at the
   a. stomach.
   b. kidney.
   c. liver.
   d. small intestine.

8. The main functional unit of the kidney is the/an
   a. glomerulus.
   b. enzyme.
   c. metabolite.
   d. nephron.

9. The body's process of transforming drugs is called
   a. distribution.
   b. metabolism.
   c. excretion.
   d. absorption.

10. When bases dissociate, they become
    a. biological.
    b. acids.
    c. ionized.
    d. unionized.

11. The _____ filter the blood and remove waste materials from it.
    a. kidneys
    b. liver
    c. gall bladder
    d. small intestine

12. Enzyme induction results in _____ metabolism of drugs.
    a. the same rate of
    b. reduced
    c. greater

13. Enzyme inhibition results in _____ metabolism of drugs.
    a. reduced
    b. greater
    c. the same rate of

14. Drug products that contain the same active ingredients in the same dosage form but different salt forms are
    a. pharmaceutical equivalents.
    b. bioequivalent drug products.
    c. pharmaceutical alternatives.
    d. antagonist drug products.

— 11 —

FACTORS AFFECTING DRUG ACTIVITY

KEY CONCEPTS

Test your knowledge by covering the information in the right-hand column.

human variability	Differences in age, weight, genetics, and gender are among the significant factors that influence the differences in medication responses among people.
age	Drug distribution, metabolism, and excretion are quite different in the neonate and infant than in adults because their organ systems are not fully developed. Children metabolize certain drugs more rapidly than adults. The elderly typically consume more drugs than other age groups. They also experience physiological changes that significantly affect drug action.
pregnancy	A number of physiological changes that occur in women in the latter stages of pregnancy tend to reduce the rate of absorption.
genetics	Genetic differences can cause differences in the types and amounts of proteins produced in the body, which can result in differences in drug action.
pharmacogenetics	A new field of study that defines the hereditary basis of individual differences.
weight	Weight adjustments may be needed for individuals whose weight is more than 50% higher than the average adult weight. Weight adjustments are also made for children, or unusually small, emaciated, or obese adult patients.
disease states	The disposition and effect of some drugs can be altered in one person but not in another by the presence of diseases other than the one for which a drug is used. Hepatic, cardiovascular, renal, and endocrine disease all increase the variability in drug response. For example, decreased blood flow from cardiovascular disorders can delay or cause erratic drug absorption.

common adverse reactions	Anorexia, nausea, vomiting, constipation, and diarrhea are among the most common adverse reactions to drugs.
allergic reactions	Almost any drug, in almost any dose, can produce an allergic or hypersensitive reaction in a patient. Anaphylactic shock is a potentially fatal hypersensitivity reaction.
teratogenicity	The ability of a substance to cause abnormal fetal development when given to pregnant women.
drug–drug interactions	These can result in either increases or decreases in therapeutic effects or adverse effects.
displacement	Displacement of one drug from protein binding sites by a second drug increases the effects of the displaced drug. Decreased intestinal absorption can occur when orally taken drugs combine to produce nonabsorbable compounds, e.g., when magnesium hydroxide and oral tetracycline bind.
enzyme induction	Caused when drugs activate metabolizing enzymes in the liver, increasing the metabolism of other drugs affected by the same enzymes.
enzyme inhibition	When a drug blocks the activity of metabolic enzymes in the liver.
urinary reabsorption	Some drugs raise urinary pH, lessening renal reabsorption, e.g., sodium bicarbonate raises pH and will cause increased elimination of phenobarbital.
additive effects	Occur when two drugs with similar pharmacological actions are taken, e.g., alcohol and a sedative together produce increased sedation.
synergism	Occurs when two drugs with different sites or mechanisms of action produce greater effects than the sum of individual effects, e.g., acetaminophen and aspirin together produce increased anticoagulation.
drug–diet interactions	The physical presence of food in the gastrointestinal tract can alter absorption by interacting chemically (e.g., certain medications and tetracycline); improving the water-solubility of some drugs by increasing bile secretion; affecting the performance of the dosage form (e.g., altering the release characteristics of polymer-coated tablets); altering gastric emptying; altering intestinal movement; altering liver blood flow. Some foods contain substances that react with certain drugs, e.g., foods containing tyramine can react with monoamine oxidase (MAO) inhibitors.

FILL IN THE KEY TERM

Answers are at the end of the book.

adverse drug reaction	enzyme inhibition	obstructive jaundice
anaphylactic shock	hepatotoxicity	pharmacogenomics
antidote	hypersensitivity	potentiation
carcinogenicity	hyperthyroidism	teratogenicity
cirrhosis	hypothyroidism	
complexation	idiosyncrasy	
displacement	nephrotoxicity	

1. _____ : An abnormal sensitivity generally resulting in an allergic reaction.

2. _____ : A potentially fatal hypersensitivity reaction that produces severe respiratory distress and cardiovascular collapse.

3. _____ : An unexpected reaction the first time a drug is taken, generally due to genetic causes.

4. _____ : Toxicity of the liver.

5. _____ : The ability of a substance to harm the kidneys.

6. _____ : The ability of a substance to cause cancer.

7. _____ : The ability of a substance to cause abnormal fetal development when given to pregnant women.

8. _____ : When one drug with no inherent activity of its own increases the activity of another drug, producing an effect.

9. _____ : Field of study that defines the hereditary basis of individual differences in ADME processes.

10. _____ : When one drug blocks the activity of metabolic enzymes in the liver.

11. _____ : When one drug is moved from protein binding sites by a second drug, resulting in increased effects of the displaced drug.

12. _____ : Obstruction of bile duct causing accumulations in the liver.

13. _____ : A drug that antagonizes the toxic effect of another.

14. _____ : A condition in which thyroid hormone secretions are below normal, often referred to as an underactive thyroid.

15. _____ : A condition in which thyroid hormone secretions are above normal, often referred to as an overactive thyroid.

16. _____ : When two different molecules associate or attach to each other.

17. _____ : A chronic and potentially fatal liver disease causing loss of function and resistance to blood flow through the liver.

18. _____ : An unintended side effect that is negative.

TRUE/FALSE

Indicate whether the statement is true or false in the blank. Answers are at the end of the book.

_____ 1. Physiological changes in pregnancy tend to increase the rate of absorption of drugs.

_____ 2. Adults experience a decrease in many physical functions between the ages of 30 and 70 years.

_____ 3. Lower cardiac output in the elderly tends to slow the distribution of drugs.

_____ 4. Foods containing tyramine, such as aged cheeses, may produce dangerous interactions with some medications.

_____ 5. Ibuprofen can cause nephrotoxicity.

_____ 6. The activity of metabolizing enzymes in the liver is reduced in hypothyroidism.

_____ 7. Some anticancer drugs are considered carcinogenic.

_____ 8. Iron salts form nonabsorbable complexes with tetracycline.

_____ 9. Phenobarbital is an example of an enzyme inducer.

_____ 10. Eating too much spinach can cause problems for patients who are taking some types of anticoagulants.

EXPLAIN WHY

Explain why these statements are true or important. Check your answers in the text. Discuss any questions you may have with your instructor.

1. Give at least three reasons why drug–drug interactions can increase the effects of drugs.

2. Give at least three reasons why drug–drug interactions can decrease the effects of drugs.

3. Give at least three reasons diet can affect drug activity.

Choose the Best Answer

Answers are at the end of the book.

1. A potentially fatal allergic reaction is called
   a. nephrotoxicity.
   b. idiosyncrasy.
   c. teratogenicity.
   d. anaphylactic shock.

2. Placebo effects can be due to
   a. pregnancy.
   b. psychological factors.
   c. body weight.
   d. gender.

3. _____ has decreased elimination in cirrhosis.
   a. Atenolol
   b. Digoxin.
   c. Metoprolol
   d. Ranitidine

4. Hypersensitivity generally happens because a patient develops
   a. anaphylaxis.
   b. anorexia.
   c. antibodies.
   d. hepatotoxicity.

5. Hepatotoxicity is associated with the
   a. central nervous system.
   b. liver.
   c. kidneys.
   d. small intestine.

6. Unpleasant physical symptoms when some drugs are discontinued is called
   a. psychological dependence.
   b. idiosyncrasy.
   c. anaphylaxis.
   d. physiological dependence.

7. Antineoplastics can cause bone marrow suppression; and this is an example of
   a. hematological effects.
   b. carcinogenicity.
   c. teratogenicity.
   d. nephrotoxicity.

8. The ability of a substance to cause abnormal fetal development when given to pregnant women is called
   a. hematological effects.
   b. idiosyncrasy.
   c. nephrotoxicity.
   d. teratogenicity.

9. _____ occurs when two drugs with similar pharmacological effects produce greater effects than the sum of individual effects when taken together.
   a. Synergism
   b. Additive effects
   c. Interference
   d. Displacement

10. Drugs that increase activity of metabolizing enzymes in the liver cause
    a. glomerular filtration.
    b. enzyme induction.
    c. renal secretion.
    d. enzyme inhibition.

11. A drug given to block or reduce toxic effects of another drug is called a(n)
    a. antidote.
    b. synergist.
    c. inducer.
    d. MAO inhibitor.

12. Amoxicillin with clavulanic acid is an example of
    a. synergism.
    b. potentiation.

13. In general, increased dietary carbohydrates _____ metabolism.
    a. increases
    b. decreases

Study Notes

Use this area to write important points you'd like to remember.

— 12 —

INFORMATION

KEY CONCEPTS

Test your knowledge by covering the information in the right-hand column.

primary literature	Original reports of clinical trials, research, and case studies; used for the most updated information.
secondary literature	General reference works based upon primary literature sources; use to find primary literature.
tertiary literature	Condensed works based on primary literature.
abstracting services	Services that summarize information from various primary sources for quick reference.
Material Safety Data Sheets (MSDSs)	OSHA required information for handling hazardous chemicals.
state regulations	Many states have Pharmacy Statutes or State Board of Pharmacy Rules and Regulations that require pharmacies to maintain specific professional literature references.
AHFS Drug Information	The authority for drug information questions. It groups drug monographs by therapeutic use.
Martindale	"The Extra Pharmacopoeia," contains information on drugs in clinical use internationally.
Merck Index	Information on chemicals, drugs, and biologicals including names, chemical structures, and physical and toxicity data.
Physicians' Desk Reference	An annual publication that contains information similar to pharmaceutical manufacturers' drug package inserts.
Drug Facts and Comparisons (DFC)	A preferred reference for comprehensive and timely drug information, containing information about prescription and OTC products.

American Drug Index   A comprehensive list of drug products that contains trade and generic drug names, phonetic pronunciations, indications, manufacturers, and schedule information in a dictionary format.

Handbook on Injectable Drugs   A collection of monographs on commercially available parenteral drugs that include preparation, storage administration, compatibility, and stability of injectable drugs.

King's Guide to Parenteral Admixtures   This reference provides information on injectable drug compatibility and stability of injectable drugs.

Red Book   Guide to products and prices, providing annual price lists of drug products including manufacturer, package size, strength, and wholesale and retail prices.

"Orange Book"   The common name for the FDA's *Approved Drug Products with Therapeutic Equivalence Evaluations.*

mobile devices   Electronic items such as smartphones, iPads, and e-readers that can be used to access drug references.

Internet   A "supernetwork" of many networks from around the world all connected to each other by telephone lines, and all using a common "language."

search engine   Internet software that searches the Web for specific information related to criteria entered by the user.

URL (uniform resource locator)   A Web address.

STUDY NOTES

Use this area to write important points or Web addresses you'd like to remember.

FILL IN THE KEY TERM

Answers are at the end of the book.

Drug Facts and Comparisons   Martindale   secondary literature
Handbook on Injectable   Material Safety Data Sheets   tertiary literature
    Drugs   (MSDS)   URL
HIPAA   "Orange Book"
Internet Service Provider (ISP)   *Physicians' Desk Reference*
King's Guide to Parenteral   primary literature
    Admixtures   *Red Book*

1. _____ : Original reports of clinical and other types of research projects and studies.

2. _____ : Condensed works based on primary literature, such as textbooks, monographs, etc.

3. _____ : Reference with updated AWPs and NDCs.

4. _____ : OSHA required information for handling hazardous chemicals.

5. _____ : General reference works based upon primary literature sources.

6. _____ : A federal law to protect the privacy of patient health records.

7. _____ : A preferred reference for comprehensive and timely drug information, containing information about prescription and OTC products.

8. _____ : Provides information similar to drug package inserts.

9. _____ : A collection of monographs on commercially available parenteral drugs that include topics such as preparation, storage, administration, compatibility, and stability.

10. _____ : Information on injectable drug compatibility and stability.

11. _____ : The "Extra Pharmacopeia" containing international drug monographs.

12. _____ : Used to determine therapeutic equivalence of brand and generic drugs.

13. _____ : A company that provides access to the Internet.

14. _____ : A Web address.

TRUE/FALSE

Indicate whether the statement is true or false in the blank. Answers are at the end of the book.

_____ 1.   Primary literature provides the largest amount of and most current source of information.

_____ 2.   Abstracting services are considered secondary literature.

_____ 3.   *Drug Facts and Comparisons* provides information on prescription and OTC drug products, using comparative tables of therapeutic groups.

_____ 4.   *AHFS* is a collection of monographs on parenteral drugs.

_____ 5.   *Handbook on Injectable Drugs* is available from USP.

_____ 6.   The "Orange Book" is available online.

_____ 7.   The *Red Book* provides pricing information.

_____ 8.   PubMed indexes primary medical literature.

_____ 9.   APhA provides a directory of accredited technician training programs.

_____ 10.   Certified technicians (CPhTs) must obtain 20 hours of continuing education credits every two years to maintain certification.

_____ 11.   Pharmacist Mutual and HPSO are examples of companies that offer pharmacy technicians liability policies.

EXPLAIN WHY

Explain why these statements are true or important. Check your answers in the text. Discuss any questions you may have with your Instructor.

1.   Why is primary literature important?

2.   Why is continuing education important?

3.   Why should technicians be familiar with pharmaceutical information sources?

4.   Why should you know how to use an Internet search engine?

CHOOSE THE BEST ANSWER

Answers are at the end of the book.

1. _____ literature contains condensed works based on primary literature, such as textbooks, monographs, etc.
   a. Orange
   b. Secondary
   c. Tertiary
   d. Abstract

2. OSHA requires pharmacies to have _____ for each hazardous chemical on hand.
   a. manufacturer sheets for documentation of safety
   b. Material Safety Data Sheets (MSDSs)
   c. mixture safety documentation sheets
   d. manufacturer's safety documentation sheets

3. _____ summarize(s) information from primary sources for quick reference.
   a. The PDR
   b. *American Drug Index*
   c. *US Pharmacist*
   d. Abstracting services

4. _____ is an example of a trade journal.
   a. *America's Pharmacist*
   b. *Drugdex*
   c. *Pharmacy Law Digest*
   d. *Pharmacy Times*

5. _____ is a collection of monographs on commercially available parenteral drugs.
   a. The *Merck Index*
   b. The "Orange Book"
   c. *Handbook on Injectable Drugs*
   d. *American Drug Index*

6. _____ is an example of a professional practice journal.
   a. *Today's Technician*
   b. *Pharmacy Times*
   c. *US Pharmacist*
   d. *The Medical Letter*

7. *The Pharmacist's Letter* is an example of a
   a. pink sheet.
   b. trade journal.
   c. professional practice journal.
   d. newsletter.

8. The name of the most comprehensive work in the pharmaceutical sciences is
   a. Goodman and Gilman's.
   b. *American Drug Index*.
   c. *Micromedex*.
   d. Remington's.

9. Remington, *The Science and Practice of Pharmacy*, is published
   a. annually.
   b. every two years.
   c. every five years.
   d. every ten years.

10. A Web address is also known as a(an)
    a. URL.
    b. dsl.
    c. browser.
    d. isp.

11. The Website address of the American Pharmacists Association is
    a. www.ashp.org.
    b. www.pharmacist.com.
    c. www.fda.gov.
    d. www.apa.gov.

12. A provider of professional liability policies for technicians:
   a. Pharmacists Mutual
   b. American Pharmacists Association
   c. American Society of Health-System Pharmacists
   d. Pharmacy Technician Certification Board

13. A _____ can be used to search the Web for information specified by the user.
   a. modem
   b. browser
   c. search engine
   d. URL

14. An example of Internet browser software:
   a. Verizon
   b. Comcast
   c. Century Link
   d. Mozilla Firefox

STUDY NOTES

Use this area to write important points or Web addresses you'd like to remember.

— 13 —

INVENTORY MANAGEMENT

KEY CONCEPTS

Test your knowledge by covering the information in the right-hand column.

inventory	A list of goods or items a business uses in its normal operations.
open formulary	One that allows purchase of any medication that is prescribed.
closed formulary	A limited list of approved medications.
wholesalers	More than three-quarters of pharmaceutical manufacturers' sales are directly to drug wholesalers, who in turn resell their inventory to hospitals, pharmacies, and other pharmaceutical dispensers. They are government licensed and regulated.
perpetual inventory	A system that maintains a continuous record of every item in inventory so that it always shows the stock on hand.
spoilage	Inappropriate storage conditions or expired products automatically determine that a product is spoiled since in either case the chemical compounds in the drug product may have degraded.
turnover	The rate at which inventory is used.
point-of-sale (POS) system	A system in which the item is deducted from inventory as it is sold or dispensed.
reorder points	Maximum and minimum inventory levels for each drug.
computer maintenance	Factors that can damage computer systems are temperature, dust, moisture, movement, vibrations, and power surges.
system backup	Pharmacy computer files must be regularly backed up or copied to an appropriate storage media.
automated dispensing system	A device that dispenses medications at point-of-use.

Material Safety Data Sheets (MSDS)	Instructions for hazardous substances such as chemotherapeutic agents that indicate when special handling and shipping is required.
online ordering	In an online ordering system, if an order can be filled as ordered, a message from the supplier will automatically confirm the order to the ordering system. The system automatically assigns to each order a purchase order number for identification.
controlled substance shipping	These substances are shipped separately and checked in by a pharmacist. A special order form must be used for Schedule II substances.
stock bottles	The bulk containers in which most medications are received from the supplier.
storage	Drugs must be stored according to manufacturer's specifications. Most drugs are kept in a fairly constant room temperature of 59°–86°F. The temperature of refrigeration should generally be 36°–46°F.
freshness	Medications should be organized in a way that will dispense the oldest items first.
point-of-use stations	In hospitals and other settings, medications are stocked in dispensing units throughout the facility that may be called supply stations or med stations.

STUDY NOTES

Use this area to write important points you'd like to remember.

FILL IN THE KEY TERM

Answers are at the end of the book.

automated dispensing system   perpetual inventory   therapeutic equivalent
closed formulary   point-of-use stations   turnover
inventory   purchase order number   unit dose
MSDS   reorder points
open formulary   stock bottles

1. _____ : One that allows purchase of any medication that is prescribed.

2. _____ : A limited list of approved medications.

3. _____ : The rate at which inventory is used, generally expressed in number of days.

4. _____ : The bulk containers in which most medications are received from the supplier.

5. _____ : A system that maintains a continuous record of every item in inventory so that it always shows the stock on hand.

6. _____ : A list of goods or items a business uses in its normal operations.

7. _____ : Minimum and maximum stock levels which determine when a reorder is placed and for how much.

8. _____ : Instructions for hazardous products.

9. _____ : Pharmaceuticals that have the same effect in patients.

10. _____ : A number assigned to each order for products that will allow it to be tracked and checked throughout the order process.

11. _____ : A device that dispenses medications at point-of-use.

12. _____ : A package containing a single dose of a medication.

13. _____ : In hospitals and other settings, medications are stocked in units throughout the facility that may also be called supply stations or med stations.

TRUE/FALSE

Indicate whether the statement is true or false in the blank. Answers are at the end of the book.

_____ 1.   The majority of pharmaceutical manufacturer sales are to wholesalers.

_____ 2.   Kirby Lester® is an example of a robotic device.

_____ 3.   Reorder points are maximum and minimum inventory levels for a product.

_____ 4.   Computerized ordering systems do not allow manual editing.

_____ 5.   Point-of-sale systems adjust inventory as medications are sold or dispensed.

_____ 6.   With computers keeping records, printed copies are not needed.

_____ 7.   Certain hazardous substances may not be shipped by air.

_____ 8.   A closed formulary allows any medication prescribed to be purchased.

_____ 9.   Refrigeration means 50°–59°F.

_____ 10. Bar codes are used to quickly identify a product.

EXPLAIN WHY

Explain why these statements are true or important. Check your answers in the text. Discuss any questions you may have with your Instructor.

1.   Why are wholesalers used?

2.   Why is knowing the turnover rate of a product important?

3.   Why are reorder points used?

4.   Why is it important to make hard copy of computerized reports?

5.   Why is it important to back up computer files?

CHOOSE THE BEST ANSWER

Answers are at the end of the book.

1. The list of medications that are approved for use in a health-care system is called a
   a. turnover.
   b. formulary.
   c. therapeutic equivalent.
   d. wholesaler.

2. Pharmaceutical equivalents that produce the same effects in patients are
   a. generic equivalents.
   b. always less expensive.
   c. always more expensive.
   d. therapeutically equivalent.

3. _____ is an expression for the rate at which inventory is used and is generally expressed in number of days.
   a. Reciprocal
   b. Turnover
   c. POS
   d. Availability

4. A general rule is that _____% of stock accounts for _____% of prescriptions.
   a. 20/80
   b. 30/70
   c. 40/60
   d. 50/50

5. An inventory system in which the item is deducted from inventory as it is dispensed is called a (an)
   a. automated dispensing unit.
   b. point-of-use system.
   c. formulary.
   d. point of sale system (POS).

6. Pyxis Med/Supply Station® is a good example of a (an)
   a. automated point-of-use storage system.
   b. automated dispensing machine.
   c. robotic dispensing machine.
   d. mobile robot.

7. Material Safety Data Sheets (MSDS) are required by _____ for hazardous substances and provide hazard, handling, clean-up, and first aid information.
   a. OSHA
   b. State Board of Pharmacy
   c. FDA
   d. DEA

8. When reconciling an order, controlled substances are shipped separately, and should be checked in by a(an)
   a. technician.
   b. pharmacy clerk.
   c. pharmacist.
   d. intern.

9. The p.o. number identifies the
   a. post office.
   b. pharmacy.
   c. point-of-sale.
   d. purchase order.

10. Walkers, wheel chairs, crutches, and bed-pans are examples of
    a. GPO.
    b. DME.
    c. DOT.
    d. EPA.

STUDY NOTES

Use this area to write important points you'd like to remember.

— 14 —

FINANCIAL ISSUES

KEY CONCEPTS

Test your knowledge by covering the information in the right-hand column.

third-party programs
Another party besides the patient or the pharmacy that pays for some or all of the cost of medication: essentially, an insurer.

pharmacy benefit manager (PBM)
A company that administers drug benefit programs for insurance companies, HMOs, and self-insured employers.

co-insurance
Essentially an agreement between the insurer and the insured to share costs.

co-pay
The portion of the cost of prescriptions that patients with third-party insurance must pay.

deductible
A set amount that must be paid by the patient for each benefit period before the insurer will cover additional expenses.

maximum allowable cost (MAC)
The amount paid by the insurer is not equal to the retail price normally charged, but is determined by a formula described in a contract between the insurer and the pharmacy. There is a maximum allowable cost (MAC) per tablet or other dispensing unit that an insurer or PBM will pay for a given product.

usual and customary (U&C)
The MAC is often determined by survey of the usual and customary (U&C) prices for a prescription within a given geographic area. This is also referred to as the UCR (usual, customary, and reasonable) price for the prescription.

prescription drug benefit cards
Cards that contain necessary billing information for pharmacies, including the patient's identification number, group number, and co-pay amount.

HMO (health maintenance organization)
Health-care networks that usually do not cover expenses incurred outside the network and often require generic substitution.

point of service (POS)	Health-care network where the patient's primary care physician must be a member and costs outside the network may be partially reimbursed.
preferred provider organization (PPO)	Health-care network that reimburses expenses outside the network at a lower rate than inside the network and usually requires generic substitution.
Medicare	National health insurance for people over the age of 65, disabled people under the age of 65, and people with kidney failure.
Medicaid	A federal-state program for the needy.
workers' compensation	Compensation for employees accidentally injured on the job.
coordination of benefits	Process to provide maximum coverage for health benefits when a patient has coverage by two plans.
online adjudication	Most prescription claims are now filed electronically by online claim submission and online adjudication of claims. In online adjudication, the technician uses the computer to determine the exact coverage for each prescription with the appropriate third party.
dispense as written (DAW)	When brand name drugs are dispensed, numbers corresponding to the reason for submitting the claim with brand name drugs are entered in a DAW (dispense as written) indicator field in the prescription system.
patient identification number	The number assigned to the patient by the insurer that is indicated on the drug benefit card. If it does not match the code for the patient in the insurer's computer (with the same sex and other information) a claim may be rejected.
age limitations	Many prescription drug plans have age limitations for children or dependents of the cardholder.
refills	Most third-party plans require that most of the medication has been taken before the plan will cover a refill of the same medication.
maintenance medications	Many managed care health programs require mail order pharmacies to fill prescriptions for maintenance medications.
rejected claims	When a claim is rejected, the pharmacy technician can telephone the insurance plan's pharmacy help desk to determine if the patient is eligible for coverage.

FILL IN THE KEY TERM

Answers are at the end of the book.

co-insurance
co-pay
deductible
dual co-pay
CMS-1500 form
coordination of benefits
CPT code

HMO
maximum allowable
    cost (MAC)
Medicaid
Medicare
online adjudication
patient assistance programs

pharmacy benefits managers
POS
PPO
prescription drug benefit cards
U&C or UCR
workers' compensation

1. _____ : Companies that administer drug benefit programs.

2. _____ : The resolution of prescription coverage through the communication of the pharmacy computer with the third-party computer.

3. _____ : An agreement for cost-sharing between the insurer and the insured.

4. _____ : The portion of the price of medication that the patient is required to pay.

5. _____ : Co-pays that have two prices: one for generic and one for brand medications.

6. _____ : The maximum price per tablet (or other dispensing unit) an insurer or PBM will pay for a given product.

7. _____ : The maximum amount of payment for a given prescription, determined by the insurer to be a reasonable price.

8. _____ : A network of providers for which costs are covered inside but not outside of the network.

9. _____ : A network of providers where the patient's primary care physician must be a member and costs outside the network may be partially reimbursed.

10. _____ : A network of providers where costs outside the network may be partially reimbursed and the patient's primary care physician need not be a member.

11. _____ : A set amount that must be paid by the patient for each benefit period before the insurer will cover additional expenses.

12. _____ : Cards that contain third-party billing information for prescription drug purchases.

13. _____ : Identifiers used for billing pharmacist-provided MTM services..

14. _____ : A federal program providing health care to people with certain disabilities age 65 and over.

15. _____ : A federal-state program, administered by the states, providing health care for the needy.

16. _____ : The standard form used by health-care providers to bill for services.

17. _____ : An employer compensation program for employees accidentally injured on the job.

18. _____ : Manufacturer sponsored prescription drug programs for the needy.

19. _____ : Process to provide maximum coverage when a patient has coverage by two plans.

TRUE/FALSE

Indicate whether the statement is true or false in the blank. Answers are at the end of the book.

_____ 1. The amount paid by a co-insurer to the pharmacy is equal to the wholesale price of a drug.

_____ 2. Medicare and Medicaid are examples of public health insurance programs.

_____ 3. A pharmacy benefits manager is a company that administers drug benefits programs.

_____ 4. Tier one drugs are usually generics.

_____ 5. Many third-party programs have drug formularies.

_____ 6. MTM is part of Medicare Part D.

_____ 7. The CMS-1500 form is used to apply for an NPI.

_____ 8. An NPI number identifies the pharmacy.

EXPLAIN WHY

Explain why these statements are true or important. Check your answers in the text. Discuss any questions you may have with your instructor.

1. If an online claim is rejected, why is it important to review the information that was originally entered before calling?

2. Why is it important to know the benefits of various third-party programs?

CHOOSE THE BEST ANSWER

Answers are at the end of the book.

1. The resolution of prescription coverage for a prescription through the communication of the pharmacy computer with the third-party computer is called
   a. PBM.
   b. online adjudication.
   c. MAC.
   d. UCR.

2. The Maximum Allowable Cost (MAC) is usually _____ the Usual and Customary (U&C) price.
   a. less than
   b. greater than
   c. equal to

3. The _____ is the maximum price per unit an insurer will pay for a product.
   a. co-insurance
   b. co-pay
   c. maximum allowable cost
   d. deductible

4. A(An) _____ is a network of providers for which costs are covered inside the network but not outside.
   a. HMO
   b. POS
   c. PPO
   d. MAC

5. _____ is a program for people over age 65 or with certain disabilities.
   a. Medicaid
   b. ADC
   c. Workers' compensation
   d. Medicare

6. The Medicare program that covers inpatient hospital expenses is
   a. Medicare Part A.
   b. Medicare Part B.
   c. Medicare Part C.
   d. Medicare Part D.

7. Procedures for billing compounded prescriptions
   a. should always be referred to the pharmacist.
   b. are not available.
   c. do not apply in community pharmacy practice.
   d. are variable, depending on the insurer or PBM.

8. When a technician receives a rejected claim "invalid birth date," this probably means
   a. the patient has Medicaid.
   b. the patient does not have coverage.
   c. the birth date submitted by the pharmacy does not match the birth date in the insurer's computer.
   d. the patient has Medicare.

9. The form used by health-care providers to apply for a National Provider Identifier (NPI) is
   a. CMS-1500.
   b. CMS-10114.
   c. a universal claim form.
   d. CPT 0116T.

10. _____ services are provided by pharmacists to some patients enrolled in Medicare Part D.
    a. MTM
    b. PDP
    c. CPT
    d. NPI

STUDY NOTES

Use this area to write important points you'd like to remember.

— 15 —

COMMUNITY PHARMACY

KEY CONCEPTS

Test your knowledge by covering the information in the right-hand column.

community pharmacy	Pharmacies that provides prescription services to the public and sell over-the-counter medications and health and beauty products.
close interaction with patients	A key characteristic of community pharmacy that allows pharmacy technicians to constantly interact with patients.
interpersonal skills	Skills involving relationships between people.
independent pharmacies	Individually owned local pharmacies.
chain pharmacies	Regional or national pharmacy chains such as CVS, Walgreens, Rite-Aid, and others.
mass merchandiser pharmacies	Regional or national stores such as Walmart, Kmart, Target, and others that have pharmacy departments.
food store pharmacies	Regional or national food store chains such as Kroger, Giant, Eagle and others that have pharmacy departments.
disease state management programs	One-on-one pharmacist-patient consultation sessions to help manage chronic diseases.
walk-in clinics	Clinics in pharmacies that are usually staffed by nurse practitioners and provide treatment for a limited number of common conditions.
pharmacist immunization programs	Depending on state law, pharmacists may administer routine vaccinations.
federal regulation	Laws such as OBRA, HIPAA, Medicare Prescription Drug Improvement and Modernization Act, CMEA, and the Red Flag Rule that are important for pharmacy technicians to know.

state regulations	Community pharmacies are most closely regulated at the state level.
transaction windows	Counter areas designated for taking prescriptions and for dispensing them to patients.
storage	Adequate shelving, cabinets, drawers, and refrigerator(s) for storing medications.
prescription counter	Counter area designated for preparing noncompounded medications.
compounding area	Counter area, usually near a sink, for preparing medications that require mixing.
prescription bins or shelves	Storage areas for completed prescriptions.
good customer service	Presenting yourself to customers in a calm, courteous, and professional manner, along with listening to and understanding customer requests for service and accurately fulfilling requests.
pharmacist's judgement	Some questions and calls require the pharmacist's judgment and these should be directed immediately to the pharmacist.
prescription in-take	The drop-off area where patients bring prescriptions that need to be filled.
patient profile	Information about the patient that is entered into the computer.
refills	When processing a refill prescription, it is necessary to check that there are refills available. In the case of a patient requesting an early refill of a controlled substance, involve the pharmacist right away.
online billing	Today's pharmacy systems generally "fill and bill" at the same time.
filing	Hard copies of prescriptions are filed by prescription number. Faxed, phoned, and electronic prescriptions must be printed or transcribed onto a paper hard copy so they can be filed.
scanning a hard copy prescription	For accuracy and improved record keeping, many pharmacies also scan the prescription into the pharmacy dispensing system.
vial	Container for dispensing tablets or capsules.
safety caps	All dispensed prescription vials and bottles must have a safety cap or child resistant cap, unless the patient requests a non-child resistant cap.

automated filling and dispensing machines	Machines that automatically fill and label pill bottles with correct quantities of ordered drugs.
counting tray	A tray designed for counting pills from a stock bottle into a prescription vial.
amber bottle	Container for dispensing liquid medications.
reconstitution	Some medications are shipped as powders but must be mixed with distilled water so they are dispensed as liquids.
Fillmaster®	A device that dispenses the exact amount of distilled water for reconstitution.
auxiliary labels	Labels regarding specific warnings, foods, or medications to avoid, potential side effects, and other cautionary statements.
final check by the pharmacist	The final step of the prescription preparation process is the final check of the product and all paperwork by the pharmacist.
signature log	Customer signatures in log are required for Medicaid and most third-party insurers, as well as Schedule V controlled substances, poisons, and certain other prescriptions (depending on state laws).
OTC products	Drug products that do not require a prescription, but are not without risks. Therefore, the technician should not recommend them to pharmacy customers.
markup	The amount of the retailer's sale price minus their purchase price.
shelf stickers	Stickers for OTC drugs and other products that can be scanned for inventory identification.
unit price	The price of a single unit of a product, such as for one ounce of a liquid cold remedy.
separation and removal of trash	In accordance with HIPAA, pharmacies must separate trash that contains protected health information (PHI). Any paperwork containing PHI must be shredded onsite, or by a contracted vendor.

IN THE WORKPLACE

Use these tools to practice and check some of your workplace skills.

Pharmacy Technician Skills Checklist
BASIC COMPUTER ENTRY SKILLS

Name:

Skill or Procedure	Self-Assessment			Supervisor Review		
	Needs to Improve	Meets or Exceeds	Needs to Improve*	Meets or Exceeds	*Plan of Action	
1. Properly interprets medical abbreviations.						
2. Understands dosage forms.						
3. Understands prescription number assignments (controlled, non-controlled).						
4. Properly enters a new patient into computer.						
5. Properly adds a new patient to an existing family file.						
6. Properly uses SIG codes.						
7. Properly adds medication allergy codes.						
8. Properly processes refill prescriptions using computer.						
9. Understands procedures for DUR screens.						
10. Properly enters third party billing (insurance) information.						
11. Properly adds a new doctor file (if doctor is not already in the database).						
12. Chooses correct drug (matches NDC).						
13. Uses appropriate DAW codes.						

Pharmacy Technician Skills Checklist
GENERAL COMPUTER ENTRY SKILLS

Name: _____

Skill or Procedure	Self-Assessment		Supervisor Review		
	Needs to Improve	Meets or Exceeds	Needs to Improve*	Meets or Exceeds	*Plan of Action
1. Properly puts new prescriptions on file (without filling).					
2. Enters and uses alternate third party plans.					
3. Enters compounded prescriptions.					
4. Generates daily reports.					
5. Generates medical expense statements.					
6. Updates inventories.					
7. Updates order quantities.					

FILL IN THE KEY TERM

Answers are at the end of the book.

auxiliary labels
counting tray
disease state management
       programs
interpersonal skills
markup

patient profile
pharmacist immunization
       program
pharmacist's judgement
prescription counter
safety caps

signature log
shelf stickers
transaction windows
unit price
walk-in clinics

1. _____ : Depending on state law, pharmacists may administer routine vaccinations.

2. _____ : Skills involving relationships between people.

3. _____ : Clinics in some pharmacies that provide treatment for a limited number of common conditions.

4. _____ : Counter areas designated for taking prescriptions and for delivering them to patients.

5. _____ : Counter area for providing noncompounded medications.

6. _____ : Some questions and calls require the pharmacist's judgement.

7. _____ : Information about the patient that is entered into the computer.

8. _____ : A book or electronic device to provide verification that a prescription was picked up.

9. _____ : The amount of the retailer's sales price minus their purchase price.

10. _____ : Child resistant caps required of all dispensed prescription vials.

11. _____ : A tray designed for counting pills.

12. _____ : Stickers with bar codes that can be scanned for inventory identification.

13. _____ : Provide one-on-one pharmacist-patient consultation to help manage chronic diseases and conditions.

14. _____ : Labels regarding specific warnings and usage information.

15. _____ : For example, the price for one ounce of a liquid cold remedy.

TRUE/FALSE

Indicate whether the statement is true or false in the blank. Answers are at the end of the book.

_____ 1. Almost two-thirds of all drugs in the United States are sold at community pharmacies.

_____ 2. Many states put limits on the number of technicians assisting the pharmacist at a given time.

_____ 3. The pharmacy technician should not recommend OTC products to pharmacy customers.

_____ 4. The dispensing code is only required for controlled substance prescriptions.

_____ 5. HIPAA regulations do not apply to disease state management services provided by pharmacists.

_____ 6. Safety caps are not used for patients who request an easy open cap.

_____ 7. Schedule II controlled substance orders must be checked and signed for by the pharmacist.

_____ 8. When a technician prepares a prescription, it is always checked by the pharmacist before dispensing to the patient.

_____ 9. Signature logs serve as proof to third-party payers that the prescription was dispensed to the patient.

_____ 10. OTC products may be purchased without a prescription because they are without risk.

_____ 11. Walk-in clinics are usually staffed by nurse practitioners.

EXPLAIN WHY

Explain why these statements are true or important. Check your answers in the text. Discuss any questions you may have with your instructor.

1. Why is the health of customers a factor in community pharmacy?

2. Why are good interpersonal skills important in community pharmacy?

3. Why is it important to look a patient in the eye and restate what they have said?

4. Why does the pharmacist check technician-filled prescriptions before dispensing to patients?

5. Why shouldn't technicians recommend OTC products?

CHOOSE THE BEST ANSWER

Answers are at the end of the book.

1. Community pharmacies within stores, like Walmart or Kmart, that are part of regional or national mass merchandise chains are
   a. chain pharmacies.
   b. mass merchandiser pharmacies.
   c. independent pharmacies.
   d. food store pharmacies.

2. Pharmacy technicians can help with immunization by
   a. taking patient information.
   b. administering the vaccine.
   c. writing prescriptions.
   d. counseling patients.

3. The refrigerator in a community pharmacy must store medications between
   a. 2° and 8° Fahrenheit.
   b. 32° and 40° Celsius.
   c. 2° and 8° Celsius.
   d. 32° and 40° Fahrenheit.

4. Medicare Part D relies on _____ to provide medication coverage to eligible patients.
   a. Medicaid
   b. patient assistance programs
   c. Prescription Drug Plans
   d. state welfare programs

5. The Red Flag Rule was enacted to
   a. help prevent identity theft.
   b. limit sales of pseudoephedrine.
   c. create PDPs.
   d. provide counseling to Medicaid patients.

6. The final check of a new prescription is performed by
   a. the pharmacist.
   b. the prescribing physician.
   c. a certified technician.
   d. the senior technician.

7. OTC product recommendations should be made by
   a. certified technicians.
   b. technicians with seniority.
   c. pharmacists.
   d. technicians with more than two years of experience.

8. When receiving orders for Schedule II controlled substances, they must be checked and signed by the
   a. certified pharmacy technician.
   b. pharmacy technician.
   c. pharmacist.
   d. third party.

9. Pharmacy technicians are responsible for all of the following EXCEPT:
   a. reordering stock.
   b. recommending OTC products to pharmacy technicians.
   c. keeping the pharmacy neat and clean.
   d. product stock duties.

10. Separation of trash in pharmacies is in accordance with
    a. HIPAA.
    b. CMEA.
    c. OBRA.
    d. PDP.

— 16 —

HOSPITAL PHARMACY

KEY CONCEPTS

Test your knowledge by covering the information in the right-hand column.

pharmacist supervision

Pharmacy technicians in the hospital work under the direct supervision of a pharmacist or supervising technician. Only a pharmacist may verify orders in the computer system and check medications being sent to the nursing floors.

patient care units

Patient rooms are divided into groups called nursing units or patient care units, with patients having similar problems often located on the same unit.

nurse's station

The work station for medical personnel on a nursing unit is called the nurse's station. Various items required for care of patients are stored there, including patient medications.

ancillary areas

Areas such as the emergency room that also use medications and are serviced by the pharmacy department.

central pharmacy

The main inpatient pharmacy in a hospital that has pharmacy satellites.

front counter

Area near the entrance of the main pharmacy where pharmacy technicians help other health-care professionals, answer phone calls, fill first doses of oral medications, and perform other duties as needed.

satellite pharmacy

A branch of the inpatient pharmacy responsible for preparing, dispensing, and monitoring medication for specific patient areas.

delivery technician

A delivery technician is responsible for transporting medications and other pharmacy supplies from the pharmacy to nursing units, ancillary areas of the hospital, and/or outpatient clinics.

outpatient pharmacy	A pharmacy attached to a hospital servicing patients who have left the hospital or who are visiting doctors in a hospital outpatient clinic.
order processing	Entering written medication orders in the computer system.
monitoring drug therapy	Retrieving drug levels, lab values, or other patient specific information from patient charts or electronic records to assist a pharmacist.
investigational drug service	A specialized pharmacy subsection that deals solely with clinical drug trials. These drug studies require a great deal of paperwork and special documentation of all doses of study medication taken by patients. Technicians frequently assist the pharmacist with this documentation and in preparing individual patient medication supplies.
inventory control	Maintaining the stock of drugs and supplies in the pharmacy.
cart fill	In hospitals that have manual cart fill, medication carts contain a 24-hour supply of medications in a patient cassette or drawer.
automation	Pharmacy systems including robots, automated dispensing cabinets.
narcotics/controlled substances	Pharmacy technicians can help coordinate narcotic drug distribution, including reviewing reports and confirming compliance with state and federal controlled substance laws.
IV/clean room	Areas designated for the preparation of sterile products.
quality assurance	Involves inspecting nursing units and other areas of the hospital that store medications to make sure medications are stored and handled in compliance with hospital policy.
chemotherapy	Additional training is important on handling and preparing hazardous materials including chemotherapy drugs.
pharmacy technician supervisor	Part of the management team responsible for training technicians, creating work schedules, and completing annual evaluations.
staff development	Providing staff training materials, reading assignments, demonstrations, and written or practical tests
formulary	A list of drugs stocked at the hospital that have been selected based on therapeutic factors as well as cost.

KEY CONCEPTS

Test your knowledge by covering the information in the right hand column.

closed formulary

A closed formulary requires physicians to order medications from the formulary list.

non-formulary

Drugs not on the formulary list.

therapeutic interchange

A policy approved by the hospital pharmacy & therapeutics committee that allows the pharmacist to change a medication order to a therapeutically equivalent formulary medication.

electronic medical record

A computerized patient medical record, also known as electronic health record.

medication order form

In the hospital, all drugs ordered for a patient are written on a medication order form and not a prescription blank as in a community pharmacy. Physicians write medication orders for hospital patients, though both nurses and pharmacists may also write orders if they are directly instructed to do so by a doctor. In addition, physician's assistants and nurse practitioners may sometimes write orders, depending upon the institution.

medication administration record

Nurses record and track medication orders on a patient specific form called the medication administration record (MAR).

computerized physician order entry (CPOE)

A computer system that allows the physician to enter the medication order directly into the hospital computer system.

standing order

A standard medication order for patients to receive medication at scheduled intervals.

PRN order

Orders for medications that are administered only on an as-needed basis.

STAT order

An order for medication to be administered immediately.

patient-specific trays

The amount of medications for a 24-hour period are placed in patient trays that are loaded into medication carts.

unit dose

A package containing the amount of drug for one dose.

prepacking

Technicians often "prepack" medications that have been supplied in bulk into unit doses. Machines that automate this process are generally used for pre-packing oral solid medications.

unit dose labels	Unit dose labels contain bar codes for identification and control. Items are scanned into the dispensing and inventory system at various stages up to dispensing. This reduces the chances of medication errors and improves documentation and inventory control.
controlled substances	A primary area of concern for inventory control is narcotics, or controlled substances, which require an exact record of the location of every item to the exact tablet or unit.
IV admixtures	A large portion of the medication used in the hospital is administered intravenously. Pharmacy technicians prepare IV admixtures, including small and large volume parenterals, parenteral nutrition therapy, and chemotherapy.
TJC	The Joint Commission on Accreditation of Healthcare Organizations, the accreditation agency for health-care organizations. Organizations undergo a TJC survey every three years.
code cart	Locked cart filled with emergency medications. All patient care areas are required to have code carts.
sharps container	Needles or other items that may cut or puncture the skin should always be thrown away in designated sharps containers.
policy and procedures manual	A manual containing information about every aspect of the job from dress code to disciplinary actions and step-by-step directions on how to perform various tasks that will be required of technicians. All departments within the hospital are required by regulating agencies to maintain this.

unit dose medications

patient trays

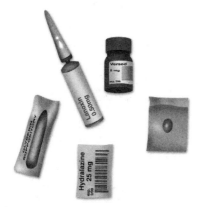

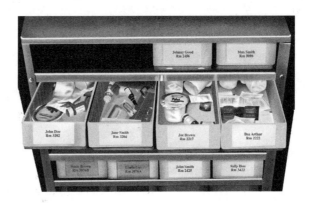

MEDICATION ORDERS

Medication order forms are an all-purpose communication tool used by the various members of the health-care team. Orders for various procedures, laboratory tests, and X-rays may be written on the form in addition to medication orders. Several medication orders may be written on one medication order form unlike pharmacy prescription blanks seen in the retail setting.

There are several different types of orders that can be written. One is a standard medication order for patients to receive a certain drug at scheduled intervals throughout the day, sometimes called a standing order. Orders for medications that are administered only on an as needed basis are called PRN medication orders. A third type of order is for a medication that is needed right away and these are referred to as STAT orders.

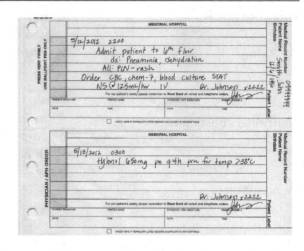

MEDICATION ADMINISTRATION RECORD

On this form every medication ordered for a patient is written down as well as the time it is administered and the person who gave the dose. These forms may be handwritten by the nursing staff or generated by the pharmacy computer system. The MAR is an important document in tracking the care of the patient because it gives a 24 hour picture of a patient's medication use. The accuracy of this document is crucial.

COMMUNITY HOSPITAL
Medication Administration Record

Room/Bed: 675-01
Patient: SMITH, JOHN
Account #: 099999999
Sex: M
Age: 48Y
Doctor: JOHNSON, P.
Allergies: PENICILLIN-->RASH

From 0730 on 02/01/13 to 0700 on 02/02/13

Diagnosis: PNEUMONIA; DEHYDRATION
Height: 5'11" weight: 75KG

Verified By: *Susie Smith, RN*

	0730-1530	1600-2300	2330-0700
5% DEXTROSE/0.9% SODIUM CHLORIDE 1 LITER BAG DOSE 125 ML/HR IV Q 8 HRS ORDER #2	800 JD	1600 SS	2400
MULTIVITAMIN TABLET DOSE: 1 TABLET P.O. DAILY ORDER #4	1000 Given @ 0900 JD		
CLARITHROMYCIN 500 MG TABLET DOSE: 500MG P.O. Q 12 HRS ORDER #5	1000 JD	2200 SS	
ACETAMINOPHEN 325 MG TABLET DOSE: 650 MG P.O. Q 4-6 HRS P.R.N. FOR TEMP>38)C ORDER # 17	1200 JD		

Init / Signature	Init / Signature
SS / *Susie Smith, RN*	___ / _____
JD / *Jane Doe, RN*	___ / _____
___ / _____	___ / _____

IN THE WORKPLACE

Some questions to ask when entering or checking a medication order.

Several questions should always be asked when entering or checking a medication order.

Question:	Example situation	
	Problem	Solution*
✓ Is the patient allergic to the ordered medication or a component of the ordered medication?	A medication order is placed for trimethoprim/sulfamoxazole (Bactrim®), but the patient has a "sulfa" allergy with the description of the allergy stating "hives".	The order should not be processed and a new medication order for a different antibiotic is required.
✓ Is the drug appropriate?	A patient is ordered a potassium IVPB. The most recent potassium lab level = 5 mEq/mL. (normal potassium = 3.5 to 5.5 mEq/mL). The medication is not indicated for this patient.	The physician should be notified that the medication is not indicated based on the current lab level.
✓ Is the dose and frequency appropriate?	An order for a patient reads, "Digoxin 0.5 mg po q 6 H." The normal dosing for digoxin is 0.125 – 0.25 mg daily.	The ordered dose would be toxic. The order should be changed.
✓ Has the drug dose/frequency been adjusted for the patient's age, weight, disease state, kidney or liver function?	A 79 year old patient with major renal dysfunction has a new medication order for Fluconazole 400 mg IV daily. Fluconazole is eliminated renally and should be adjusted for renal dysfunction.	The patient's renal function should be calculated and the dose adjusted appropriately.
✓ Is the drug formulation and route most appropriate for the patient?	A patient has an order for an IV medication but the patient is tolerating oral feeds.	Discuss with the physician and change the drug to the oral formulation.
✓ Are there any drug interactions that require changes in the order or increased monitoring that the physician should be made aware of?	A new order for amiodarone is received for a patient who is also on warfarin. There is an interaction between amiodarone and warfarin which increases the risk for the patient to bleed.	The physician should be made aware of the interaction and recommended to monitor the patient more closely.
✓ Does the new order therapeutically duplicate another drug the patient is already taking?	A medication order for pantoprazole is ordered for a patient with currently active order for omeprazole. Both medications are proton pump inhibitors and work in the same way.	There would be no additive effect to using both medications. The order needs to be clarified with the physician and one of the orders discontinued.
✓ Is the drug on the hospital formulary? If not, can the medication be therapeutically interchanged?	Famotidine 20mg BID is ordered but the formulary H₂-blocker is ranitidine.	A therapeutic substitution is made to ranitidine 150 mg BID per hospital protocol.
✓ Is the medication "restricted" and need approval from a specific service in the hospital?	Vancomycin 1 g IV q 12 H is ordered for a patient. Vancomycin is restricted by the infectious disease service and it has not yet been approved for this patient.	The infectious disease service should be notified and approval received before processing the order.
✓ Should the medication be limited to a certain number of days due to hospital policy or an automatic stop order?	An order is written for ketoralac 30 mg IV q 6H x 10 days. Hospital policy and manufacturer recommendations limit the length of therapy to 5 days.	The order is changed to 5 days of therapy.

*Unless there is a hospital policy in place to the contrary, all changes in medication orders need to be authorized by the physician before they are changed.

IN THE WORKPLACE

A sample extemporaneous compounding worksheet.

Extemporaneous Compounding Work sheet
Department of Pharmacy
University Medical Center

NAME OF PRODUCT: OMEPRAZOLE ORAL SUSPENSION 2 mg/mL

Hospital Lot No: _____   **Prepared on:** ____/____/____   **Expires on:** ____/____/____

INGREDIENTS	MFR	LOT #	EXP DATE	QUANTITY	MADE BY	CHKD BY
Omeprazole (Prilosec®) 20 mg capsules				5		
Sodium Bicarbonate 8.4% (1 mEq/mL)				q.s. 50 mL		

Compounding Instructions:
1. Empty capsules into beaker.
2. Add sodium bicarbonate solution.
3. Gently stir (about 15 minutes) until a white suspension is formed.
4. Transfer to amber-colored bottle.

Stability:
45 days at 4°C

Auxilliary Labels required:
SHAKE WELL
REFRIGERATE
PROTECT FROM LIGHT

References:
Ann Pharmacother, 2000;34:600-605.
Am J Health Syst Pharm, 1999;56(suppl 4): S18-21

IN THE WORKPLACE

A sample orientation checklist.

UNIVERSITY MEDICAL CENTER
Orientation Checklist

NAME: _____   POSITION: _____   HIRE DATE: _____

Pharmacy ORIENTATION SKILL CHECKLIST (outline of competency requirements)	EVALUATION			
	Reviewed (date/initial)	Verbalizes Understanding (date/initial)	Demonstrates Skill (date/initial)	COMMENTS
INTRODUCTION AND TOUR Introduce to all personnel				
Tour pharmacy department - Central pharmacy and pharmacy satellites				
Tour main pathways from department to different areas in hospital				
GENERAL INFORMATION Mailbox				
Phone etiquette/personal calls				
Regular and Holiday schedule				
Vacation and Sick time off				
Time clock (punching in/out)				
PERSONAL NEEDS Dress code				
Cloak storage/locker				
Lunch and coffee breaks				
SECURITY AND SAFETY Exposure control				
Proper waste disposal				
Material Safety Data Sheets (MSDS)				
Mass Casualty Disaster Plan				
COMPUTER ENVIRONMENT / ORDER PROCESSING Computer system (CPOE, Entry and Retrieval, Allergy, Patient Profiles, etc.)				
Order Verification (R.Ph. only)				
Printing labels				
Filling orders				
Managing missing doses				
Delivery schedule/tube system				
Restocking automated dispensing cabinets				
Down-time procedures				
POLICY AND PROCEDURE MANUAL Receipt of manual				
EMPLOYEE HANDBOOK Receipt of handbook				
JOB DESCRIPTION PERFORMANCE EVALUATION				

Pharmacy ORIENTATION SKILL CHECKLIST (outline of competency requirements)	EVALUATION			
	Reviewed (date/initial)	Verbalizes Understanding (date/initial)	Demonstrates Skill (date/initial)	COMMENTS
IV SOLUTIONS				
Clean room usage and monitoring				
IV solution preparation procedures				
Aseptic technique				
IV Scheduling – 12-hour batching				
IV area restocking routine				
Total Parenteral Nutrition solutions				
Chemotherapy preparation				
Checking IV solutions (RPh only)				
IV admixture infection control consideration				
MISCELLANEOUS				
Narcotic replenishment				
Narcotic delivery/Narcotics in IV Rom				
Inventory requests				
Servicing ancillary areas				
Borrowing/lending				
Outpatient pharmacy services – Hours of operation				
Crash cart trays/crash cart re-issue				
Investigational drugs				
Repackaging request				
Ethyl alcohol requisitions				
Inventory check/order process				
Requisitioning from General Stores and Materials Management				
Restricted drug programs/Approvals				
On-call coordinator, clinical staff, Pharmacist-In-Charge				
Non-formulary drugs				
Pager system				
Unit-dose cassette process and exchange (Adults/Peds)				

37-0111.1

Most hospital pharmacies utilize a "Pharmacy Technician Orientation Checklist." Once each skill has been demonstrated, the checklist is initialed by the technician and the supervisor. Upon completion it is placed in the pharmacy technician's personnel file.

FILL IN THE KEY TERM

Answers are at the end of the book.

central pharmacy   medication administration   PRN order
clean rooms   record (MAR)   reconstitute
code carts   nurse's station   standing order
CPOE   outpatient pharmacy   STAT order
electronic medical record   pharmacy satellite   unit dose
inpatient pharmacy   policy and procedures manual   unit inspection

1. _____ : Addition of water or other diluent to a powdered drug form to make a solution or suspension.

2. _____ : A system in which the prescriber enters orders directly into the computer system.

3. _____ : A computerized patient medical record.

4. _____ : A package containing the amount of a drug required for one dose.

5. _____ : A standard medication order for patients to receive medication at scheduled intervals.

6. _____ : An order for medication to be administered only on an as needed basis.

7. _____ : An order for medication to be administered immediately.

8. _____ : A form that tracks the medications administered to a patient.

9. _____ : A locked cart of medications designed for emergency use only.

10. _____ : The main inpatient pharmacy in a hospital that has satellite pharmacies.

11. _____ : A pharmacy located in a hospital that serves only those patients in the hospital and its ancillary areas.

12. _____ : A branch of the inpatient pharmacy.

13. _____ : Work station for medical personnel located on a nursing unit.

14. _____ : Areas designed for the preparation of sterile products.

15. _____ : A pharmacy attached to a hospital servicing patients who have left the hospital or who are visiting doctors in a hospital outpatient clinic.

16. _____ :   Documentation of required policies, procedures, and disciplinary actions in a hospital.

17. _____ :   A review of a nursing unit to ensure compliance with hospital medication policies.

TRUE/FALSE

Indicate whether the statement is true or false in the blank. Answers are at the end of the book.

_____ 1.   Technicians working the front counter do not handle phone calls.

_____ 2.   Medication carts in hospitals contain a 72–hour supply of medications.

_____ 3.   Technicians often prepare IV admixtures in hospitals.

_____ 4.   The pharmacy technician supervisor is often responsible for training technicians.

_____ 5.   Lot numbers and expiration dates are not needed in bulk compounding logs.

_____ 6.   All departments within a hospital are required to maintain a policy and procedure manual.

_____ 7.   The pharmacy inventory staff is often responsible for removal of drug recalls from the pharmacy inventory.

EXPLAIN WHY

Explain why these statements are true or important. Check your answers in the text. Discuss any questions you may have with your instructor.

1. Why can several medication orders be written on a single medication order form?

2. Why is it important for technicians to be familiar with the policy and procedures manual for their department?

CHOOSE THE BEST ANSWER

Answers are at the end of the book.

1. All of the following are ancillary areas EXCEPT
   a. radiology.
   b. nurse's station.
   c. emergency room.
   d. cardiac catheterization lab.

2. A health-care provider who assists with the evaluation, treatment, and care of patients with breathing problems:
   a. PCT
   b. RT
   c. LPN
   d. PA

3. A health-care provider who is concerned with factors such as a patient's ability to pay for medications is a(an)
   a. Pharm.D.
   b. R.Ph.
   c. N.P.
   d. M.S.W.

4. Includes preparing and delivering medications for drug studies:
   a. investigational drug service
   b. unit dose
   c. cart fill
   d. inventory control

5. A pharmacy attached to a hospital that serves patients who have left the hospital or who are visiting doctors in a hospital outpatient clinic is a(an)
   a. inpatient pharmacy.
   b. pharmacy satellite.
   c. central pharmacy.
   d. outpatient pharmacy.

6. Pharmacy technicians working in this satellite require special training and chemotherapy certification from the pharmacy department.
   a. oncology
   b. pediatric
   c. OR
   d. radiology

7. Each individual drawer in a medication cart is filled with
   a. the most commonly used medications for a given floor.
   b. large volume parenteral that do not require patient specific labeling.
   c. controlled substances only.
   d. daily medication for a given patient.

8. The unit dose package type used or ointments and creams is a(an)
   a. plastic blister.
   b. ampule.
   c. tube.
   d. vial.

9. Orders for medications that are needed right away are called
   a. PRN orders.
   b. parenteral.
   c. STAT orders.
   d. standing orders.

10. A locked cart of medications designed for emergency use is called a
    a. PCU.
    b. code cart.
    c. satellite.
    d. IP.

11. Rooms designed for the preparation of sterile products are called
    a. satellites.
    b. clean rooms.
    c. CPs.
    d. PCUs.

12. Which of the following agencies is responsible for approving hospitals so they may receive Medicaid reimbursement?
    a. BOP
    b. TJC
    c. HCFA
    d. DPH

— 17 —

Other Environments

Key Concepts

Test your knowledge by covering the information in the right-hand column.

mail order pharmacy	Delivery of prescriptions by mail (primarily for maintenance therapy). Mail order pharmacies are generally large-scale operations that are highly automated. They use assembly line processing in which each step in the prescription fill process is completed or managed by a person who specializes in that step.
maintenance therapy	Therapy for chronic conditions that include depression, gastrointestinal disorders, heart disease, hypertension, and diabetes.
regulation	Mail order pharmacies must follow federal and state requirements in processing prescriptions, but are not necessarily licensed in each state to which they send medications.
pharmacist review	Pharmacists review mail order prescriptions before and after filling.
online drugstore	A type of mail order pharmacy that uses the Internet to advertise and take orders for drugs.
home care	Care in the home, generally supervised by a registered nurse who works with a physician, pharmacist, and others to administer a care plan that involves the patient or another caregiver.
home infusion	Infusion administered in the home, the fastest growing area of home health care. The primary therapies provided by home infusion services are: antibiotic therapy, parenteral nutrition, pain management, and chemotherapy.
infusion pumps	Pumps that control infusion. There are pumps for specific therapies or multiple therapies, as well as ambulatory pumps that can be worn by patients.

patient education	In home infusion, the patient or their caregiver is educated about their therapy: how to self-administer, monitor, report problems, and so on.
admixture preparation	The same rules apply to preparing parenteral admixtures in the home infusion setting as in the hospital.
long-term care	Facilities that provide care for people unable to care for themselves because of mental or physical impairment. Because of limited resources, most long-term care facilities will contract out dispensing and clinical pharmacy services.
distributive pharmacist	A long-term care pharmacist responsible for making sure patients receive the correct medicines that were ordered.
consultant pharmacist	A long-term care pharmacist who develops and maintains an individualized pharmaceutical plan for every long-term care resident.
emergency kits	Locked kits containing emergency medications, similar to code carts used in hospitals.
automated dispensing systems	Automated units that dispense medications at the point of use.
nuclear pharmacy	Specially licensed and regulated pharmacies that prepare and dispense radiopharmaceuticals.

TRUE/FALSE

Indicate whether the statement is true or false in the blank. Answers are at the end of the book.

_____ 1. Generally drugs cost less in the United States than in Canada.

_____ 2. Mail order pharmacies are often used to handle maintenance medications.

_____ 3. Code carts are never found in long-term care facilities.

_____ 4. Antibiotic therapy is a common home infusion service used in treating AIDS related and other infections.

_____ 5. On the home care team, the technician works under the supervision of a home care aide.

_____ 6. Institutional care always provides better quality of life for the patient than home care.

_____ 7. Nuclear pharmacies typically operate 365 days a year.

_____ 8. PET scans use radiopharmaceuticals.

EXPLAIN WHY

Explain why these statements are true or important. Check your answers in the text. Discuss any questions you may have with your Instructor.

1. Why is mail order pharmacy growing so rapidly?

2. Why would maintenance drugs be well suited to mail order delivery?

3. Why is patient education important in home infusion?

4. Why is home infusion growing so rapidly?

5. Why is storage of admixtures an issue in home infusion?

6. Why is hazardous waste an issue in home infusion?

CHOOSE THE BEST ANSWER

Answers are at the end of the book.

1. In the United States, a mail order pharmacy can provide services to
   a. only the states where the company has pharmacies.
   b. only the state of the main campus.
   c. only the state of the main campus and adjacent states.
   d. any state in the United States

2. A medication that is required on a continuing basis for the treatment of a chronic condition is called
   a. PRN medication.
   b. PO medication.
   c. STAT medication.
   d. maintenance medication.

3. Medication counseling for mail order pharmacies is done by
   a. registered nurses.
   b. certified technicians.
   c. nurses.
   d. pharmacists.

4. In some long-term care facilities the medication carts are usually filled with enough medications to last
   a. one week.
   b. one day.
   c. one month.
   d. 24 hours.

5. Medications used from emergency kits in long-term care pharmacies are charged to
   a. the patient.
   b. the pharmacy.
   c. the long-term care facility.
   d. none of the above.

6. The type of infusion therapy that usually involves infusion of narcotics for patients with painful terminal illness or severe chronic pain is called
   a. laxative therapy.
   b. maintenance therapy.
   c. pain management therapy.
   d. infection therapy.

7. Regulation of hazardous waste procedures associated with chemotherapy applies to all of the following EXCEPT:
   a. storage.
   b. disposal.
   c. transportation.
   d. pricing.

8. Which member of the home care team is responsible for educating the patient?
   a. R.Ph.
   b. physician
   c. registered nurse
   d. Pharm.D.

9. Radiopharmaceuticals are considered
   a. hazardous materials.
   b. OTC medications.
   c. safe to store in unrestricted areas.
   d. exempt narcotics.

10. Body badges for technicians that work with radiopharmaceuticals are typically monitored
   a. weekly.
   b. monthly.
   c. quarterly.
   d. yearly.

STUDY NOTES

Use this area to write important points you'd like to remember.

— 18 —

COMMON DRUGS & THEIR USES

CLASSIFICATION OF DRUGS

There are thousands of drugs used in pharmacy. A basic familiarity with these drugs and their uses will enhance your skills as a pharmacy technician.

Drugs may be classified in different ways. One way is *based on their main therapeutic indication or action*. An example of such a group name would be **antibiotic**, which describes drugs that work by destroying pathogenic organisms (microorganisms that cause disease). Another example of a group name would be **analgesic**, which describes drugs that are used in the alleviation of pain. Following is a sample list of such group names:

Analgesics
Anesthetic Agents
Anti-infectives
Antineoplastics
Cardiovascular Agents
Dermatologicals
Electrolytic Agents
Gastrointestinal & Urinary
    Tract Agents
Hematological Agents

Hormones & Modifiers
Immunobiologic Agents
Musculoskeletal Agents
Neurological Agents
Ophthalmic & Otic Agents
Psychotropic Agents
Respiratory Agents

Another arrangement of drugs is by *specific classification based on how the drug actually works*. Drugs classified this way generally share these characteristics:

1. similar chemical structure
2. similar mechanism of action
3. similar effects (including side effects)

An example of such a classification is the **cephalosporins,** which is found in the antibiotics group. Drugs in the cephalosporins classification share the above mentioned characteristics with each other but not necessarily with other antibiotics, which may have different characteristics. Another example of such a group would be **xanthine derivatives**, which are found in the bronchodilators group.

COMMON DRUGS & THEIR USES — 18

Example:

Trade Name	Generic Name	Group	Classification
Keflex	Cephalexin	Antibiotic	Cephalosporin
Theo-Dur	Theophylline	Bronchodilator	Xanthine Derivative

Below is a sample list of such classifications:

Angiotensin Converting Enzyme inhibitors (ACE inhibitors)
α-adrenergic agonists
β-blockers
Calcium channel blockers
Cephalosporins
Corticosteroids
Histamine$_2$ blockers
Loop Diuretics

For national certification exams, you will need to know the main groups of drugs used in the retail and hospital setting. More specific classifications are not emphasized. You will learn most of this information on the job: as you handle these medications over and over again, you'll see which drugs are the most commonly used and which are not.

STUDY TIP — DRUG CARDS

A good way to help you remember the most common drugs used in pharmacy is to create drug cards. Drug cards are easy to make by writing information about drugs on small index cards. You can then use these to study until you have memorized the information.

Information needed on your drug card:

1. Trade name of drug

2. Generic name of drug

3. Classification

KEY CONCEPTS

Test your knowledge by covering the information in the right-hand column.

USAN	The United States Adopted Names Council (USAN) designates nonproprietary names for drugs.
drug classes	Group names for drugs that have similar activities or are used for the same type of diseases and disorders.
stems	Common stems or syllables that are used to identify the different drug classes and in making new nonproprietary names. They are approved and recommended by the USAN.
neurotransmitter	Substances that carry the impulses from one neuron to another.
blocker	Another name for an antagonist drug—because antagonists block the action of a neurotransmitter.
homeostasis	The state of equilibrium of the body.
mimetic	Another term for an agonist drug—because agonists imitate or "mimic" the action of the neurotransmitter.
analgesia	A state in which pain is not felt even though a painful condition exists.
antipyretic	Reduces fever.
opiate-type analgesics	Drugs related to morphine and codeine that can be habit forming and are used for pain relief.
narcotic analgesics	Same as opiate-type analgesics.
salicylates	Drugs related to aspirin that are used to relieve mild to moderate pain, and have anti-inflammatory and antipyretic properties.
NSAIDs	Nonsteroidal anti-inflammatory drugs that have anti-inflammatory, antipyretic, and analgesic properties.
acetaminophen	A drug that relieves mild to moderate pain and has antipyretic properties.
local anesthetics	Drugs that block pain conduction from peripheral nerves to the central nervous system without causing a loss of consciousness.
surgical anesthesia	The stage of anesthesia in which surgery can be safely conducted.
medullary paralysis	An overdose of anesthesia that paralyzes the respiratory and heart centers of the medulla, leading to death.
antibiotic (antimicrobial)	Drug that destroys microorganisms.
antiviral	Drug that attacks a virus.

antifungal	Drug that destroys fungi or inhibits growth of fungi.
antimycobacterial	Drug that attacks the organisms that cause tuberculosis and leprosy.
antiprotozoal	Drug that destroys protozoa.
anthelmintic	Drug that destroys worms.
bactericidal	Bacteria killing.
bacteriostatic	Bacteria inhibiting.
virustatic	Drug that inhibits the growth of viruses.
antineoplastic	Drug that inhibits new growth of cancer cells.
lymphocyte	A type of white blood cell that releases antibodies that destroy disease cells.
metastasis	When cancer cells spread beyond their original site.
neoplasm	A new and abnormal tissue growth, often referring to cancer cells.
remission	A state in which cancer cells are inactive.
arrhythmia	An abnormal heart rhythm.
cardiac cycle	The contraction and relaxation of the heart that pumps blood through the cardiovascular system.
diastolic pressure	The minimum blood pressure when the heart relaxes; the second number in a blood pressure reading.
electrocardiogram (EKG or ECG)	A graph of the heart's rhythm.
embolism	A clot that has traveled in the bloodstream to a point where it obstructs flow.
myocardium	Heart muscle.
systolic pressure	The maximum blood pressure when the heart contracts; the first number in a blood pressure reading.
thrombus	A blood clot.
antianginals	Drugs used to treat cardiac related chest pain (angina).
antiarrhythmics	Drugs used to treat irregular heart rhythms.
antihypertensives	Drugs used to reduce a sustained elevation in blood pressure.
vasopressors	Drugs used to increase blood pressure.
antihyperlipidemics	Drugs used to lower high levels of cholesterol.

KEY CONCEPTS

Test your knowledge by covering the information in the right-hand column.

thrombolytics	Drugs used to dissolve blood clots.
anticoagulants	Drugs used to prevent blood clot formation.
beta blockers	Drugs that reduce the oxygen demands of the heart muscle.
calcium channel blockers	Drugs that relax the heart by reducing heart conduction.
diuretics	Drugs that decrease blood pressure by decreasing blood volume.
ACE inhibitors	The "pril" drugs that relax the blood vessels.
vasodilators	Drugs that relax and expand the blood vessels.
dermatological	A product that is used to treat a skin condition.
integumentary system	The skin.
anion	A negatively charged ion.
cation	A positively charged ion.
dissociation	When a compound breaks down and separates into smaller components.
electrolytes	A substance that in solution forms ions that conduct an electrical current.
extracellular fluids	The fluid outside the body's individual cells found in plasma and tissue fluid.
intracellular fluids	Cell fluid.
interstitial fluid	Tissue fluid.
ions	Electrically charged particles.
vaccine	A suspension containing infectious agents used to boost the body's immune system response.
chyme	The semiliquid form of food as it enters the intestinal tract.
peristalsis	The wavelike motion of the intestines that moves food through them.
enzymes	Substances in the body that help the body to break down molecules.
antidiarrheals	Drugs used to treat diarrhea.
antiemetics	Drugs used to treat nausea and vomiting.
antacids	Drugs used to neutralize acid.

laxatives	Drugs that promote defecation.
stool softeners	Drugs that promote mixing of fatty and watery internal substances to soften the stool's contents and ease the evacuation of feces.
hematological agents	Drugs that affect the blood.
fibrin	The fiber that serves as the structure for clot formation.
anemia	A decrease in hemoglobin or red blood cells.
hemostatic drugs	Drugs that prevent excessive bleeding.
hormones	Chemicals that are secreted in the body by the endocrine system's ductless glands.
corticosteroid	Hormonal steroid substances produced by the cortex of the adrenal gland.
endocrine system	The system of hormone secreting glands.
hyperthyroidism	Overproduction of thyroid hormone.
hypothyroidism	Underproduction of thyroid hormone.
insulin	A hormone that controls the body's use of glucose.
glucagon	A hormone that helps convert amino acid to glucose.
diabetes mellitus	A condition in which the body does not produce enough insulin or is unable to use insulin efficiently.
serum glucose	Blood sugar.
androgens	Male sex hormones.
estrogen	Female sex characteristic hormone that is involved in calcium and phosphorus conservation.
progesterone	Female sex characteristic hormone that is involved in ovulation prevention.
testosterone	The primary androgen (male sex hormone).
gout	A painful inflammatory condition in which excess uric acid accumulates in the joints.
rheumatoid arthritis	A chronic and often progressive inflammatory condition with symptoms that include swelling, feelings of warmth, and joint pain.
osteoarthritis	A disorder characterized by weight-bearing bone deterioration, decreasing range of motion, pain, and deformity.
Parkinson's disease	A progressive neuromuscular condition.
Alzheimer's disease	A progressive dementia condition.

KEY CONCEPTS

Test your knowledge by covering the information in the right-hand column.

epilepsy   A neurologic disorder characterized by seizures.

migraine headaches   A type of headache associated with possible auras and pain.

ophthalmic agents   Drugs used to treat conditions of the eye.

conjunctivitis   Inflammation of the eyelid lining.

glaucoma   A disorder characterized by high pressure within the eye.

mydriatics   Drugs that dilate the pupil.

sedatives   Drugs that are intended to relax and calm.

hypnotics   Drugs that are intended to induce sleep.

bipolar disorder   A disorder characterized by mood swings.

depression   A disorder characterized by low mood.

asthma   A condition characterized by chronic airway inflammation.

emphysema   A condition associated with chronic airway obstruction.

antihistamines   Drugs that replace histamine at histamine receptor sites.

decongestants   Drugs that cause mucous membrane vasoconstriction.

antitussives   Drugs that are used to treat coughs.

bronchodilators   Drugs that are used to relieve bronchospasm.

Study Notes

Use this area to write important points you'd like to remember.

FILL IN THE BLANKS

Match the drug classifications with the generic drug names. Answers are at the end of the book.

Analgesic	**Cardiovascular Agent**	**Psychotropic Agent**
Anesthetic	**Dermatological Agent**	**Respiratory Agent**
Antidiabetic	**Electrolytic Agent**	
Anti-infective	**Gastrointestinal Agent**	
Antineoplastic	**Musculoskeletal Agent**	

Generic Name   **Drug Classification**

1. Albuterol _____

2. Alprazolam _____

3. Amlodipine _____

4. Amoxicillin/Clavulanate _____

5. Ampicillin _____

6. Atenolol _____

7. Atorvastatin _____

8. Azithromycin _____

9. Carisoprodol _____

10. Carvedilol _____

11. Cefaclor _____

12. Cetirizine _____

13. Ciprofloxacin _____

14. Citalopram _____

15. Clarithromycin _____

16. Clopidogrel _____

17. Clotrimazole/Betamethasone _____

18. Diltiazem _____

19. Docusate sodium _____

20. Doxazosin _____

21. Escitalopram _____

22. Fluconazole _____

23. Fluticasone _____

24. Furosemide _____

25. Glyburide _____

26. Heparin _____

27. Hydrocortisone cream _____

28. Ibuprofen _____

29. Insulin _____

30. Lactulose _____

31. Levofloxacin _____

32. Lisinopril _____

33. Loperamide _____

34. Metoprolol _____

35. Nifedipine _____

36. Nitroglycerin _____

37. Omeprazole _____

38. Pantoprazole _____

39. Potassium chloride _____

40. Procaine _____

41. Sertraline _____

42. Silver sulfadiazine _____

43. Sodium chloride _____

44. Tamoxifen _____

45. Tramadol _____

46. Trimethobenzamide _____

47. Trimethoprim/Sulfamethoxazole _____

48. Warfarin _____

MATCH THE BRAND AND GENERIC NAMES

In the following exercises, match each brand name with its generic name. The list of the Top 200 Brand Name Drugs (Appendix A) and the Top 200 Brand Name Drugs by Classification (Appendix B) should be helpful. Answers are at the end of the book.

ANALGESICS

Brand Name	Generic Name
1. Tylenol w/Codeine _____	a. tramadol
2. Ultram _____	b. butalbital/acetaminophen/caffeine
3. Fioricet _____	c. aspirin enteric-coated
4. Ecotrin _____	d. tramadol HCl/acetaminophen
5. Percocet _____	e. hydrocodone/acetaminophen
6. Ultracet _____	f. oxycodone w/acetaminophen
7. Vicodin _____	g. acetaminophen w/codeine

ANTI-INFECTIVES

Brand Name	Generic Name
1. Bactrim _____	a. azithromycin
2. Augmentin _____	b. cephalexin
3. Keflex _____	c. amoxicillin/clavulanate
4. Vibramycin _____	d. trimethoprim/sulfamethoxazole
5. Cleocin _____	e. metronidazole
6. Zithromax _____	f. clarithromycin
7. Flagyl _____	g. clindamycin
8. Biaxin _____	h. doxycycline

CARDIOVASCULAR AGENTS

Brand Name	Generic Name
1. Betapace _____	a. sotalol
2. Zocor _____	b. carvedilol
3. Pravachol _____	c. warfarin
4. Coreg _____	d. lovastatin

CARDIOVASCULAR AGENTS (cont'd)

Brand Name	Generic Name
5. Vasotec _____	e. simvastatin
6. Mevacor _____	f. pravastatin
7. Coumadin _____	g. gemfibrozil
8. Lopid ____	h. enalapril

DERMATOLOGICALS

Brand Name	Generic Name
1. Elocon _____	a. clotrimazole/betamethasone
2. Monistat _____	b. mupirocin
3. Hytone _____	c. clobetasol
4. Lotrisone _____	d. ketoconazole
5. Temovate _____	e. fluocinonide
6. Bactroban _____	f. mometasone
7. Nizoral _____	g. hydrocortisone
8. Lidex _____	h. miconazole

GASTROINTESTINAL AGENTS

Brand Name	Generic Name
1. Zantac _____	a. dicyclomine
2. Protonix _____	b. omeprazole
3. Tigan _____	c. ranitidine
4. Bentyl _____	d. pantoprazole
5. Pepcid _____	e. famotidine
6. Zofran _____	f. diphenoxylate w/atropine
7. Lomotil _____	g. trimethobenzamide
8. Prilosec _____	h. ondansetron

MATCH THE BRAND AND GENERIC NAMES (cont'd)

Answers are at the end of the book.

HORMONES & MODIFIERS: ADRENAL CORTICOSTEROIDS

Brand Name	Generic Name
1. Sterapred _____	a. prednisone
2. Medrol _____	b. methylprednisolone
3. Prelone _____	c. prednisolone
4. Kenalog _____	d. triamcinolone

HORMONES & MODIFIERS: ORAL ANTIDIABETICS

Brand Name	Generic Name
1. Glucovance _____	a. metformin
2. Diabeta _____	b. glimepiride
3. Amaryl _____	c. glyburide
4. Glucotrol _____	d. glipizide
5. Glucophage _____	e. glyburide/metformin

MUSCULOSKELETAL AGENTS

Brand Name	Generic Name
1. Flexeril _____	a. allopurinol
2. Soma _____	b. cyclobenzaprine
3. Fosamax _____	c. carisoprodol
4. Zanaflex _____	d. tizanidine
5. Robaxin _____	e. methocarbamol
6. Zyloprim _____	f. alendronate

NEUROLOGICAL AGENTS

Brand Name	Generic Name
1. Dilantin _____	a. amphetamine salt combination
2. Requip _____	b. methylphenidate
3. Concerta _____	c. benztropine
4. Cogentin _____	d. carbidopa/levodopa
5. Adderall _____	e. ropinirole

NEUROLOGICAL AGENTS (cont'd)

Brand Name	Generic Name
6. Tegretol _____	f. gabapentin
7. Sinemet _____	g. phenytoin
8. Neurontin _____	h. carbamazepine

PSYCHOTROPIC AGENTS

Brand Name	Generic Name
1. Xanax _____	a. alprazolam
2. Zoloft _____	b. lorazepam
3. Buspar _____	c. clonazepam
4. Prozac _____	d. diazepam
5. Ativan _____	e. buspirone
6. Celexa _____	f. sertraline
7. Valium _____	g. fluoxetine
8. Klonopin _____	h. citalopram

RESPIRATORY AGENTS

Brand Name	Generic Name
1. Allegra _____	a. fluticasone
2. QVAR _____	b. fexofenadine
3. Tessalon _____	c. promethazine
4. Vistaril _____	d. beclomethasone
5. Phenergan _____	e. hydroxyzine pamoate
6. Ventolin _____	f. benzonatate
7. Flonase _____	g. albuterol

TRUE/FALSE

Indicate whether the statement is true or false in the blank. Answers are at the end of the book.

_____ 1. Once a suggested nonproprietary name for a drug is officially approved, it becomes the generic name of the drug.

_____ 2. Meperidene is a naturally occurring opiate.

_____ 3. Medullary paralysis is associated with an overdose of analgesic.

_____ 4. Ringworm is a type of fungal infection.

_____ 5. Vasopressors are used to treat hypertension.

_____ 6. Some antacids have significant drug interactions with tetracycline.

_____ 7. Hematopoietic drugs are used to treat excessive bleeding.

_____ 8. Insulin is a cure for diabetes.

_____ 9. Calcium channel blockers are sometimes used to prevent migraine headaches.

_____ 10. Meprobamate is a barbiturate.

EXPLAIN WHY

Explain why these statements are true or important. Check your answers in the text. Discuss any questions you may have with your instructor.

1. Why would an antibiotic not be appropriate for treating viral infections?

2. Why is it important for pharmacy technicians to be careful when handling antineoplastic drugs?

3. Why is it important for patients with diabetes to use a glucometer?

CHOOSE THE BEST ANSWER

Answers are at the end of the book.

1. The _____ designates nonproprietary names for drugs.
   a. manufacturer
   b. FDA
   c. USAN
   d. DEA

2. _____ is a neurotransmitter.
   a. Estrogen
   b. Testosterone
   c. Insulin
   d. Epinephrine

3. A common, naturally occurring opiate-type drug is
   a. codeine.
   b. cocaine.
   c. meperidine.
   d. propoxyphene.

4. An inhalation anesthetic is
   a. propofol.
   b. isoflurane.
   c. etomidate.
   d. methohexital.

5. An antifungal drug is
   a. metronidazole.
   b. nystatin.
   c. indinavir.
   d. tetracycline.

6. The term used to denote the presence of a life-threatening cancerous group of cells or tumor is
   a. malignant.
   b. remission.
   c. benign.
   d. viral.

7. Drugs that decrease blood pressure by decreasing blood volume are called
   a. beta blockers.
   b. calcium channel blockers.
   c. diuretics.
   d. vasodilators.

8. Drugs that act to increase blood pressure are
   a. vasodilators.
   b. antihypertensives.
   c. vasopressors.
   d. ACE inhibitors.

9. A type of skin cancer:
   a. basal cells.
   b. keratoses.
   c. dandruff.
   d. cellulitus

10. The histamine receptor antagonist with the most drug interactions is
    a. ranitidine.
    b. cimetidine.
    c. famotidine.
    d. nizatidine.

11. A commonly ordered stool softener is
    a. docusate sodium.
    b. lactulose.
    c. bismuth subsalicylate.
    d. loperamide.

12. _____ is used for vitamin B12 deficiency.
    a. Vitamin K
    b. Cyanocobalamin
    c. Ferrous sulfate
    d. Plasminogen

13. A posterior lobe hormone of the pituitary gland:
    a. oxytocin.
    b. thyroid.
    c. insulin.
    d. glucagon.

14. A drug that reduces uric acid and is used to treat gout is
    a. celecoxib.
    b. ibuprofen.
    c. allopurinol.
    d. cyclobenzaprine.

15. A drug commonly used to treat epilepsy is
    a. phenobarbital.
    b. sumatriptan.
    c. tacrine.
    d. donepezil.

TOP 200 BRAND NAME DRUGS

Following is a list of the Top 200 Brand Name Drugs cross-referenced with corresponding generic drug names and classifications. Rankings are based on Drug Topic's 2010 Top 200 list (available at http://drugtopics.modernmedicine.com/Pharmacy+Facts+&+Figures).

	Brand Name	Generic Name	Classification
1.	Lipitor	atorvastatin	Cardiovascular, Antihyperlipidemic
2.	Nexium	esomeprazole	Gastrointestinal, Antacid/Antiulcer
3.	Plavix	clopidogrel	Cardiovascular
4.	Singulair	montelukast	Respiratory
5.	Lexapro	escitalopram	Psychotropic, Antidepressant
6.	Crestor	rosuvastatin	Cardiovascular, Antihyperlipidemic
7.	Synthroid	levothyroxine	Hormones & Modifiers, Thyroid
8.	ProAir HFA	albuterol	Respiratory, Bronchodilator
9.	Advair Diskus	fluticasone and salmeterol	Respiratory
10.	Cymbalta	duloxetine	Psychotropic
11.	Diovan	valsartan	Cardiovascular, Antihypertensive*
12.	Ventolin HFA	albuterol	Respiratory, Bronchodilator
13.	Diovan HCT	hydrochlorothiazide and valsartan	Cardiovascular, Antihypertensive*
14.	Actos	pioglitazone	Hormones & Modifiers, Oral antidiabetic
15.	Seroquel	quetiapine	Psychotropic, Antipsychotic
16.	Levaquin	levofloxacin	Anti-infective
17.	Lantus	Insulin glargine	Hormones & Modifiers, Insulin
18.	Nasonex	mometasone	Respiratory
19.	Viagra	sildenafil	Hormones & Modifiers, Phosphodiesterase inhibitor
20.	Lyrica	pregabalin	Neurological
21.	Celebrex	celecoxib	Analgesic, NSAID
22.	Concerta	methylphenidate	Psychotropic/Neurologic/ADHD
23.	Spiriva	tiotropium	Respiratory
24.	Premarin tablets	conjugated estrogens	Hormones & Modifiers, Estrogen
25.	Effexor XR	venlafaxine	Psychotropic, Antidepressant
26.	Tricor	fenofibrate	Cardiovascular, Antihyperlipidemic
27.	Zetia	ezetimibe	Cardiovascular, Antihyperlipidemic
28.	Vytorin	ezetimibe and simvastatin	Cardiovascular, Antihyperlipidemic
29.	OxyContin	oxycodone	Analgesic, Opiate
30.	Abilify	aripiprazole	Psychotropic, Antipsychotic
31.	Loestrin 24 Fe	ethinyl estradiol and norethindrone and iron	Hormones & Modifiers, Contraceptive

An asterisk next to a drug's classification indicates there are additional common uses for that drug.

Brand Name	Generic Name	Classification
32. Vyvanse	lisdexamfetamine	Psychotropic
33. Cialis	tadalafil	Hormones & Modifiers, Phosphodiesterase inhibitor
34. Suboxone	buprenorphine and naloxone	Psychotropic, Drug dependency
35. Aricept	donepezil	Neurological, Anti-Alzheimer's
36. Benicar	olmesartan	Cardiovascular, Antihypertensive*
37. Januvia	sitagliptin	Hormones & Modifiers, Oral antidiabetic
38. Lunesta	eszopiclone	Psychotropic, Hypnotic
39. Ambien CR	zolpidem	Psychotropic, Hypnotic
40. Niaspan	niacin	Cardiovascular, Antihyperlipidemic
41. Xalatan	latanoprost	Ophthalmic, Antiglaucoma
42. Levoxyl	levothyroxine	Hormones & Modifiers, Thyroid
43. Benicar HCT	olmesartan and hydrochlorothiazide	Cardiovascular, Antihypertensive*
44. Flovent HFA	fluticasone	Respiratory
45. NuvaRing	etonogestrel and ethinyl estradiol	Hormones & Modifiers, Contraceptive
46. Lovaza	omega-3 fatty acid	Cardiovascular, Antihyperlipidemic
47. Yaz	drosperinone and ethinyl estradiol	Hormones & Modifiers, Contraceptive
48. NovoLog	insulin aspart (rDNA origin)	Hormones & Modifiers, Insulin
49. Combivent	ipratropium and albuterol	Respiratory
50. Namenda	memantine	Neurological, Anti-Alzheimer's
51. Detrol LA	tolterodine	Urinary
52. Ortho Tri Cyclen	norgestimate and ethinyl estradiol	Hormones & Modifiers, Contraceptive
53. Lantus SoloSTAR	insulin glargine (rDNA origin)	Hormones & Modifiers, Insulin
54. Proventil HFA	albuterol	Respiratory, Bronchodilator
55. Aciphex	rabeprazole	Gastrointestinal, Antacid/Antiulcer
56. Avapro	irbesartan	Cardiovascular, Antihypertensive*
57. Bystolic	nebivolol	Cardiovascular, Antihypertensive*
58. Adderall XR	dextroamphetamine and amphetamine	Psychotropic/Neurologic/ADHD
59. Symbicort	formoterol and budesonide	Respiratory
60. Zyprexa	olanzapine	Psychotropic, Antipsychotic
61. Trilipix	fenofibrate	Cardiovascular, Antihyperlipidemic
62. Boniva	ibandronate	Musculoskeletal, Osteoporitic
63. Avodart	dutasteride	Urinary
64. Glipizide XL	glipizide	Hormones & Modifiers, Oral antidiabetic
65. Pristiq	desvenlafaxine	Psychotropic, Antidepressant

TOP 200 BRAND NAME DRUGS

	Brand Name	Generic Name	Classification
66.	Lidoderm	lidocaine transdermal	Anesthetic, Local
67.	Humalog	insulin lispro	Hormones & Modifiers, Insulin
68.	Vigamox	moxifloxacin ophthalmic	Ophthalmic
69.	Evista	raloxifene	Musculoskeletal, Osteoporitic
70.	Flomax	tamsulosin	Urinary
71.	Chantix	varenicline	Psychotropic, Drug dependency
72.	Avalide	irbesartan and hydrochlorothiazide	Cardiovascular, Antihypertensive*
73.	Protonix	pantoprazole	Gastrointestinal, Antacid/Antiulcer
74.	Cozaar	losartan	Cardiovascular, Antihypertensive*
75.	Vivelle-DOT	estradiol	Hormones & Modifiers, Estrogen
76.	Vesicare	solifenacin	Urinary
77.	Prempro	conjugated estrogens and medroxyprogesterone	Hormones & Modifiers
78.	Avelox	moxifloxacin	Anti-infective
79.	Dexilant/Kapidex	dexlansoprazole	Gastrointestinal
80.	Focalin XR	dexmethylphenidate	Psychotropic/Neurologic/ADHD
81.	Strattera	atomoxetine	Psychotropic
82.	Xopenex HFA	levalbuterol	Respiratory, Bronchodilator
83.	Actonel	risedronate	Musculoskeletal, Osteoporitic
84.	Travatan Z	travoprost	Ophthalmic, Antiglaucoma
85.	Levemir	insulin detemir (rDNA origin)	Hormones & Modifiers, Insulin
86.	Lumigan	bimatoprost	Ophthalmic, Antiglaucoma
87.	Apri	desogestrel and ethinyl estradiol	Hormones & Modifiers, Contraceptive
88.	Levitra	vardenafil	Hormones & Modifiers, Phosphodiesterase inhibitor
89.	Geodon oral	ziprasidone	Psychotropic, Antipsychotic
90.	Micardis	telmisartan	Cardiovascular, Antihypertensive*
91.	Exforge	amlodipine and valsartan	Cardiovascular, Antihypertensive*
92.	Coumadin tabs	warfarin	Cardiovascular, Anticoagulant
93.	Janumet	metformin and sitagliptin	Hormones & Modifiers, Oral antidiabetic
94.	Ciprodex otic	ciprofloxacin and dexamethasone	Otic
95.	Valtrex	valacyclovir	Anti-infective, Antiviral
96.	Restasis	cyclosporine	Ophthalmic
97.	Seroquel XR	quetiapine	Psychotropic, Antipsychotic
98.	Micardis HCT	telmisartan and hydrochlorothiazide	Cardiovascular, Antihypertensive*
99.	Actonel 150	risedronate	Musculoskeletal, Osteoporitic

Brand Name	Generic Name	Classification
100. Lotrel	amlodipine and benazepril	Cardiovascular, Antihypertensive*
101. Tussionex	hydrocodone and chlorpheniramine	Respiratory
102. Prometrium	progesterone	Hormones & Modifiers, Progestin
103. AndroGel	testosterone	Hormones & Modifiers, Androgen
104. Kariva	desogestrel and ethinyl estradiol	Hormones & Modifiers, Contraceptive
105. Patanol	olopatadine	Ophthalmic
106. Voltaren gel	diclofenac topical	Analgesic, NSAID
107. Hyzaar	losartan and hydrochlorothiazide	Cardiovascular, Antihypertensive*
108. Thyroid, Armour	desiccated thyroid	Hormones & Modifiers, Thyroid
109. Nasacort AQ	triamcinolone	Respiratory
110. Coreg CR	carvedilol	Cardiovascular, Antihypertensive*
111. QVAR	beclomethasone	Respiratory
112. Pataday	olopatadine	Ophthalmic
113. Xyzal	levocetirizine	Respiratory, Antihistamine
114. Humulin N	insulin (human recombinant)	Hormones & Modifiers, Insulin
115. Vagifem	estrogen	Hormones & Modifiers, Estrogen
116. Toprol XL	metoprolol	Cardiovascular, Antihypertensive*
117. Byetta	exenatide	Hormones & Modifiers
118. NovoLog Mix 70/30	insulin aspart protamine and insulin aspart (rDNA origin)	Hormones & Modifiers, Insulin
119. Veramyst	fluticasone	Respiratory
120. Azor	amlodipine and olmesartan	Cardiovascular, Antihypertensive*
121. Caduet	amlodipine and atorvastatin	Cardiovascular, Antihyperlipidemic, Antihypertensive*
122. Welchol	colesevelam	Cardiovascular, Antihyperlipidemic
123. Actoplus Met	metformin and pioglitazone	Hormones & Modifiers, Oral antidiabetic
124. Provigil	modafinil	Psychotropic
125. Epipen	epinephrine	Respiratory
126. Aggrenox	aspirin and dipyridamole	Cardiovascular
127. Dilantin	phenytoin	Neurological, Antiepileptic
128. Enablex	darifenacin	Urinary
129. Alphagan P	brimonidine	Ophthalmic, Antiglaucoma
130. Premarin vaginal	conjugated estrogens	Hormones & Modifiers, Estrogen
131. Xopenex	levalbuterol	Respiratory, Bronchodilator
132. Uroxatral	alfuzosin	Urinary
133. Asmanex	mometasone	Respiratory

TOP 200 BRAND NAME DRUGS

Brand Name	Generic Name	Classification
134. Prevacid SoluTab	lansoprazole	Gastrointestinal, Antacid/Antiulcer
135. Moviprep	Polyethylene glycol electrolyte	Gastrointentinal
136. Avandia	rosiglitazone	Hormones & Modifiers, Oral antidiabetic
137. Tekturna	aliskiren	Cardiovascular, Antihypertensive*
138. Propecia	finasteride	Hormones & Modifiers
139. Ortho Evra	norelgestromin and ethinyl estradiol	Hormones & Modifiers, Contraceptive
140. Solodyn	minocycline	Anti-infective
141 Humulin 70/30	insulin (human recombinant)	Hormones & Modifiers, Insulin
142 Lanoxin	digoxin	Cardiovascular, Antiarrhythmic
143. Asacol	mesalamine	Gastrointestinal
144. Prevacid	lansoprazole	Gastrointestinal, Antacid/Antiulcer
145. Atacand	candesartan	Cardiovascular, Antihypertensive*
146. Nitrostat	nitroglycerin	Cardiovascular
147. Combigan	brimonidine and timolol	Ophthalmic, Antiglaucoma
148. HalfLytely Bowel Prep Kit	PEG-3350, sodium chloride, sodium bicarbonate and potassium chloride for oral solution and bisacodyl	Gastrointestinal, Laxative
149. Relpax	eletriptan	Neurological, Antimigraine
150. Novolin 70/30	human insulin isophane suspension and regular, human insulin injection (rDNA origin)	Hormones & Modifiers, Insulin
151. Femara	letrozole	Antineoplastic, Hormone
152. Tamiflu	oseltamivir	Anti-infective, Antiviral
153. Zovirax topical	acyclovir	Dermatological
184. Lovenox	enoxaparin	Cardiovascular, Anticoagulant
155. Zymar	gatifloxacin	Ophthalmic
156. Maxalt	rizatriptan	Neurological, Antimigraine
157. Estrace vaginal	estradiol	Hormones & Modifiers, Estrogen
158. Exelon patch	rivastigmine	Neurological, Anti-Alzheimer's
159. Intuniv	guanfacine extended-release	Psychotropic
160. Allegra-D 24	fexofenadine and pseudoephedrine	Respiratory
161. Astrepo 0.15%	azelastine	Respiratory, Antihistamine
162. Maxalt MLT	rizatriptan	Neurological, Antimigraine
163. Arimidex	anastrozole	Antineoplastic, Hormone
164. Amitiza	lubiprostone	Gastrointestinal
165. Doryx	doxycycline	Anti-infective
166. Differin	adapalene	Dermatological

Brand Name	Generic Name	Classification
167. Clarinex	desloratadine	Respiratory, Antihistamine
168. Lotemax	loteprednol	Ophthalmic
169. Astelin	azelastine	Respiratory, Antihistamine
170. Transderm-Scop	scopolamine	Gastrointestinal
171. Humulin R	insulin (human recombinant)	Hormones & Modifiers, Insulin
172. Levothroid	levothyroxine	Hormones & Modifiers, Thyroid
173. Advair HFA	fluticasone and salmeterol	Respiratory
174. Truvada	tenofovir/emtricitabine	Anti-Infective, Antiviral
175. Nuvigil	armodafinil	Psychotropic
176. SF 5000 Plus	fluoride	Dental
177. Yasmin 28	drospirenone and ethinyl estradiol	Hormones & Modifiers, Contraceptive
178. Bactroban	mupirocin	Dermatological
179. Ranexa	ranolazine	Cardiovascular, Antiangina
180. Metadate CD	methylphenidate	Psychotropic
181. Lamictal	lamotrigine	Neurological, Antiepileptic*
182. Atrovent HFA	ipratropium	Respiratory
183. Simcor	niacin	Cardiovascular, Antihyperlipidemic
184. Opana ER	oxymorphone	Analgesic, Opiate
185. Rhinocort Aqua	budesonide	Respiratory
186. Humalog Mix 75/25	insulin lispro protamine suspension mixed with soluble insulin lispro	Hormones & Modifiers, Insulin
187. Carafate	sucralfate	Gastrointestinal, Antacid/Antiulcer
188. Norvir	ritonavir	Anti-infective, Antiviral
189. Aspir-Low	aspirin and dipyridamole	Cardiovascular
190. BenzaClin	clindamycin and benzoyl peroxide	Dermatological
191. Skelaxin	metaxalone	Musculoskeletal, Muscle relaxant
192. Duac Care System	clindamycin and benzoyl peroxide	Dermatological
193. Wellbutrin XL	bupropion	Psychotropic, Antidepressant
194. Arthrotec	diclofenac and misoprostol	Analgesic, NSAID
195. Epiduo	adapalene and benzoyl peroxide	Dermatological
196. Pulmicort Flexhaler	budesonide	Respiratory
197. Omnaris	ciclesonide	Respiratory
198. Ortho Tri-Cyclen	norgestimate and ethinyl estradiol	Hormones & Modifiers, Contraceptive
199. Prandin	repaglinide	Hormones & Modifiers, Oral antidiabetic
200. Nevanac	nepafenac	Ophthalmic

TOP 200 BRAND NAME DRUGS BY CLASSIFICATION

Following is a list of the Top 200 Brand Name Drugs organized by classification and cross-referenced with corresponding generic drug names. Drugs included are based on rankings in Drug Topic's 2010 Top 200 list at http://drugtopics.modernmedicine.com/Pharmacy+Facts+&+Figures.

Class/Type	Brand Name	Generic Name
Analgesics		
NSAID	Arthrotec	diclofenac and misoprostol
NSAID	Celebrex	celecoxib
NSAID	Voltaren gel	diclofenac topical
Opiate	Opana ER	oxymorphone
Opiate	OxyContin	oxycodone
Anesthetic Agents		
Local	Lidoderm	lidocaine transdermal
Anti-infectives		
Anti-Infective	Avelox	moxifloxacin
Anti-Infective	Doryx	doxycycline
Anti-Infective	Levaquin	ofloxacin
Anti-Infective	Solodyn	minocycline
Antiviral	Norvir	ritonavir
Antiviral	Tamiflu	oseltamivir
Antiviral	Truvada	tenofovir/emtricitabine
Antiviral	Valtrex	valacyclovir
Antineoplastic Agents		
Hormone	Arimidex	anastrozole
Hormone	Femara	letrozole
Cardiovascular Agents		
Cardiovascular	Aggrenox	aspirin and dipyridamole
Cardiovascular	Aspir-Low	aspirin and dipyridamole
Cardiovascular	Nitrostat	nitroglycerin
Cardiovascular	Plavix	clopidogrel
Anti-anginal	Ranexa	ranolazine
Antiarrhythmic	Lanoxin	digoxin
Anticoagulant	Coumadin	warfarin

*An asterisk next to a drug's classification indicates there are additional common uses for that drug.

Class/Type	Brand Name	Generic Name
Anticoagulant	Lovenox	enoxaparin
Antihyperlipidemic	Crestor	rosuvastatin
Antihyperlipidemic	Lipitor	atorvastatin
Antihyperlipidemic	Lovaza	omega-3 fatty acid
Antihyperlipidemic	Niaspan	niacin
Antihyperlipidemic	Simcor	niacin
Antihyperlipidemic	Tricor	fenofibrate
Antihyperlipidemic	Trilipix	fenofibrate
Antihyperlipidemic	Vytorin	ezetimibe and simvastatin
Antihyperlipidemic	Welchol	colesevelam
Antihyperlipidemic	Zetia	ezetimibe
Antihyperlipidemic, antihypertensive*	Caduet	amlodipine and atorvastatin
Antihypertensive*	Atacand	candesartan
Antihypertensive*	Avalide	irbesartan and hydrochlorothiazide
Antihypertensive*	Avapro	irbesartan
Antihypertensive*	Azor	amlodipine and olmesartan
Antihypertensive*	Benicar	olmesartan
Antihypertensive*	Benicar HCT	olmesartan and hydrochlorothiazide
Antihypertensive*	Bystolic	nebivolol
Antihypertensive*	Coreg CR	carvedilol
Antihypertensive*	Cozaar	losartan
Antihypertensive*	Diovan	valsartan
Antihypertensive*	Diovan HCT	hydrochlorothiazide and valsartan
Antihypertensive*	Exforge	amlodipine and valsartan
Antihypertensive*	Hyzaar	losartan and hydrochlorothiazide
Antihypertensive*	Lotrel	amlodipine and benazepril
Antihypertensive*	Micardis	telmisartan
Antihypertensive*	Micardis HCT	telmisartan and hydrochlorothiazide
Antihypertensive*	Tekturna	aliskiren
Antihypertensive*	Toprol XL	metoprolol

Dental

Dental	SF 5000 Plus	fluoride

Dermatologicals

Dermatological	Bactroban	mupirocin
Dermatological	BenzaClin	clindamycin and benzoyl peroxide
Dermatological	Differin	adapalene
Dermatological	Duac Care System	clindamycin and benzoyl peroxide
Dermatological	Epiduo	adapalene and benzoyl peroxide
Dermatological	Zovirax topical	acyclovir

TOP 200 BRAND NAME DRUGS BY CLASSIFICATION

Class/Type	Brand Name	Generic Name
Gastrointestinal & Urinary Tract Agents		
Gastrointentinal	Moviprep	polyethylene glycol electrolyte
Gastrointestinal	Amitiza	lubiprostone
Gastrointestinal	Asacol	mesalamine
Gastrointestinal	Dexilant/Kapidex	dexlansoprazole
Gastrointestinal	Transderm-Scop	scopolamine
Antacid/antiulcer	Aciphex	rabeprazole
Antacid/antiulcer	Carafate	sucralfate
Antacid/antiulcer	Nexium	esomeprazole
Antacid/antiulcer	Prevacid	lansoprazole
Antacid/antiulcer	Prevacid SoluTab	lansoprazole
Antacid/antiulcer	Protonix	pantoprazole
Laxative	HalfLytely bowel prep	peg-3350, sodium chloride, sodium bicarbonate, and potassium chloride
Urinary	Avodart	dutasteride
Urinary	Detrol LA	tolterodine
Urinary	Enablex	darifenacin
Urinary	Flomax	tamsulosin
Urinary	Uroxatral	alfuzosin
Urinary	Vesicare	solifenacin
Hormones & Modifiers		
Hormones & Modifiers	Byetta	exenatide
Hormones &Modifiers	Prempro	conjugated estrogens and medroxyprogesterone
Hormones & Modifiers	Propecia	finasteride
Androgen	AndroGel	testosterone
Contraceptive	Apri	desogestrel and ethinyl estradiol
Contraceptive	Kariva	desogestrel and ethinyl estradiol
Contraceptive	Loestrin 24 Fe	ethinyl estradiol and norethindrone and iron
Contraceptive	NuvaRing	etonogestrel and ethinyl estradiol
Contraceptive	Ortho Evra	norelgestromin and ethinyl estradiol
Contraceptive	Ortho Tri-Cyclen	norgestimate and ethinyl estradiol
Contraceptive	Ortho Tri-Cyclen Lo	norgestimate and ethinyl estradiol
Contraceptive	Yasmin 28	drospirenone and ethinyl estradiol
Contraceptive	Yaz	drosperinone and ethinyl estradiol
Estrogen	Estrace vaginal	estradiol

Class/Type	Brand Name	Generic Name
Estrogen	Premarin tabs	conjugated estrogens
Estrogen	Premarin vaginal	conjugated estrogens
Estrogen	Vagifem	estrogen
Estrogen	Vivelle-DOT	estradiol
Insulin	Humalog	insulin lispro
Insulin	Humalog Mix 75/25 Pen	insulin lispro protamine suspension mixed with soluble insulin lispro
Insulin	Humulin 70/30	insulin (human recombinant)
Insulin	Humulin N	insulin (human recombinant)
Insulin	Humulin R	insulin (human recombinant)
Insulin	Lantus	insulin glargine
Insulin	Lantus SoloSTAR	insulin glargine (rDNA origin)
Insulin	Levemir	insulin detemir (rDNAorigin)
Insulin	Novolin 70/30	human insulin isophane suspension and regular, human insulin injection (rDNA origin)
Insulin	NovoLog	insulin aspart (rDNA origin)
Insulin	NovoLog Mix 70/30	insulin aspart protamine and insulin aspart (rDNA origin)
Oral antidiabetic	Actoplus Met	metformin and pioglitazone
Oral antidiabetic	Actos	pioglitazone
Oral antidiabetic	Avandia	rosiglitazone
Oral antidiabetic	Glipizide XL	glipizide
Oral antidiabetic	Janumet	metformin and sitagliptin
Oral antidiabetic	Januvia	sitagliptin
Oral antidiabetic	Prandin	repaglinide
Phosphodiesterase inhibitor	Cialis	tadalafil
Phosphodiesterase inhibitor	Levitra	vardenafil
Phosphodiesterase inhibitor	Viagra	sildenafil
Progestins	Prometrium	progesterone
Thyroid	Levothroid	levothyroxine
Thyroid	Levoxyl	levothyroxine
Thyroid	Synthroid	levothyroxine
Thyroid	Thyroid, Armour	dessicated thyroid

Musculoskeletal Agents

Muscle relaxant	Skelaxin	metaxalone
Osteoporitics	Actonel	risedronate
Osteoporitics	Actonel 150	risedronate
Osteoporitics	Boniva	ibandronate
Osteoporitics	Evista	raloxifene

Neurological Agents

Neurological	Lyrica	pregabalin
Anti-Alzheimer's	Aricept	donepezil

TOP 200 BRAND NAME DRUGS BY CLASSIFICATION

Class/Type	Brand Name	Generic Name
Neurological Agents, cont'd		
Anti-Alzheimer's	Exelon Patch	rivastigmine
Anti-Alzheimer's	Namenda	memantine
Antiepileptic*	Lamictal	lamotrigine
Antiepileptic*	Dilantin	phenytoin
Antimigraine	Maxalt	rizatriptan
Antimigraine	Maxalt MLT	rizatriptan
Antimigraine	Relpax	eletriptan
Ophthalmic & Otic Agents		
Ophthalmic	Lotemax	loteprednol
Ophthalmic	Nevanac	nepafenac
Ophthalmic	Pataday	olopatadine
Ophthalmic	Patanol	olopatadine
Ophthalmic	Restasis	cyclosporine
Ophthalmic	Vigamox	moxifloxacin ophthalmic
Ophthalmic	Zymar	gatifloxacin
Antiglaucoma	Alphagan P	brimonidine
Antiglaucoma	Combigan	brimonidine and timolol
Antiglaucoma	Lumigan	bimatoprost
Antiglaucoma	Travatan Z	travoprost
Antiglaucoma	Xalatan	latanoprost
Otic	Ciprodex otic	ciprofloxacin and dexamethasone
Psychotropic Agents		
Psychotropic	Cymbalta	duloxetine
Psychotropic	Intuniv	guanfacine extended-release
Psychotropic	Nuvigil	armodafinil
Psychotropic	Provigil	modafinil
Psychotropic	Strattera	atomoxetine
Antidepressant	Effexor XR	venlafaxine
Antidepressant	Lexapro	escitalopram
Antidepressant	Pristiq	desvenlafaxine
Antidepressant	Wellbutrin XL	bupropion
Antipsychotic	Abilify	aripiprazole
Antipsychotic	Geodon oral	ziprasidone
Antipsychotic	Seroquel	quetiapine

Class/Type	Brand Name	Generic Name
Antipsychotic	Seroquel XR	quetiapine
Antipsychotic	Zyprexa	olanzapine
Drug dependency	Chantix	varenicline
Drug dependency	Suboxone	buprenorphine and naloxone
Hypnotic	Ambien CR	zolpidem
Hypnotic	Lunesta	eszopiclone
Psychotropic/neurologic/ADHD	Adderall XR	dextroamphetamine and amphetamine
Psychotropic/neurologic/ADHD	Concerta	methylphenidate
Psychotropic/neurologic/ADHD	Focalin XR	dexmethylphenidate
Psychotropic/neurologic/ADHD	Metadate CD	methylphenidate
Psychotropic/neurologic/ADHD	Vyvanse	lisdexamfetamine

Respiratory Agents

Class/Type	Brand Name	Generic Name
Respiratory	Advair Diskus	fluticasone and salmeterol
Respiratory	Advair HFA	fluticasone and salmeterol
Respiratory	Allegra-D 24 Hour	fexofenadine and pseudoephedrine
Respiratory	Asmanex	mometasone
Respiratory	Atrovent HFA	ipratropium
Respiratory	Combivent	ipratropium and albuterol
Respiratory	Epipen	epinephrine
Respiratory	Flovent HFA	fluticasone
Respiratory	Nasacort AQ	triamcinolone
Respiratory	Nasonex	mometasone
Respiratory	Omnaris	ciclesonide
Respiratory	Pulmicort Flexhaler	budesonide
Respiratory	Qvar	beclomethasone
Respiratory	Rhinocort Aqua	budesonide
Respiratory	Singulair	montelukast
Respiratory	Spiriva	tiotropium
Respiratory	Symbicort	formoterol and budesonide
Respiratory	Tussionex	hydrocodone and chlorpheniramine
Respiratory	Veramyst	fluticasone
Antihistamine	Astelin	azelastine
Antihistamine	Astepro 0.15%	azelastine
Antihistamine	Clarinex	desloratadine
Antihistamine	Xyzal	levocetirizine
Bronchodilator	ProAir HFA	albuterol
Bronchodilator	Proventil HFA	albuterol
Bronchodilator	Ventolin HFA	albuterol
Bronchodilator	Xopenex	levalbuterol
Bronchodilator	Xopenex HFA	levalbuterol

COMMON GENERIC DRUGS BY CLASSIFICATION

Many drugs are commonly dispensed as generics to provide a cost savings to patients. The following list contains generic drug names and is organized by classification.

Class/Type	Generic Name
Analgesics	
Analgesic	aspirin
Analgesic	butalbital/acetaminophen/caffeine
Analgesic	tramadol
NSAID	diclofenac sodium
NSAID	etodolac
NSAID	ibuprofen
NSAID	meloxicam
NSAID	nabumetone
NSAID	naproxen
Opiate	acetaminophen/codeine
Opiate	fentanyl transdermal
Opiate	hydrocodone/acetaminophen
Opiate	methadone
Opiate	morphine sulfate
Opiate	oxycodone
Anesthetic Agents	
Anesthetic	procaine
Anti-infectives	
Anti-infective	amoxicillin
Anti-infective	amoxicillin/clavulanate
Anti-infective	ampicillin
Anti-infective	azithromycin
Anti-infective	cefaclor
Anti-infective	cefdinir
Anti-infective	cephalexin
Anti-infective	ciprofloxacin
Anti-infective	clarithromycin
Anti-infective	clindamycin
Anti-infective	levofloxacin
Anti-infective	metronidazole
Anti-infective	nitrofurantoin
Anti-infective	penicillin VK

An asterisk next to a drug's classification indicates there are additional common uses for that drug.

Class/Type	Generic Name
Anti-infective	trimethoprim/sulfamethoxazole
Anti-infective	tetracycline
Antifungal	fluconazole
Antifungal	nystatin
Antiviral	acyclovir

Antineoplastic Agents

Antineoplastic*	tamoxifen
Antimetabolite*	methotrexate

Cardiovascular Agents

Cardiovascular	carvedilol
Cardiovascular	clopidogrel
Cardiovascular	isosorbide mononitrate
Antianginal	nitroglycerin
Anticoagulant	heparin
Anticoagulant	warfarin
Antihyperlipidemic	atorvastatin
Antihyperlipidemic	gemfibrozil
Antihyperlipidemic	lovastatin
Antihyperlipidemic	pravastatin
Antihyperlipidemic	simvastatin
Antihypertensive*	amlodipine
Antihypertensive*	atenolol
Antihypertensive*	benazepril
Antihypertensive*	bisoprolol
Antihypertensive*	clonidine
Antihypertensive*	diltiazem
Antihypertensive*	doxazosin
Antihypertensive*	enalapril
Antihypertensive*	fosinopril sodium
Antihypertensive*	furosemide
Antihypertensive*	hydrochlorothiazide
Antihypertensive*	lisinopril
Antihypertensive*	metoprolol
Antihypertensive*	nadolol
Antihypertensive*	nifedipine
Antihypertensive*	propranolol
Antihypertensive*	ramipril
Antihypertensive*	spironolactone
Antihypertensive*	terazosin
Antihypertensive*	torsemide
Antihypertensive*	triamterene/hydrochlorothiazide
Antihypertensive*	verapamil

COMMON GENERIC DRUGS BY CLASSIFICATION

Class/Type	Generic Name
Dermatologicals	
Dermatological	clotrimazole/betamethasone
Dermatological	hydrocortisone cream/ointment
Dermatological	silver sulfadiazine
Electrolytes	
Electrolyte	potassium chloride
Electrolyte	sodium chloride
Gastrointestinal & Urinary Tract Agents	
Gastrointestinal	metoclopramide
Gastrointestinal	phentermine
Antacid/Antiulcer	famotidine
Antacid/Antiulcer	pantoprazole
Antidiarrheal	diphenoxylate/atropine
Antiemetic	meclizine
Antiemetic	trimethobenzamide
Antispasmodic	hyoscyamine
laxative	docusate Sodium
laxative	lactulose
laxative	polyethylene glycol
Urinary	finasteride
Urinary	oxybutynin
Urinary	phenazopyridine
Hormones & Modifiers	
Adrenal corticosteroid	dexamethasone
Adrenal corticosteroid	methylprednisolone
Adrenal corticosteroid	prednisolone
Adrenal corticosteroid	prednisone
Antidiabetic	insulin
Oral antidiabetic	glimepiride
Oral antidiabetic	glipizide
Oral antidiabetic	glyburide
Oral antidiabetic	metformin
Estrogen	estradiol
Progestins	medroxyprogesterone
Antigout	allopurinol

Class/Type	Generic Name
Musculoskeletal Agents	
Muscle relaxant	baclofen
Muscle relaxant	carisoprodol
Muscle relaxant	cyclobenzaprine
Muscle relaxant	tizanidine
Osteoporitics	alendronate
Neurological Agents	
Neurological	benztropine
Antiparkinsonian	carbidopa/levodopa
ADHD	amphetamine salt combination
ADHD	methylphenidate
Antiepileptic	carbamazepine
Antiepileptic	gabapentin
Antiepileptic	lamotrigine
Antiepileptic	phenobarbital
Antiepileptic	phenytoin
Psychotropic Agents	
Psychotropic	alprazolam
Psychotropic	buspirone
Psychotropic	clonazepam
Psychotropic	diazepam
Psychotropic	lithium carbonate
Psychotropic	lorazepam
Antidepressant	amitriptyline
Antidepressant*	bupropion
Antidepressant	citalopram
Antidepressant	doxepin
Antidepressant	escitalopram
Antidepressant	fluoxetine
Antidepressant	mirtazapine
Antidepressant	nortriptyline
Antidepressant	paroxetine
Antidepressant	sertraline
Antidepressant	trazodone
Antidepressant	venlafaxine
Antipsychotic	risperidone
Hypnotic	temazepam
Hypnotic	zolpidem
Respiratory Agents	
Antihistamine	hydroxyzine
Antihistamine	promethazine
Antitussive	benzonatate
Bronchodilator	albuterol

TOP 50 CANADIAN DRUGS

Following is a list of the top 50 dispensed medication products in Canada cross-referenced with corresponding generic drug names and the classifications used in this text. Rankings are based on IMS Brograns' Top 50 Dispensed Medications in Canada, 2010 (available at http:// www.imshealth.com/deployedfiles/ims/Global/North%20America/Canada/Home%20Page%20 Content/Pharma%20Trends/Top50Dispensed_En_11.pdf).

Rank	Product	Generic Name	Classification
1.	Synthroid	levothyroxine sodium	Hormones & Modifiers, Thyroid
2.	Crestor	rosuvastatin	Cardiovascular, Antihyperlipidemic
3.	Lipitor	atorvastatin	Cardiovascular, Antihyperlipidemic
4.	Apo-Furosemide	furosemide	Cardiovascular, Antihypertensive*
5.	Teva-Amoxicillin	amoxicillin	Anti-infective
6.	Nexium	esomeprazole magnesium	Gastrointestinal, Antacid/Antiulcer
7.	Teva-Venlafaxine XR	venlafaxine	Psychotropic, Antidepressant
8.	Apo-Ramipril	ramipril	Cardiovascular, Antihypertensive*
9.	Apo-Hydro	hydrochlorothiazide	Cardiovascular, Antihypertensive*
10.	Plavix	clopidogrel	Cardiovascular
11.	Apo-Atorvastatin	atorvastatin	Cardiovascular, Antihyperlipidemic
12.	Teva-Rabeprazole	rabeprazole	Gastrointestinal, Antacid/Antiulcer
13.	Ativan	lorazepam	Psychotropic
14.	Coversyl	perindopril	Cardiovascular, Antihypertensive*
15.	Celebrex	celecoxib	Analgesic, NSAID
16.	Apo-Salvent CFC FR	salbutamol (albuterol)	Respiratory, Bronchodilator
17.	Sandoz-Bisoprolol	bisoprolol	Cardiovascular, Antihypertensive*
18.	Apo-Lorazepam	lorazepam	Psychotropic
19.	Avapro	irbesartan	Cardiovascular, Antihypertensive*
20.	Diovan	valsartan/hydrochlorothiazide	Cardiovascular, Antihypertensive*
21.	Eltroxin	levothyroxine sodium	Hormones & Modifiers, Thyroid
22.	Ratio-Lenoltec #3	codeine/acetaminophen/caffeine	Analgesic, Opiate
23.	Adalat XL	nifedipine	Cardiovascular, Antihypertensive*
24.	Nasonex	mometasone	Respiratory
25.	Ventolin HFA	salbutamol (albuterol)	Respiratory, Bronchodilator
26.	Ratio-Oxycocet	oxycodone/acetaminophen	Analgesic, Opiate
27.	Tylenol with Codeine #3	codeine/acetaminophen	Analgesic, Opiate

An asterisk next to a drug's classification indicates there are additional common uses for that drug.

Rank	Product	Generic Name	Classification
28.	Flovent HFA	fluticasone propionate	Respiratory
29.	Actonel	risedronate	Musculoskeletal, Osteoporotic
30.	Lyrica	pregabalin	Neurological
31.	Atacand	candesartan cilexitil	Cardiovascular, Antihypertensive*
32.	Ratio-Metformin	metformin HCl	Hormones & Modifiers, Oral antidiabetic
33.	Taro-Warfarin	warfarin sodium	Cardiovascular, Anticoagulant
34.	Pro-AAS EC-80	aspirin, delayed release	Analgesic, Salicylate*
35.	Ran-Pantoprazole	pantoprazole	Gastrointestinal, Antacid/Antiulcer
36.	Teva-Metoprolol	metoprolol tartrate	Cardiovascular, Antihypertensive*
37.	Cipralex	escitalopram	Psychotropic, Antidepressant
38.	Ezetrol	ezetimibe	Cardiovascular, Antihyperlipidemic
39.	Flomax CR	tamsulosin	Urinary
40.	Apo-Naproxen	naproxen	Analgesic, NSAID
41.	Apo-Prednisone	prednisone	Hormones & Modifiers, Adrenal corticosteroid
42.	Apo-Metformin	metformin HCl	Hormones & Modifiers, Oral antidiabetic
43.	Teva-Hydrochlorothiazide	hydrochlorothiazide	Cardiovascular, Antihypertensive*
44.	Coumadin	warfarin sodium	Cardiovascular, Anticoagulant
45.	Apo-Oxazepam	oxazepam	Psychotropic
46.	Alesse	levonorgestrel/ethinyl estradiol	Hormones & Modifiers, Oral contraceptive
47.	Diovan HCT	valsartan/hydrochlorothiazide	Cardiovascular, Antihypertensive*
48.	Apo-Metoprolol	metoprolol tartrate	Cardiovascular, Antihypertensive*
49.	Spiriva	tiotropium bromide	Respiratory
50.	Yasmin	drospirenone/ethinyl estradiol	Hormones & Modifiers, Oral contraceptive

COMMONLY REFRIGERATED DRUGS

Many products must be stored at refrigerated temperatures to ensure stability. Following is a list of commonly refrigerated drugs. As per the manufacturer's product information, some products need to be refrigerated immediately upon receipt from the manufacturer. Others may be stored at room temperature but will require refrigeration once reconstituted or when a diluent is added. A few drugs are stored in the refrigerator at the pharmacy but can be kept at room temperature when in use by the patient. For reconstituted products, the manufacturer will provide information as to how long the product is stable once reconstituted.

Brand Name & Dosage Form	Generic Name
ActHib vials	haemophilus b conjugate vaccine (tetanus toxoid conjugate)
Actimmune vials	interferon gamma-1b
Adacel vials	tetanus toxoid, reduced diphtheria toxoid, acellular pertussis vaccine adsorbed (Tdap) vaccine
Alcaine ophthalmic solution	proparacaine
Amoxil suspension	amoxicillin
Anectine vials	succinylcholine chloride
Aspirin Uniserts suppositories	aspirin
Atgam vials	lymphocyte immune globulin
Augmentin suspension	amoxicillin/clavulanic acid
Avonex syringes	interferon beta-1a
Azasite ophthalmic solution	azithromycin
BACiiM vials	bacitracin
Benzamycin gel	erythromycin/benzoyl peroxide
Bicillin syringes	penicillin G benzathine
Cardizem vials	diltiazem hydrochloride
Caverject vials	alprostadil
Ceftin suspension	cefuroxime axetil
Cefzil suspension	cefprozil
Cerebyx vials	fosphenytoin sodium
Cipro suspension	ciprofloxacin
Combipatch transdermal patch	estradiol/norethindrone
Copaxone	glatiramer acetate
DDAVP vials	desmopressin
Digibind vials	digoxin immune Fab
Enbrel syringes	etanercept
Engerix-B vials	hepatitis B vaccine
Epogen vials	epoetin alfa
Genotropin cartridges	somatropin
Havrix vials, syringes	hepatitis A vaccine

Brand Name & Dosage Form	Generic Name
Hemabate vial	carboprost tromethamine
Humalog vials, pens	insulin lispro
Humira syringes	adalimumab
Humulin R vials	regular insulin
Infergen vials	interferon alfacon-1
Kaletra solution, capsules	lopinavir/ritonavir
Lactinex tablets	lactobacillus acidophilus/bulgaricus
Lantus vials, pens	insulin glargine
Leukeran tablets	chlorambucil
Meruvax vials	rubella virus vaccine live
Methergine vials	methylergonovine maleate
Miacalcin nasal spray	calcitonin salmon
MMR II vials	measles, mumps, rubella virus vaccine live
Mycostatin pastilles	nystatin
Neupogen vials, syringes	filgrastim
Nimbex vials	cisatracurium besylate
Norditropin cartridges	somatropin
Norvir soft gels	ritonavir
Neulasta syringe	pegfilgrastim
Neurontin suspension	gabapentin
Pavulon	pancuronium bromide
Phenergan suppositories	promethazine
Pneumovax 23 vaccine	pneumococcal vaccine polyvalent
Premarin Secule® vials	conjugated estrogens
RabAvert vial	rabies vaccine
Rapamune solution	sirolimus
Rebetron	ribavirin/interferon alfa-2b
Regranex gel	becaplermin
Risperdal Consta kits	risperidone
Sandostatin vials	octreotide acetate
Survanta vials	beractant
Tamiflu suspension	oseltamivir phosphate
Thyrolar tablets	liotrix
Tracrium vials	atracurium besylate
Veetids suspension	penicillin V
VePesid capsules	etoposide
Vibramycin suspension	doxycycline
Viroptic ophthalmic solution	trifluridine
Xalatan ophthalmic solution	latanoprost
Zemuron vials	rocuronium bromide
Zithromax suspension	azithromycin

PHARMACY TECHNICIAN LABS

The following pages contain exercises to provide hands-on activities to accompany each of the chapters in *The Pharmacy Technician, Fifth Edition*. The labs that follow are intended to provide students with opportunities for engaging experiences to enhance learning of some concepts associated with the chapters.

Supplies for labs: A pencil, a pen, a bound composition book, index cards (your instructor may have a preference for what size you should use), and a highlighter.

You will need access to the Internet to complete these labs. Web addresses current at the time of printing have been included in the exercises. If you find a printed Web address is not available when you are working on the exercise, you may wish to use a different link.

You should use a bound notebook such as a composition book to serve as a lab notebook for documenting your lab activities. Throughout the labs, you should make notes and write the answers to any questions in your lab notebook.

Learning activities for learning the brand names, generic names, and classifications of the top 200 brand name drugs have been separated by classification, and dispersed throughout each of the labs to make memorization of information more manageable.

DRUG CARDS

Drug cards can be a great study tool for memorizing information about drugs. It is suggested that you prepare and learn the information on your drug cards in advance of working on each lab. That way, you can build on the foundational knowledge with your lab experiences.

INSTRUCTIONS FOR MAKING DRUG CARDS

1. Use pencil to write on the index card so you can easily change or correct any information. Use highlighters to color-code your cards, giving each type of information a different color. You may wish to include additional information to customize the information for your drug cards.

2. Write the brand name of the drug on the front of the index card.

3. Write the generic name and classification on the backside of the index card. You can use a different color of highlighter for the generic name and the classification.

4. Your instructor may want you to add additional cards for commonly used generic drugs or your instructor may provide additional information for you to include on each drug card. You can use online resources such as Medline Plus of the National Library of Medicine website, http://www.nlm.nih.gov/medlineplus/.

5. Study and memorize the information you have written on your drug cards. You can test yourself by looking at the brand names on the front and trying to remember the information on the back, or looking at the information on the back and trying to remember the brand names of the drugs.

LAB ONE

DRUG CARDS

Make drug cards for the following drugs. (See page 201 for instructions on making drug cards.)

Brand Name	Generic Name	Classification
Celebrex	celecoxib	Analgesic, NSAID
Voltaren gel	diclofenac topical	Analgesic, NSAID
Arthrotec	diclofenac and misoprostol	Analgesic, NSAID
OxyContin	oxycodone	Analgesic, opiate
Opana ER	oxymorphone	Analgesic, opiate
Lidoderm	lidocaine transdermal	Anesthetic, ocal
Skelaxin	metaxalone	Musculoskeletal, Muscle relaxant
Boniva	ibandronate	Musculoskeletal, Osteoporitics
Evista	raloxifene	Musculoskeletal, Osteoporitics
Actonel	risedronate	Musculoskeletal, Osteoporitics
Actonel 150	risedronate	Musculoskeletal, Osteoporitic

LAB ACTIVITIES

1. Visit the FDA website, http://www.fda.gov/, and click on the Drugs tab. What items are listed in the Spotlight box? (Write your answers in your lab notebook.)

2. Visit the website for QS/1® http://qs1.com/ and click on the Products & Modules tab. Then select the NRx Pharmacy Management link, http://www.qs1.com/products/pharmacy/nrx-pharmacy-management/. Once at the the NRx Pharmacy Management site, click on the View Demo link, http://www.qs1.com/products/pharmacy/nrx-pharmacy-management/#!prettyPhoto[flash]/0/ and watch the demo. List the activities from the Computers in Pharmacy spread of the main text that are provided by the NRx Pharmacy Management software.

3. Visit the website for the American Society of Health-System Pharmacists, http://www.ashp.org/, and click on the link for Accreditation, http://www.ashp.org/menu/Accreditation.aspx. Once in the accreditation website, click on the link for Technician Training Directory, http://www.ashp.org/menu/Accreditation/TechnicianTrainingDirectory. Search for the accredited technician training programs in your state and write the names of the programs in your lab notebook.

4. Visit the Pharmacy Technician Certification Board website, http://www.ptcb.org/, and click on the tab for Certification. Click on the link for Candidate Guidebook for the most current information about the PTCE exam.

5. Visit http://www.nhanow.com/pharmacy-technician.aspx, the NHA website for the ExCPT exam. Click on the link for the Pharmacy Technician Candidate Handbook for the most current information about the ExCPT exam.

6. Visit the Medline Plus website of the National Library of Medicine, http://www.nlm.nih.gov/medlineplus/.

a. Search Medline Plus for Oxycontin and select the druginfo result for oxycodone (http://www.nlm.nih.gov/medlineplus/druginfo/meds/a682132.htm) to answer the following questions:

1. Why is this medication prescribed?
2. What storage conditions are needed for this medicine?
3. What are other brand names for oxycodone products?
4. What are brand names for combination products containing oxycodone and what does each product contain?
5. Read the pronunciation of oxycodone at the top of the page and correctly pronounce oxycodone.

b. Search Medline Plus for Celebrex and select the druginfo result for celecoxib (http://www.nlm.nih.gov/medlineplus/druginfo/meds/a699022.html) to answer the following questions:

1. Why is this medication prescribed?
2. What storage conditions are needed for this medicine?
3 Are there any other brand names for celecoxib products?
4. Read the pronunciation of celecoxib at the top of the page and correctly pronounce celecoxib.

c. Search Medline Plus for Boniva and select the druginfo result for ibandronate (http://www.nlm.nih.gov/medlineplus/druginfo/meds/a605035.html) to answer the following questions:

1. Why is this medication prescribed?
2. What storage conditions are needed for this medicine?
3. Are there any other brand names for ibandronate products?
4. Read the pronunciation of ibandronate at the top of the page and correctly pronounce ibandronate.

LAB TWO

DRUG CARDS

Make drug cards for the following drugs. (See page 201 for instructions on making drug cards.)

Brand Name	Generic Name	Classification
Levaquin	ofloxacin	Anti-Infective
Avelox	moxifloxacin	Anti-Infective
Solodyn	minocycline	Anti-Infective
Doryx	doxycycline	Anti-Infective
Valtrex	valacyclovir	Anti-Infective, Antiviral
Tamiflu	oseltamivir	Anti-Infective, Antiviral
Truvada	tenofovir/emtricitabine	Anti-Infective, Antiviral
Norvir	ritonavir	Anti-Infective, Antiviral
Femara	letrozole	Antineoplastic, Hormone
Arimidex	anastrozole	Antineoplastic, Hormone

LAB ACTIVITIES

1. Visit the FDA video gallery website for drugs, http://www.accessdata.fda.gov/scripts/video/drugs.cfm, and select two videos to watch. Write two sentence summaries about the videos in your lab notebook.

2. Visit the FDA website for Drug Safety Communications, http://www.fda.gov/Drugs/DrugSafety/ucm199082.htm. List two current drug safety communications.

3. Visit the DEA website for the Pharmacist's Manual, http://www.deadiversion.usdoj.gov/pubs/manuals/pharm2/index.html. Click on the link for Section VIII – Ordering Controlled Substances, http://www.deadiversion.usdoj.gov/pubs/manuals/pharm2/pharm_manual.htm#8, and explain how additional DEA Form 222 order forms can be requested from the DEA.

4. Visit the website for the National Association of Boards of Pharmacy, http://www.nabp.net/, and click on the link for Boards of Pharmacy, http://www.nabp.net/boards-of-pharmacy. Click on the link for your state (if in the United States) or province (if in Canada) and write down the website address for your board of pharmacy.

5. Visit the website for The Joint Commission, http://www.jointcommission.org/, and click on the Accreditation link, http://www.jointcommission.org/accreditation/accreditation_main.aspx. List three types of health-care organizations that are accredited by TJC.

6. Visit the Medline Plus website of the National Library of Medicine, http://www.nlm.nih.gov/medlineplus/.

a. Search Medline Plus for Levaquin and select the druginfo result for levofloxacin (http://www.nlm.nih.gov/medlineplus/druginfo/meds/a697040.html) to answer the following questions:

1. Why is this medication prescribed?
2. What storage conditions are needed for this medicine?
3. Are there any special dietary instructions? What auxiliary label could be used for this dietary instruction?
4. Read the pronunciation of levofloxacin at the top of the page and correctly pronounce levofloxacin.

b. Search Medline Plus for Valtrex and select the druginfo result for valacyclovir (http://www.nlm.nih.gov/medlineplus/druginfo/meds/a695010.html) to answer the following questions:

1. Why is this medication prescribed?
2. What storage conditions are needed for this medicine?
3. Are there any other brand names for valacyclovir products?
4. Read the pronunciation of valacyclovir at the top of the page and correctly pronounce valacyclovir.

c. Search Medline Plus for Tamiflu and select the druginfo result for oseltamivir (http://www.nlm.nih.gov/medlineplus/druginfo/meds/a699040.html) to answer the following questions:

1. Why is this medication prescribed?
2. How should the suspension be used?
3. What storage conditions are needed for this medicine?
4. Are there any other brand names for oseltamivir products?
5. Read the pronunciation of oseltamivir at the top of the page and correctly pronounce oseltamivir.

LAB THREE

DRUG CARDS

Make drug cards for the following drugs. (See page 201 for instructions on making drug cards.)

Brand Name	Generic Name	Classification
Diovan	valsartan	Cardiovascular, Antihypertensive
Diovan HCT	hydrochlorothiazide and valsartan	Cardiovascular, Antihypertensive
Benicar	olmesartan	Cardiovascular, Antihypertensive
Benicar HCT	olmesartan and hydrochlorothiazide	Cardiovascular, Antihypertensive
Avapro	irbesartan	Cardiovascular, Antihypertensive
Bystolic	nebivolol	Cardiovascular, Antihypertensive
Avalide	irbesartan and hydrochlorothiazide	Cardiovascular, Antihypertensive
Cozaar	losartan	Cardiovascular, Antihypertensive
Micardis	telmisartan	Cardiovascular, Antihypertensive
Exforge	amlodipine and valsartan	Cardiovascular, Antihypertensive
Micardis HCT	telmisartan and hydrochlorothiazide	Cardiovascular, Antihypertensive
Lotrel	amlodipine and benazepril	Cardiovascular, Antihypertensive
Hyzaar	losartan and hydrochlorothiazide	Cardiovascular, Antihypertensive
Coreg CR	carvedilol	Cardiovascular, Antihypertensive
Toprol XL	metoprolol	Cardiovascular, Antihypertensive
Azor	amlodipine and olmesartan	Cardiovascular, Antihypertensive
Tekturna	aliskiren	Cardiovascular, Antihypertensive
Atacand	candesartan	Cardiovascular, Antihypertensive

LAB ACTIVITIES

1. Visit the website for the National Library of Medicine, http://www.nlm.nih.gov/, and click on the link for Medline Plus, http://www.nlm.nih.gov/medlineplus/. Search the medical dictionary feature for the following terms and write the definitions in your lab notebook: hypoglycemia, hyperthyroidism, cardiomyopathy, and sublingual.

2. Visit the website for the National Library of Medicine, http://www.nlm.nih.gov/, and click on the link for Medline Plus, http://www.nlm.nih.gov/medlineplus/. Click on the link for Medical Encyclopedia, http://www.nlm.nih.gov/medlineplus/encyclopedia.html. Find and watch the videos on the following organ systems:

    a. cardiovascular, http://www.nlm.nih.gov/medlineplus/ency/anatomyvideos/000023.htm

    b. endocrine glands, http://www.nlm.nih.gov/medlineplus/ency/anatomyvideos/000048.htm

    c. lymphatics, http://www.nlm.nih.gov/medlineplus/ency/anatomyvideos/000084.htm

3. Visit the Medline Plus website of the National Library of Medicine http://www.nlm.nih.gov/medlineplus/.

    a. Search Medline Plus for Benicar and select the druginfo result for olmesartan, (http://www.nlm.nih.gov/medlineplus/druginfo/meds/a603006.htm) to answer the following questions:

    1. Why is this medication prescribed?
    2. What storage conditions are needed for this medicine?
    3. What are other brand names for olmesartan products (including combination products)?
    4. Read the pronunciation of olmesartan at the top of the page and correctly pronounce olmesartan.

    b. Search Medline Plus for Benicar HCT and select the druginfo result for olmesartan and hydrochlorothiazide, (http://www.nlm.nih.gov/medlineplus/druginfo/meds/a611030.html) to answer the following questions:

    1. What two medications are contained in this product?
    2. Read the pronunciation of olmesartan and hydrochlorothiazide at the top of the page and correctly pronounce olmesartan and hydrochlorothiazide.
    3. Click on the link for hydrochlorothiazide. Why is hydrochlorothiazide prescribed?

    c. Search Medline Plus for Toprol XL and select the druginfo result for metoprolol, (http://www.nlm.nih.gov/medlineplus/druginfo/meds/a682864.html) to answer the following questions:

    1. Why is this medication prescribed? What is noted about extended-release metoprolol?
    2. What storage conditions are needed for this medicine?
    3. Are there any other brand names for metoprolol products? What other products contain metoprolol?
    4. Read the pronunciation of metoprolol at the top of the page and correctly pronounce metoprolol.

LAB FOUR

DRUG CARDS

Make drug cards for the following drugs. (See page 201 for instructions on making drug cards.)

Brand Name	Generic Name	Classification
Plavix	clopidogrel	Cardiovascular
Aggrenox	aspirin and dipyridamole	Cardiovascular
Nitrostat	nitroglycerin	Cardiovascular
Aspir-Low	aspirin and dipyridamole	Cardiovascular
Ranexa	ranolazine	Cardiovascular, Anti-angina
Lanoxin	digoxin	Cardiovascular, Antiarrhythmic
Coumadin	warfarin	Cardiovascular, Anticoagulant
Lovenox	enoxaparin	Cardiovascular, Anticoagulant
Lipitor	atorvastatin	Cardiovascular, Antihyperlipidemic
Crestor	rosuvastatin	Cardiovascular, Antihyperlipidemic
Tricor	fenofibrate	Cardiovascular, Antihyperlipidemic
Zetia	ezetimibe	Cardiovascular, Antihyperlipidemic
Vytorin	ezetimibe and simvastatin	Cardiovascular, Antihyperlipidemic
Niaspan	niacin	Cardiovascular, Antihyperlipidemic
Lovaza	omega-3 fatty acid	Cardiovascular, Antihyperlipidemic
Trilipix	fenofibrate	Cardiovascular, Antihyperlipidemic
Welchol	colesevelam	Cardiovascular, Antihyperlipidemic
Simcor	niacin	Cardiovascular, Antihyperlipidemic
Caduet	amlodipine and atorvastatin	Cardiovascular, Antihyperlipidemic, Antihypertensive

LAB ACTIVITIES

1. Visit the website for the Institute for Safe Medication Practices, http://www.ismp.org/, and click on the link for High Alert Medications Consumer Leaflets http://www.ismp.org/tools/highalertMedications/default.asp. List 10 medications that have High Alert Medications Consumer Leaflets and print the leaflet for warfarin. List the colors of warfarin tablets that are associated with each strength.

2. Visit the website for the Institute for Safe Medication Practices, http://www.ismp.org/, and click on the link for Tools, http://www.ismp.org/tools/default.asp. Click on the link for the Error-Prone Abbreviations List, http://www.ismp.org/tools/errorproneabbreviations.pdf, and print the list. Write the intended meaning for the following abbreviations in your lab notebook and the possible misinterpretations: AD, AS, AU, OD, OS, OU, OD, OS, OU. Also, indicate the better way to communicate the intended meaning.

3. Visit the Medline Plus website of the National Library of Medicine, http://www.nlm.nih.gov/medlineplus/.

   a. Search Medline Plus for Lanoxin and select the druginfo result for digoxin oral (http://www.nlm.nih.gov/medlineplus/druginfo/meds/a682301.html) to answer the following questions:

   1. Why is this medication prescribed?
   2. What storage conditions are needed for this medicine?
   3. What are other brand names for digoxin products?
   4. Read the pronunciation of digoxin at the top of the page and correctly pronounce digoxin.

   b. Search Medline Plus for Coumadin and select the druginfo result for warfarin (http://www.nlm.nih.gov/medlineplus/druginfo/meds/a682277.html) to answer the following questions:

   1. Why is this medication prescribed?
   2. What storage conditions are needed for this medicine?
   3. What is the special precaution noted about aspirin or aspirin-containing products? What auxiliary label could be used for this precaution?
   4. What is another brand name for a warfarin product?
   5. Read the pronunciation of warfarin at the top of the page and correctly pronounce warfarin.

   c. Search Medline Plus for Lovaza and select the druginfo result for omega-3-acid ethyl esters (http://www.nlm.nih.gov/medlineplus/druginfo/meds/a607065.html) to answer the following questions:

   1. Why is this medication prescribed?
   2. What storage conditions are needed for this medicine?
   3. Read the pronunciation of omega-3-acid ethyl esters at the top of the page and correctly pronounce omega-3-acid ethyl esters.

4. Prescriptions

   a. A prescription was written by Dr. Alice Chan for Andy Apple (date of birth 7/14/1953) for Lanoxin 0.25 mg #30, Sig: i tab daily, 2 refills. You check the patient's profile and the patient is not taking any other medications. The patient has no medication allergies. The patient pays cash for his prescriptions. Prepare a prescription label for this prescription using an index card formatted like the example shown on page 210 or prepare a computer-generated label if a computer pharmacy software system is available.

b. A prescription was written by Dr. Alice Chan for Bobby Banana (date of birth 2/24/1948) for Coumadin 5 mg #30, Sig: i tab daily, No refills. You check the patient's profile and the patient is not taking any other medications. The patient has no medication allergies. The patient pays cash for his prescriptions. Prepare a prescription label for this prescription using an index card formatted like the example shown below or prepare a computer-generated label if a computer pharmacy software system is available.

c. A prescription was written by Dr. Alice Chan for Carol Crumb (date of birth 9/4/1943) for Lovaza 1 g #120, Sig: ii caps b.i.d., 2 refills. You check the patient's profile and the patient is not taking any other medications. The patient has no medication allergies. The patient pays cash for her prescriptions. Prepare a prescription label for this prescription using an index card formatted like the example shown below or prepare a computer-generated label if a computer pharmacy software system is available.

Pharmacy Name	
Address	
Phone Number	
Rx Number	**Dr.**
Patient	
Directions	
Drug	
Date	**R.Ph.** _____**Refills**

STUDY NOTES

Use this area to write important points you'd like to remember.

LAB FIVE

DRUG CARDS

Make drug cards for the following drugs. (See page 201 for instructions on making drug cards.)

Brand Name	Generic Name	Classification
Synthroid	levothyroxine	Hormones & Modifiers, Thyroid
Thyroid, Armour	dessicated thyroid	Hormones & Modifiers, Thyroid
Prempro	conjugated estrogens and medroxyprogesterone	Hormones & Modifiers
Propecia	finasteride	Hormones & Modifiers
AndroGel	testosterone	Hormones & Modifiers, Androgen
Premarin tabs	conjugated estrogens	Hormones & Modifiers, Estrogen
Vivelle-DOT	estradiol	Hormones & Modifiers, Estrogen
Vagifem	estrogen	Hormones & Modifiers, Estrogen
Premarin vaginal	conjugated estrogens	Hormones & Modifiers, Estrogen
Estrace vaginal	estradiol	Hormones & Modifiers, Estrogen
Prometrium	progesterone	Hormones & Modifiers, Progestins
Levoxyl	levothyroxine	Hormones & Modifiers, Thyroid
Levothroid	levothyroxine	Hormones & Modifiers, Thyroid

LAB ACTIVITIES

1. Visit the Medline Plus website of the National Library of Medicine, http://www.nlm.nih.gov/medlineplus/.

   a. Search Medline Plus for Synthroid and select the druginfo result for levothyroxine (http://www.nlm.nih.gov/medlineplus/druginfo/meds/a682461.html) to answer the following questions:

   1. Why is this medication prescribed?
   2. What storage conditions are needed for this medicine?
   3. What are other brand names for levothyroxine products?
   4. Read the pronunciation of levothyroxine at the top of the page and correctly pronounce levothyroxine.

b. Search Medline Plus for Propecia and select the druginfo result for finasteride (http://www.nlm.nih.gov/medlineplus/druginfo/meds/a698016.html) to answer the following questions:

1. Why is this medication prescribed?
2. What storage conditions are needed for this medicine?
3. What is another brand name for a finasteride product?
4. What are the special precautions for finasteride products?
5. Read the pronunciation of finasteride at the top of the page and correctly pronounce finasteride.

c. Search Medline Plus for Androgel and select the druginfo result for testosterone topical (http://www.nlm.nih.gov/medlineplus/druginfo/meds/a605020.html) to answer the following questions:

1. What is the important warning in a red box for this medication?
2. Why is this medication prescribed?
3. What storage conditions are needed for this medicine?
4. What is another brand name for a testosterone topical product?
5. What are the special precautions for testosterone products?
6. Read the pronunciation of testosterone at the top of the page and correctly pronounce testosterone.

2. Prescriptions

a. A prescription was written by Dr. Alice Chan for Donna Dimple (date of birth 7/14/1953) for Synthroid 0.1 mg DAW #30, Sig: i tab daily, 2 refills. You check the patient's profile and the patient is not taking any other medications. The patient has no medication allergies. The patient pays cash for her prescriptions. Prepare a prescription label for this prescription using an index card formatted like the example shown on page 210 or prepare a computer-generated label if a computer pharmacy software system is available.

b. A prescription was written by Dr. Alice Chan for Eddy Elmer (date of birth 2/24/1948) for Propecia 1mg #30, Sig: i tab daily, 2 refills. You check the patient's profile and the patient is not taking any other medications. The patient has no medication allergies. The patient pays cash for his prescriptions. Prepare a prescription label for this prescription using an index card formatted like the example shown on page 210 or prepare a computer-generated label if a computer pharmacy software system is available.

c. A prescription was written by Dr. Alice Chan for Curt Crumb (date of birth 9/4/1943) for Androgel 1% Packets #30, Sig: i packet daily, 2 refills. You check the patient's profile and the patient is not taking any other medications. The patient has no medication allergies. The patient pays cash for his prescriptions. Prepare a prescription label for this prescription using an index card formatted like the example shown on page 210 or prepare a computer-generated label if a computer pharmacy software is available. When filling the prescription you notice the symbol C-III on the package. What does the C-III mean?

LAB SIX

DRUG CARDS

Make drug cards for the following drugs. (See page 201 for instructions on making drug cards.)

Brand Name	Generic Name	Classification
Moviprep	polyethylene glycol electrolyte	Gastrointentinal
Dexilant/Kapidex	dexlansoprazole	Gastrointestinal
Asacol	mesalamine	Gastrointestinal
Amitiza	lubiprostone	Gastrointestinal
Transderm-Scop	scopolamine	Gastrointestinal
Nexium	esomeprazole	Gastrointestinal, Antacid/Antiulcer
Aciphex	rabeprazole	Gastrointestinal, Antacid/Antiulcer
Protonix	pantoprazole	Gastrointestinal, Antacid/Antiulcer
Prevacid SoluTab	lansoprazole	Gastrointestinal, Antacid/Antiulcer
Prevacid	lansoprazole	Gastrointestinal, Antacid/Antiulcer
Carafate	sucralfate	Gastrointestinal, Antacid/Antiulcer
HalfLytely bowel prep	PEG-3350, sodium chloride, sodium bicarbonate and potassium chloride	Gastrointestinal, Laxative

LAB ACTIVITIES

1. Visit the Medline Plus website of the National Library of Medicine, http://www.nlm.nih.gov/medlineplus/.

a. Search Medline Plus for polyethylene glycol electrolyte solution and select the druginfo result for polyethylene glycol electrolyte solution (http://www.nlm.nih.gov/medlineplus/druginfo/meds/a601097.html) to answer the following questions:

1. Why is this medication prescribed?
2. What storage conditions are needed for this medicine?
3. What are other brand names for polyethylene glycol electrolyte solution products?
4. Read the pronunciation of polyethylene glycol at the top of the page and correctly pronounce polyethylene glycol.

b. Search Medline Plus for Transderm-Scop and select the druginfo result for scopolamine patch (http://www.nlm.nih.gov/medlineplus/druginfo/meds/a682509.html) to answer the following questions:

1. Why is this medication prescribed?
2. What storage conditions are needed for this medicine?
3. What are the special precautions for scopolamine patch products?
4. Read the pronunciation of scopolamine at the top of the page and correctly pronounce scopolamine.

c. Search Medline Plus for Prevacid Solutab and select the druginfo result for lansoprazole (http://www.nlm.nih.gov/medlineplus/druginfo/meds/a695020.html) to answer the following questions:

1. Why is this medication prescribed?
2. What storage conditions are needed for this medicine?
3. What are other brand names for lansoprazole products?
4. What are the special precautions for lansoprazole products?
5. Read the pronunciation of lansoprazole at the top of the page and correctly pronounce lansoprazole.

2. Prescriptions

a. A prescription was written by Dr. Alice Chan for Derrick Dimple (date of birth 7/14/1953) for Moviprep Disp 2 liters, Sig: 8 oz q15 min x4 doses, repeat 90 min later, then drink 1 l of clear liquid evening before procedure, no refills. You check the patient's profile and the patient is not taking any other medications. The patient has no medication allergies. The patient pays cash for his prescriptions. Prepare a prescription label for this prescription using an index card formatted like the example shown on page 210 or prepare a computer-generated label if a computer pharmacy software system is available.

b. A prescription was written by Dr. Alice Chan for George Grace (date of birth 2/24/1948) for Transderm-Scop #4, Sig: Start: evening prior to surgery. Info: remove patch 24h after surgery; do not cut patch. No refills. You check the patient's profile and the patient is not taking any other medications. The patient has no medication allergies. The patient pays cash for his prescriptions. Prepare a prescription label for this prescription using an index card formatted like the example shown on page 210 or prepare a computer-generated label if a computer pharmacy software system is available.

c. A prescription was written by Dr. Alice Chan for Cindy Current (date of birth 9/4/1943) for Prevacid Solutab 30 mg #30, Sig: i PO daily, before breakfast, 2 refills. You check the patient's profile and the patient is not taking any other medications. The patient has no medication allergies. The patient pays cash for her prescriptions. Prepare a prescription label for this prescription using an index card formatted like the example shown on page 210 or prepare a computer-generated label if a computer pharmacy software system is available.

LAB SEVEN

DRUG CARDS

Make drug cards for the following drugs. (See page 201 for instructions on making drug cards.)

Brand Name	Generic Name	Classification
SF 5000 Plus	fluoride	Dental
Zovirax topical	acyclovir	Dermatological
Differin	adapalene	Dermatological
Bactroban	mupirocin	Dermatological
BenzaClin	clindamycin and benzoyl peroxide	Dermatological
Duac Care System	clindamycin and benzoyl peroxide	Dermatological
Epiduo	adapalene and benzoyl peroxide	Dermatological

LAB ACTIVITIES

1. Visit the Medline Plus website of the National Library of Medicine, http://www.nlm.nih.gov/medlineplus/.

a. Search Medline Plus for SF 5000 Plus and select the druginfo result for fluoride (http://www.nlm.nih.gov/medlineplus/druginfo/meds/a682727.html) to answer the following questions:

1. Why is this medication prescribed?
2. What storage conditions are needed for this medicine?
3. What are other brand names for fluoride products?
4. Read the pronunciation of fluoride at the top of the page and correctly pronounce fluoride.

b. Search Medline Plus for Differin and select the druginfo result for adapalene (http://www.nlm.nih.gov/medlineplus/druginfo/meds/a604001.html) to answer the following questions:

1. Why is this medication prescribed?
2. What storage conditions are needed for this medicine?
3 What are the special precautions for adapalene products?
4. Read the pronunciation of adapalene at the top of the page and correctly pronounce adapalene.

c. Search Medline Plus for Benzaclin and select the druginfo result for clindamycin and benzoyl peroxide topical (http://www.nlm.nih.gov/medlineplus/druginfo/meds/a603021.html) to answer the following questions:

1. Why is this medication prescribed?
2. What storage conditions are needed for this medicine?
3. What are other brand names for clindamycin and benzoyl peroxide products?
4. What are the special precautions for clindamycin and benzoyl peroxide products?
5. Read the pronunciation of clindamycin and benzoyl peroxide at the top of the page and correctly pronounce clindamycin and benzoyl peroxide.

2. Prescriptions

a. A prescription was written by Dr. Alice Chan for David Noodle (date of birth 7/14/1953) for SF 5000 Plus Disp. 51 g, Sig: Apply a thin ribbon of SF 5000 Plus to toothbrush. Brush thoroughly for two minutes, preferably at bedtime, 3 refills. You check the patient's profile and the patient is not taking any other medications. The patient has no medication allergies. The patient pays cash for his prescriptions. Prepare a prescription label for this prescription using an index card formatted like the example shown on page 210 or prepare a computer-generated label if a computer pharmacy software system is available.

b. A prescription was written by Dr. Alice Chan for Sara Sunny (date of birth 2/24/1948) for Differin 0.1% Cream Disp. 45 g, Sig: daily hs. 1 refill. You check the patient's profile and the patient is not taking any other medications. The patient has no medication allergies. The patient pays cash for her prescriptions. Prepare a prescription label for this prescription using an index card formatted like the example shown on page 210 or prepare a computer-generated label if a computer pharmacy software system is available.

c. A prescription was written by Dr. Alice Chan for Tom Tree (date of birth 9/4/1943) for Benzaclin Disp. 25 g, Sig: apply b.i.d., 2 refills. You check the patient's profile and the patient is not taking any other medications. The patient has no medication allergies. The patient pays cash for his prescriptions. Prepare a prescription label for this prescription using an index card formatted like the example shown on page 210 or prepare a computer-generated label if a computer pharmacy software system is available.

LAB EIGHT

DRUG CARDS

Make drug cards for the following drugs. (See page 201 for instructions on making drug cards.)

Brand Name	Generic Name	Classification
Lantus	insulin glargine	Hormones & Modifiers, Insulin
NovoLog	insulin aspart (rDNA origin)	Hormones & Modifiers, Insulin
Lantus SoloSTAR	insulin glargine (rDNA origin)	Hormones & Modifiers, Insulin
Humalog	insulin lispro	Hormones & Modifiers, Insulin
Levemir	insulin detemir (rDNA origin)	Hormones & Modifiers, Insulin
Humulin N	insulin (human recombinant)	Hormones & Modifiers, Insulin
NovoLog Mix 70/30	insulin aspart protamine and insulin aspart (rDNA origin)	Hormones & Modifiers, Insulin
Humulin 70/30	insulin (human recombinant)	Hormones & Modifiers, Insulin
Novolin 70/30	human insulin isophane suspension and regular, human insulin injection (rDNA origin)	Hormones & Modifiers, Insulin
Humulin R	insulin (human recombinant)	Hormones & Modifiers, Insulin
Humalog Mix 75/25 Pen	insulin lispro protamine suspension mixed with soluble insulin lispro	Hormones & Modifiers, Insulin
Byetta	exenatide	Hormones & Modifiers

LAB ACTIVITIES

1. Visit the Medline Plus website of the National Library of Medicine, http://www.nlm.nih.gov/medlineplus/.

a. Search Medline Plus for Lantus and select the druginfo result for insulin glargine (rDNA origin) injection (http://www.nlm.nih.gov/medlineplus/druginfo/meds/a600027.html) to answer the following questions:

1. Why is this medication prescribed?
2. What storage conditions are needed for this medicine?
3. Read the pronunciation of insulin glargine at the top of the page and correctly pronounce insulin glargine.

b. Search Medline Plus for Levemir and select the druginfo result for insulin detemir (rDNA Origin) injection (http://www.nlm.nih.gov/medlineplus/druginfo/meds/a606012.html) to answer the following questions:

1. Why is this medication prescribed?
2. What storage conditions are needed for this medicine?
3. Read the pronunciation of insulin detemir at the top of the page and correctly pronounce insulin detemir.

c. Search Medline Plus for Byetta and select the druginfo result for exenatide injection (http://www.nlm.nih.gov/medlineplus/druginfo/meds/a605034.html) to answer the following questions:

1. Why is this medication prescribed?
2. What storage conditions are needed for this medicine?
3. What are the special precautions for exenatide products?
4. Read the pronunciation of exenatide at the top of the page and correctly pronounce exenatide.
5. Follow the link to the FDA Medication Guide for Byetta.

2. Prescriptions

a. A prescription was written by Dr. Alice Chan for David Noodle (date of birth 7/14/1953) for Lantus SoloSTAR 100 Units/ml Disp. #5 g, Sig: 10 units SC qhs, 8 refills. Another prescription was written for Pen Needles Disp #60, Sig: use b.i.d. for Lantus injections. 8 refills. You check the patient's profile and the patient is not taking any other medications. The patient has no medication allergies. The patient pays cash for his prescriptions. Prepare prescription labels for these prescriptions using an index card formatted like the example shown on page 210 or prepare computer-generated labels if a computer pharmacy software system is available.

b. A prescription was written by Dr. Alice Chan for Sara Sunny (date of birth 2/24/1948) for Levemir 100 Units/ml Disp 10 ml, Sig: 10 units SC b.i.d. 5 refills. You check the patient's profile and the patient is not taking any other medications. Another prescription was written for Insulin syringes and needles 3/10 cc Disp #60, Sig: use b.i.d. for insulin injections. 5 refills. The patient has no medication allergies. The patient pays cash for her prescriptions. Prepare prescription labels for these prescriptions using an index card formatted like the example shown on page 210 or prepare computer-generated labels if a computer pharmacy software system is available.

c. A prescription was written by Dr. Alice Chan for Tom Tree (date of birth 9/4/1943) for Byetta 5 mcg/0.02 ml Disp. 1 pen, Sig 5 mcg SC b.i.d. within 1h before am and pm meals. 2 refills. Another prescription was written for Pen Needles Disp #60, Sig: use b.i.d. for Byetta injections. 2 refills. You check the patient's profile and the patient is not taking any other medications. The patient has no medication allergies. The patient pays cash for his prescriptions. Prepare prescription labels for these prescriptions using an index card formatted like the example shown on page 210 or prepare computer-generated labels if a computer pharmacy software system is available.

LAB NINE

DRUG CARDS

Make drug cards for the following drugs. (See page 201 for instructions on making drug cards.)

Brand Name	Generic Name	Classification
Actos	pioglitazone	Hormones & Modifiers, Oral antidiabetic
Januvia	sitagliptin	Hormones & Modifiers, Oral antidiabetic
Glipizide XL	glipizide	Hormones & Modifiers, Oral antidiabetic
Janumet	metformin and sitagliptin	Hormones & Modifiers, Oral antidiabetic
Actoplus Met	metformin and pioglitazone	Hormones & Modifiers, Oral antidiabetic
Avandia	rosiglitazone	Hormones & Modifiers, Oral antidiabetic
Prandin	repaglinide	Hormones & Modifiers, Oral antidiabetic

LAB ACTIVITIES

1. Visit the Medline Plus website of the National Library of Medicine http://www.nlm.nih.gov/medlineplus/.

   a. Search Medline Plus for Actos and select the druginfo result for pioglitazone (http://www.nlm.nih.gov/medlineplus/druginfo/meds/a699016.html) to answer the following questions:

   1. Why is this medication prescribed?
   2. What storage conditions are needed for this medicine?
   3. What are other brand names for pioglitazone products?
   4. Read the pronunciation of pioglitazone at the top of the page and correctly pronounce pioglitazone.

   b. Search Medline Plus for Januvia and select the druginfo result for sitagliptin (http://www.nlm.nih.gov/medlineplus/druginfo/meds/a606023.html) to answer the following questions:

   1. Why is this medication prescribed?
   2. What storage conditions are needed for this medicine?
   3. What are other brand names for sitagliptin products?
   4. What are the special precautions for sitagliptin products?
   5. Read the pronunciation of sitagliptin at the top of the page and correctly pronounce sitagliptin.

c. Search Medline Plus for Prandin and select the druginfo result for repaglinide (http://www.nlm.nih.gov/medlineplus/druginfo/meds/a600010.html) to answer the following questions:

1. Why is this medication prescribed?
2. What storage conditions are needed for this medicine?
3. What is the brand name of another repaglinide product?
4. What are the special precautions for repaglinide products?
5. Read the pronunciation of repaglinide at the top of the page and correctly pronounce repaglinide.

2. Prescriptions

a. A prescription was written by Dr. Alice Chan for Donna Green (date of birth 7/14/1953) for Actos 15 mg Disp. #30 g, Sig: i daily, 3 refills. You check the patient's profile and the patient is not taking any other medications. The patient has no medication allergies. The patient pays cash for her prescriptions. Prepare a prescription label for this prescription using an index card formatted like the example shown on page 210 or prepare a computer-generated label if a computer pharmacy software system is available.

b. A prescription was written by Dr. Alice Chan for Susan Knight (date of birth 2/24/1948) for Januvia 100 mg Disp. #30, Sig: i daily a.m., 5 refills. You check the patient's profile and the patient is not taking any other medications. The patient has no medication allergies. The patient pays cash for her prescriptions. Prepare a prescription label for this prescription using an index card formatted like the example shown on page 210 or prepare a computer-generated label if a computer pharmacy software system is available.

c. A prescription was written by Dr. Alice Chan for Tony Green (date of birth 9/4/1943) for Prandin 0.5 mg Disp. #90, Sig: i a.c., 3 refills. You check the patient's profile and the patient is not taking any other medications. The patient has no medication allergies. The patient pays cash for his prescriptions. Prepare a prescription label for this prescription using an index card formatted like the example shown on page 210 or prepare a computer-generated label if a computer pharmacy software system is available.

LAB TEN

DRUG CARDS

Make drug cards for the following drugs. (See page 201 for instructions on making drug cards.)

Brand Name	Generic Name	Classification
Loestrin 24 Fe	ethinyl estradiol and norethindrone and iron	Hormones & Modifiers, Contraceptive
NuvaRing	etonogestrel and ethinyl estradiol	Hormones & Modifiers, Contraceptive
Yaz	drosperinone and ethinyl estradiol	Hormones & Modifiers, Contraceptive
Ortho Tri-Cyclen Lo	norgestimate and ethinyl estradiol	Hormones & Modifiers, Contraceptive
Apri	desogestrel and ethinyl estradiol	Hormones & Modifiers, Contraceptive
Kariva	desogestrel and ethinyl estradiol	Hormones & Modifiers, Contraceptive
Ortho Evra	norelgestromin and ethinyl estradiol	Hormones & Modifiers, Contraceptive
Yasmin 28	drospirenone and ethinyl estradiol	Hormones & Modifiers, Contraceptive
Ortho Tri-Cyclen	norgestimate and ethinyl estradiol	Hormones & Modifiers, Contraceptive

LAB ACTIVITIES

1. Visit the Medline Plus website of the National Library of Medicine, http://www.nlm.nih.gov/medlineplus/.

a. Search Medline Plus for Loestrin 24 Fe and select the druginfo result for estrogen and progestin (oral contraceptives) (http://www.nlm.nih.gov/medlineplus/druginfo/meds/a601050.html) to answer the following questions:

1. Why is this medication prescribed?
2. What storage conditions are needed for this medicine?
3. What are five other brand names for oral contraceptive products?

b. Search Medline Plus for Nuvaring and select the druginfo result for ethinyl estradiol and etonogestrel vaginal ring (http://www.nlm.nih.gov/medlineplus/druginfo/meds/a604032.html) to answer the following questions:

1. Why is this medication prescribed?
2. What storage conditions are needed for this medicine?
3. What are the special precautions for ethinyl estradiol and etonogestrel vaginal ring products?
4. What is a special dietary instruction for this product?
5. Read the pronunciation of ethinyl estradiol and etonogestrel at the top of the page and correctly pronounce ethinyl estradiol and etonogestrel.

c. Search Medline Plus for Ortho Evra and select the druginfo result for ethinyl estradiol and norelgestromin transdermal (http://www.nlm.nih.gov/medlineplus/druginfo/meds/a602006.html) to answer the following questions:

1. Why is this medication prescribed?
2. What storage conditions are needed for this medicine?
3 What are the special precautions for ethinyl estradiol and norelgestromin transdermal products?
4. Read the pronunciation of ethinyl estradiol and norelgestromin at the top of the page and correctly pronounce ethinyl estradiol and norelgestromin.

2. Prescriptions

a. A prescription was written by Dr. Alice Chan for Debbie Downey (date of birth 7/14/1953) for Loestrin 24 Fe Disp. #28 g, Sig: i daily, 11 refills. You check the patient's profile and the patient is not taking any other medications. The patient has no medication allergies. The patient pays cash for her prescriptions. Prepare a prescription label for this prescription using one of the labels on pp. 230–233 or prepare a computer-generated label if a computer pharmacy software system is available.

b. A prescription was written by Dr. Alice Chan for Susan Knight (date of birth 2/24/1948) for Nuvaring Disp. #1, Sig: 1 ring PV x3wk, off x1wk. 11 refills. You check the patient's profile and the patient is not taking any other medications. The patient has no medication allergies. The patient pays cash for her prescriptions. Prepare a prescription label for this prescription using an index card formatted like the example shown on page 210 or prepare a computer-generated label if a computer pharmacy software system is available.

c. A prescription was written by Dr. Alice Chan for Tonia Simpson (date of birth 9/4/1943) for Ortho Evra Disp. #1 box, Sig: apply 1 patch qwk x3wk, off x1wk, 11 refills. You check the patient's profile and the patient is not taking any other medications. The patient has no medication allergies. The patient pays cash for her prescriptions. Prepare a prescription label for this prescription using an index card formatted like the example shown on page 210 or prepare a computer-generated label if a computer pharmacy software system is available.

LAB ELEVEN

DRUG CARDS

Make drug cards for the following drugs. (See page 201 for instructions on making drug cards.)

Brand Name	Generic Name	Classification
Lyrica	pregabalin	Neurological
Aricept	donepezil	Neurological, Anti-Alzheimer's
Namenda	memantine	Neurological, Anti-Alzheimer's
Exelon Patch	rivastigmine	Neurological, Anti-Alzheimer's
Lamictal	lamotrigine	Neurological, Antiepileptic
Dilantin	phenytoin	Neurological, Antiepileptic
Relpax	eletriptan	Neurological, Anti-migraine
Maxalt	rizatriptan	Neurological, Anti-migraine
Maxalt MLT	rizatriptan	Neurological, Anti-migraine
Concerta	methylphenidate	Psychotropic–Neurological, ADHD
Vyvanse	lisdexamfetamine	Psychotropic–Neurological, ADHD
Adderall XR	dextroamphetamine and amphetamine	Psychotropic–Neurological, ADHD
Focalin XR	dexmethylphenidate	Psychotropic–Neurological, ADHD
Strattera	atomoxetine	Psychotropic–Neurological, ADHD
Metadate CD	methylphenidate	Psychotropic–Neurological, ADHD

LAB ACTIVITIES

1. Visit the Medline Plus website of the National Library of Medicine http://www.nlm.nih.gov/medlineplus/.

   a. Search Medline Plus for Exelon Patch and select the druginfo result for rivastigmine transdermal (http://www.nlm.nih.gov/medlineplus/druginfo/meds/a607078.html) to answer the following questions:

   1. Why is this medication prescribed?
   2. What storage conditions are needed for this medicine?
   3. Read the pronunciation of rivastigmine transdermal at the top of the page and correctly pronounce rivastigmine transdermal.

   b. Search Medline Plus for Relpax and select the druginfo result for eletriptan (http://www.nlm.nih.gov/medlineplus/druginfo/meds/a603029.html) to answer the following questions:

1. Why is this medication prescribed?
2. What storage conditions are needed for this medicine?
3. What are the special precautions for eletriptan products?
4. Read the pronunciation of eletriptan at the top of the page and correctly pronounce eletriptan.

c. Search Medline Plus for Strattera and select the druginfo result for atomoxetine (http://www.nlm.nih.gov/medlineplus/druginfo/meds/a603013.html) to answer the following questions:

1. Why is this medication prescribed?
2. What storage conditions are needed for this medicine?
3. What are the special precautions for atomoxetine products?
4. Read the pronunciation of atomoxetine at the top of the page and correctly pronounce atomoxetine.

2. Prescriptions

a. A prescription was written by Dr. Alice Chan for Donna Green (date of birth 7/14/1933) for Exelon Patch 4.6 mg Disp. #30 g, Sig: i daily, 3 refills. You check the patient's profile and the patient is not taking any other medications. The patient has no medication allergies. The patient pays cash for her prescriptions. Prepare a prescription label for this prescription using an index card formatted like the example shown on page 210 or prepare a computer-generated label if a computer pharmacy software system is available.

b. A prescription was written by Dr. Alice Chan for Steve Day (date of birth 2/24/1948) for Relpax 40 mg Disp. #6 Sig: i at onset, may repeat X 1 after 2 hours as directed. 1 refill. You check the patient's profile and the patient is not taking any other medications. The patient has no medication allergies. The patient pays cash for his prescriptions. Prepare a prescription label for this prescription using an index card formatted like the example shown on page 210 or prepare a computer-generated label if a computer pharmacy software system is available.

c. A prescription was written by Dr. Alice Chan for Terry Stevens (date of birth 9/4/2001) for Strattera 80 mg Disp. #30, Sig: i daily. No refills. You check the patient's profile and the patient is not taking any other medications. The patient has no medication allergies. The patient pays cash for his prescriptions. Prepare a prescription label for this prescription using an index card formatted like the example shown on page 210 or prepare a computer-generated label if a computer pharmacy software system is available.

LAB TWELVE

DRUG CARDS

Make drug cards for the following drugs. (See page 201 for instructions on making drug cards.)

Brand Name	Generic Name	Classification
Vigamox	moxifloxacin ophthalmic	Ophthalmic
Restasis	cyclosporine	Ophthalmic
Patanol	olopatadine	Ophthalmic
Pataday	olopatadine	Ophthalmic
Zymar	gatifloxacin	Ophthalmic
Lotemax	loteprednol	Ophthalmic
Nevanac	nepafenac	Ophthalmic
Xalatan	latanoprost	Ophthalmic, Antiglaucoma
Travatan Z	travoprost	Ophthalmic, Antiglaucoma
Lumigan	bimatoprost	Ophthalmic, Antiglaucoma
Alphagan P	brimonidine	Ophthalmic, Antiglaucoma
Combigan	brimonidine and timolol	Ophthalmic, Antiglaucoma
Ciprodex otic	ciprofloxacin and dexamethasone	Otic

LAB ACTIVITIES

1. Visit the Medline Plus website of the National Library of Medicine, http://www.nlm.nih.gov/medlineplus/.

a. Search Medline Plus for Restasis and select the druginfo result for cyclosporine ophthalmic (http://www.nlm.nih.gov/medlineplus/druginfo/meds/a604009.html) to answer the following questions:

1. Why is this medication prescribed?
2. What storage conditions are needed for this medicine?
3. Read the pronunciation of cyclosporine at the top of the page and correctly pronounce cyclosporine.

b. Search Medline Plus for Xalatan and select the druginfo result for latanoprost (http://www.nlm.nih.gov/medlineplus/druginfo/meds/a697003.html) to answer the following questions:
1. Why is this medication prescribed?

2. What storage conditions are needed for this medicine?

3. What are the special precautions for latanoprost products?

4. Read the pronunciation of latanoprost at the top of the page and correctly pronounce latanoprost.

c. Search Medline Plus for Ciprodex Otic and select the druginfo result for ciprofloxacin and dexamethasone otic (http://www.nlm.nih.gov/medlineplus/ druginfo/meds/a607010.html) to answer the following questions:

1. Why is this medication prescribed?

2. How should the medicine be used?

3. What storage conditions are needed for this medicine?

4. What are the special precautions for ciprofloxacin and dexamethasone otic products?

5. Read the pronunciation of ciprofloxacin and dexamethasone at the top of the page and correctly pronounce ciprofloxacin and dexamethasone.

2. Prescriptions

a. A prescription was written by Dr. Alice Chan for Sally Jones (date of birth 7/14/1953) for Restasis 0.05% Disp. #30 g, Sig: i gtt in each eye q 12h, 3 refills. You check the patient's profile and the patient is not taking any other medications. The patient has no medication allergies. The patient pays cash for her prescriptions. Prepare a prescription label for this prescription using an index card formatted like the example shown on page 210 or prepare a computer-generated label if a computer pharmacy software system is available.

b. A prescription was written by Dr. Alice Chan for Jenny Smith (date of birth 2/24/1948) for Xalatan 0.005% Disp. 1 bottle, Sig: i gtt o.d. q.d. h.s. 5 refills. You check the patient's profile and the patient is not taking any other medications. The patient has no medication allergies. The patient pays cash for her prescriptions. Prepare a prescription label for this prescription using an index card formatted like the example shown on page 210 or prepare a computer-generated label if a computer pharmacy software system is available.

c. A prescription was written by Dr. Alice Chan for Chad Doe (date of birth 9/4/1943) for Ciprodex Otic Disp. 7.5 ml, Sig: 4 gtt in both ears bid x7 days, no refills. You check the patient's profile and the patient is not taking any other medications. The patient has no medication allergies. The patient pays cash for his prescriptions. Prepare a prescription label for this prescription using an index card formatted like the example shown on page 210 or prepare a computer-generated label if a computer pharmacy software system is available.

LAB THIRTEEN

DRUG CARDS

Make drug cards for the following drugs. (See page 201 for instructions on making drug cards.)

Brand Name	Generic Name	Classification
Cymbalta	duloxetine	Psychotropic
Provigil	modafinil	Psychotropic
Intuniv	guanfacine extended-release	Psychotropic
Nuvigil	armodafinil	Psychotropic
Lexapro	escitalopram	Psychotropic, Antidepressant
Effexor XR	venlafaxine	Psychotropic, Antidepressant
Pristiq	desvenlafaxine	Psychotropic, Antidepressant
Wellbutrin XL	bupropion	Psychotropic, Antidepressant
Seroquel	quetiapine	Psychotropic, Antipsychotic
Abilify	aripiprazole	Psychotropic, Antipsychotic
Zyprexa	olanzapine	Psychotropic, Antipsychotic
Geodon oral	ziprasidone	Psychotropic, Antipsychotic
Seroquel XR	quetiapine	Psychotropic, Antipsychotic
Suboxone	buprenorphine and naloxone	Psychotropic, Drug dependency
Chantix	varenicline	Psychotropic, Drug dependency
Lunesta	eszopiclone	Psychotropic, Hypnotic
Ambien CR	zolpidem	Psychotropic, Hypnotic

LAB ACTIVITIES

1. Visit the Medline Plus website of the National Library of Medicine http://www.nlm.nih.gov/medlineplus/.

   a. Search Medline Plus for Nuvigil and select the druginfo result for armodafinil (http://www.nlm.nih.gov/medlineplus/druginfo/meds/a607067.html) to answer the following questions:

   1. Why is this medication prescribed?
   2. What are special dietary instructions for this medicine?
   3. What storage conditions are needed for this medicine?
   4. Read the pronunciation of armodafinil at the top of the page and correctly pronounce armodafinil.

   b. Search Medline Plus for Suboxone and select the druginfo result for buprenorphine sublingual (http://www.nlm.nih.gov/medlineplus/druginfo/meds/a605002.html) to answer the following questions:

1. Why is this medication prescribed?
2. What are special dietary instructions for this medicine?
3. What is the difference between Subutex and Suboxone?
4. What storage conditions are needed for this medicine?
5. What are special precautions for buprenorphine and naloxone products?
6. Read the pronunciation of buprenorphine at the top of the page and correctly pronounce buprenorphine.

c. Search Medline Plus for Ambien CR and select the druginfo result for zolpidem (http://www.nlm.nih.gov/medlineplus/druginfo/meds/a693025.html) to answer the following questions:

1. Why is this medication prescribed?
2. What is the difference between Ambien, Ambien CR, Edluar, Intermezzo, and Zolpimist?
3. What storage conditions are needed for this medicine?
4. What are the special precautions for zolpidem products?
5. Read the pronunciation of zolpidem at the top of the page and correctly pronounce zolpidem.

2. Prescriptions

a. A prescription was written by Dr. Alice Chan for Donna Green (date of birth 7/14/1953) for Nuvigil 150 mg Disp. #30 g, Sig: i daily in the morning, 3 refills. You check the patient's profile and the patient is not taking any other medications. The patient has no medication allergies. The patient pays cash for her prescriptions. Prepare a prescription label for this prescription using an index card formatted like the example shown on page 210 or prepare a computer-generated label if a computer pharmacy software system is available. When filling the prescription you notice the symbol C-IV on the package. What does the C-IV mean?

b. A prescription was written by Dr. Alice Chan for Susan Knight (date of birth 2/24/1948) for Suboxone 2 mg /0.5 mg Disp. #30, Sig: i s.l. daily. No refills. You check the patient's profile and the patient is not taking any other medications. The patient has no medication allergies. The patient pays cash for her prescriptions. Prepare a prescription label for this prescription using an index card formatted like the example shown on page 210 or prepare a computer-generated label if a computer pharmacy software system is available. When filling the prescription you notice the symbol C-III on the package. What does the C-III mean?

c. A prescription was written by Dr. Alice Chan for Tony Green (date of birth 9/4/1943) for Ambien CR 12.5 mg Disp. #30, Sig: i h.s., 1 refill. You check the patient's profile and the patient is not taking any other medications. The patient has no medication allergies. The patient pays cash for his prescriptions. Prepare a prescription label for this prescription using an index card formatted like the example shown on page 210 or prepare a computer-generated label if a computer pharmacy software system is available. When filling the prescription you notice the symbol C-IV on the package. What does the C-IV mean?

LAB FOURTEEN

DRUG CARDS

Make drug cards for the following drugs. (See page 201 for instructions on making drug cards.)

Brand Name	Generic Name	Classification
Singulair	montelukast	Respiratory
Advair Diskus	fluticasone and salmeterol	Respiratory
Nasonex	mometasone	Respiratory
Spiriva	tiotropium	Respiratory
Flovent HFA	fluticasone	Respiratory
Combivent	ipratropium and albuterol	Respiratory
Symbicort	formoterol and budesonide	Respiratory
Tussionex	hydrocodone and chlorpheniramine	Respiratory
Nasacort AQ	triamcinolone	Respiratory
Qvar	beclomethasone	Respiratory
Veramyst	fluticasone	Respiratory
Epipen	epinephrine	Respiratory
Asmanex	mometasone	Respiratory
Allegra-D 24 Hour	fexofenadine and pseudoephedrine	Respiratory
Advair HFA	fluticasone and salmeterol	Respiratory
Atrovent HFA	ipratropium	Respiratory
Rhinocort Aqua	budesonide	Respiratory
Pulmicort Flexhaler	budesonide	Respiratory
Omnaris	ciclesonide	Respiratory
Xyzal	levocetirizine	Respiratory, Antihistamine
Astepro 0.15%	azelastine	Respiratory, Antihistamine
Clarinex	desloratadine	Respiratory, Antihistamine
Astelin	azelastine	Respiratory, Antihistamine
ProAir HFA	albuterol	Respiratory, Bronchodilator
Ventolin HFA	albuterol	Respiratory, Bronchodilator
Proventil HFA	albuterol	Respiratory, Bronchodilator
Xopenex HFA	levalbuterol	Respiratory, Bronchodilator
Xopenex	levalbuterol	Respiratory, Bronchodilator

1. Visit the Medline Plus website of the National Library of Medicine, http://www.nlm.nih.gov/medlineplus/.

a. Search Medline Plus for Spiriva and select the druginfo result for tiotropium oral inhalation (http://www.nlm.nih.gov/medlineplus/druginfo/meds/a604018.html) to answer the following questions:

1. Why is this medication prescribed?
2. What storage conditions are needed for this medicine?
3. Read the pronunciation of tiotropium at the top of the page and correctly pronounce tiotropium.

b. Search Medline Plus for Epipen and select the druginfo result for epinephrine injection (http://www.nlm.nih.gov/medlineplus/druginfo/meds/a603002.html) to answer the following questions:

1. Why is this medication prescribed?
2. What storage conditions are needed for this medicine?
3. What are other brand names for epinephrine products?
4. What are the special precautions for epinephrine products?
5. Read the pronunciation of epinephrine at the top of the page and correctly pronounce epinephrine.

c. Search Medline Plus for ProAir HFA and select the druginfo result for albuterol inhalation (http://www.nlm.nih.gov/medlineplus/druginfo/meds/a682145.html) to answer the following questions:

1. Why is this medication prescribed?
2. What storage conditions are needed for this medicine?
3. What are the special precautions for albuterol products?
4. What are other brand names for albuterol products?
5. Read the pronunciation of albuterol at the top of the page and correctly pronounce albuterol.

2. Prescriptions

a. A prescription was written by Dr. Alice Chan for Deanna Gray (date of birth 7/14/1933) for Spiriva 18 mcg Disp. #30 g, Sig: i cap inhaled daily, 6 refills. You check the patient's profile and the patient is not taking any other medications. The patient has no medication allergies. The patient pays cash for her prescriptions. Prepare a prescription label for this prescription using an index card formatted like the example shown on page 210 or prepare a computer-generated label if a computer pharmacy software system is available.

b. A prescription was written by Dr. Alice Chan for Jay Day (date of birth 2/24/1948) for Epipen Disp. #2 Sig: i IM as directed. 1 refill. You check the patient's profile and the patient is not taking any other medications. The patient has no medication allergies. The patient pays cash for his prescriptions. Prepare a prescription label for this prescription using an index card formatted like the example shown on page 210 or prepare a computer-generated label if a computer pharmacy software system is available.

c. A prescription was written by Dr. Alice Chan for Troy Schmidt (date of birth 9/4/2001) for ProAir HFA 8.5 g Disp. #1, Sig: 2 puffs inhaled q4-6h prn, 6 refills. You check the patient's profile and the patient is not taking any other medications. The patient has no medication allergies. The patient pays cash for his prescriptions. Prepare a prescription label for this prescription using an index card formatted like the example shown on page 210 or prepare a computer-generated label if a computer pharmacy software system is available.

STUDY NOTES

Use this area to write important points you'd like to remember.

LAB FIFTEEN

DRUG CARDS

Make drug cards for the following drugs. (See page 201 for instructions on making drug cards.)

Brand Name	Generic Name	Classification
Detrol LA	tolterodine	Urinary
Avodart	dutasteride	Urinary
Flomax	tamsulosin	Urinary
Vesicare	solifenacin	Urinary
Enablex	darifenacin	Urinary
Uroxatral	alfuzosin	Urinary
Viagra	sildenafil	Hormones & Modifiers, Phosphodiesterase inhibitor
Cialis	tadalafil	Hormones & Modifiers, Phosphodiesterase inhibitor
Levitra	vardenafil	Hormones & Modifiers, Phosphodiesterase inhibitor

LAB ACTIVITIES

1. Visit the Medline Plus website of the National Library of Medicine, http://www.nlm.nih.gov/medlineplus/.

   a. Search Medline Plus for Flomax and select the druginfo result for tamsulosin (http://www.nlm.nih.gov/medlineplus/druginfo/meds/a698012.html) to answer the following questions:

   1. Why is this medication prescribed?
   2. What storage conditions are needed for this medicine?
   3. What are other brand names for tamsulosin products?
   4. Read the pronunciation of tamsulosin at the top of the page and correctly pronounce tamsulosin.

b. Search Medline Plus for Vesicare and select the druginfo result for solifenacin (http://www.nlm.nih.gov/medlineplus/druginfo/meds/a605019.html) to answer the following questions:

1. Why is this medication prescribed?
2. What storage conditions are needed for this medicine?
3. What is a special dietary instruction for this product?
4. What are the special precautions for solifenacin products?
5. Read the pronunciation of solifenacin at the top of the page and correctly pronounce solifenacin.

c. Search Medline Plus for Cialis and select the druginfo result for tadalafil (http://www.nlm.nih.gov/medlineplus/druginfo/meds/a604008.html) to answer the following questions:

1. Why is this medication prescribed?
2. What storage conditions are needed for this medicine?
3. What is a special dietary instruction for this product?
4. What are the special precautions for tadalafil products?
5. Read the pronunciation of tadalafil at the top of the page and correctly pronounce tadalafil.

2. Prescriptions

a. A prescription was written by Dr. Alice Chan for Dustin George (date of birth 7/14/1933) for Flomax 0.4 mg Disp. #30 g, Sig: i cap daily, 6 refills. You check the patient's profile and the patient is not taking any other medications. The patient has no medication allergies. The patient pays cash for his prescriptions. Prepare a prescription label for this prescription using an index card formatted like the example shown on page 210 or prepare a computer-generated label if a computer pharmacy software system is available.

b. A prescription was written by Dr. Alice Chan for Jay Day (date of birth 2/24/1948) for Vesicare 10 mg Disp. #30 Sig: i daily. 1 refill. You check the patient's profile and the patient is not taking any other medications. The patient has no medication allergies. The patient pays cash for his prescriptions. Prepare a prescription label for this prescription using an index card formatted like the example shown on page 210 or prepare a computer-generated label if a computer pharmacy software system is available.

c. A prescription was written by Dr. Alice Chan for Troy Schmidt (date of birth 9/4/1952) for Cialis 2.5 mg Disp. #15, Sig: i prn prior to sexual activity. 6 refills. You check the patient's profile and the patient is not taking any other medications. The patient has no medication allergies. The patient pays cash for his prescriptions. Prepare a prescription label for this prescription using an index card formatted like the example shown on page 210 or prepare a computer-generated label if a computer pharmacy software system is available.

Pharmacy Technician Certification Exam (PTCE)

Practice Exam

The following multiple choice questions are in the *choose the best answer format* of the national Pharmacy Technician Certification Examination (PTCE) offered by the Pharmacy Technician Certification Board (PTCB). There are four possible answers with only one answer being the most correct. Many of these questions can be answered through a careful review of this workbook. However, others require knowledge gained from practice as a technician. Answers for all questions can be found on page 264.

Since the time limit for taking the National Exam is two hours, you may want to test your ability to answer the questions under a time limit, or you may simply wish to time yourself to see how long it takes you. There are 90 questions here, the same number as on the exam. If you wish to have a similar experience, you can allow yourself two hours to answer these questions.

For more information on the Pharmacy Technician Certification Exam, see the preface of this Workbook.

Answers are on page 264.

1. The pharmacist has asked you to obtain a MedWatch Form 3500 so s/he can report
   a. an adverse event regarding a veterinary product.
   b. an adverse event regarding a drug.
   c. an adverse event regarding a vaccine.
   d. an adverse event regarding a prescribing error.

2. Medications for ophthalmic administration are usually available in
   a. sterile hypotonic drops or sterile ointment.
   b. sterile hypertonic drops or sterile ointment.
   c. hypotonic solution or hypotonic suspension.
   d. sterile isotonic drops or sterile ointment.

3. A Class _____ drug recall is the most serious.
   a. I
   b. II
   c. III
   d. IV

4. You receive a prescription for Mary Jones and note there are two patients with that name in your computer system. To prevent errors, the best course of action is
   a. process the prescription for the patient who gets the most prescriptions filled at your pharmacy.
   b. ask a colleague which Mary Jones you should choose.
   c. verify the birthdate of the patient.
   d. process the prescription for the patient with the fewest allergies.

5. An excellent resource for a list of commonly confused drug names is
   a. ISMP www.ismp.org.
   b. APhA www.pharmacist.com.
   c. USP www.usp.org.
   d. NABP www.nabpnet.org.

6. Biological safety cabinets protect personnel and the environment from
   a. light.
   b. temperature.
   c. contamination.
   d. freezing.

7. _____ is a pharmacy technician responsibility.
   a. Checking that the patient knows how to take the medication
   b. Checking that the patient understands the expected benefits of taking the medication
   c. Counseling patients
   d. Quickly locating the correct medication for dispensing

8. The form number for ordering Schedule II drugs is
   a. DEA Form 121.
   b. DEA Form 200.
   c. DEA Form 222.
   d. DEA Form 240.

9. Patient package inserts (PPIs) for oral contraceptive refills are required to be provided to patients
   a. only for new prescriptions.
   b. for new prescription and refills if 30 days have lapsed since the patient received a PPI.
   c. every six months.
   d. once a year.

10. How much cough syrup will a patient take in 24 hours if the dose is two teaspoonsful every six hours?
    a. 20 ml
    b. 30 ml
    c. 40 ml
    d. 80 ml

11. The smallest gelatin capsule used for extemporaneous compounding is size
    a. 10.
    b. 8.
    c. 5.
    d. 000.

12. Coring can occur when
    a. the needle is longer than the ampule.
    b. the patient has an allergy to latex.
    c. the needle is not correctly removed from the vial.
    d. the needle is not correctly inserted into the vial.

13. Furosemide or Lasix® is used as
    a. an analgesic.
    b. an anti-inflammatory agent.
    c. a sedative.
    d. a diuretic.

14. The infusion rate of an IV is over 12 hours. The total exact volume is 800 ml. What would be the infusion rate in mls per minute?
    a. 0.56 ml/minute
    b. 1.11 ml/minute
    c. 2.7 ml/minute
    d. none of the above

15. You have a 70% solution of dextrose. How many grams of dextrose is in 400 ml of this solution?
    a. 700 grams
    b. 460 grams
    c. 280 grams
    d. 120 grams

16. The standard pediatric dose for cefazolin is 20 mg/kg/day. The order is written for 150 mg TID. The infant weighs 8 lb. This dose is
    a. too high.
    b. too low.
    c. within guidelines.
    d. none of the above

17. Federal law requires pharmacies to have available for inspection Copy 3 of the DEA Form 222 for a period of _____ year(s).
    a. 1
    b. 4
    c. 3
    d. 2

18. An IV order calls for the addition of 45 mEq of $CaCO_3$ (calcium carbonate). You have a 25 ml vial of $CaCO_3$ 4.4mEq/ml. How many ml of this concentrate do you need to add to this IV?
    a. 5.6 ml
    b. 8.4 ml
    c. 10.2 ml
    d. 12.8 ml

19. Which of the following is true about high-alert medications?
    a. High-alert medications are medications that are known to cause significant harm to the patient if an error is made.
    b. High-alert medications are medications that are expensive.
    c. High-alert medications are medications that only come in generic.
    d. High-alert medications are always multi-source.

20. Which of the following is true about medication guides?
    a. Medication guides are part of the FDA-approved labeling.
    b. Manufacturers are required to provide medication guides for all FDA-approved drugs.
    c. Medication guides are written by the dispensing pharmacist.
    d. Medication guides are written by the technician who fills the prescription.

21. A pharmacy wants to markup a product by 30 percent. How much would an item cost with this markup, if its original cost was $4.50?
    a. $5.85
    b. $6.23
    c. $6.40
    d. $7.10

22. Federal law requires an exact inventory must be kept for
    a. phenobarbital.
    b. alprazolam.
    c. carisoprodal.
    d. morphine sulfate.

23. The Material Safety Data Sheets (MSDS)
    a. provide protocols for fire hazards in the pharmacy setting.
    b. provide safety codes by OSHA in the storage of inventory.
    c. provide information concerning hazardous substances.
    d. none of the above

24. How much diluent do you need to add to 4 gm of powder to get a concentration of 500 mg/ml?
    a. 0.8 ml
    b. 8 ml
    c. 1.0 ml
    d. 10 ml

25. Bedside Medication Verification (BMV) in hospitals utilizes
    a. nurse's bar-coded name badge, patient's bar-coded arm band, and medication bar code.
    b. patient's bar-coded arm band and medication bar code only.
    c. nurse's bar-coded name badge and medication bar code only.
    d. nurse's bar-coded name badge and patient's bar-coded arm band only.

26. For most medication stock bottles, the bar code includes
    a. the product's NDC code.
    b. the pharmacist's license number.
    c. the technician's registration number.
    d. the DEA number of the pharmacy.

27. The last set of digits of the NDC are indicative of
    a. the manufacturer.
    b. product identification.
    c. package size.
    d. none of the above.

28. The approximate size container for the dispensing of 180 ml of liquid medication would be?
    a. 2 ounces
    b. 4 ounces
    c. 6 ounces
    d. 8 ounces

29. A patient asks whether he/she can take a certain medication with another one? As a pharmacy technician what should you do?
    a. Inform the patient that you see no problem.
    b. Provide the patient with a drug insert.
    c. Request the patient see the pharmacist for a consult.
    d. Try to sell the patient some Mylanta®.

30. The doctor writes: ii gtts OU bid. What does this mean?
    a. two drops in the left eye twice a day
    b. two drops in the right eye twice a day
    c. two drops in each eye twice a day
    d. two drops in the right ear twice a day

31. Investigational drugs are regulated by the
    a. FDA.
    b. CMS.
    c. DEA.
    d. Board of Pharmacy.

32. Which of the following books is used for the FDA's list of approved drug products?
   a. *Merck Index*
   b. *Red Book*
   c. "Orange Book"
   d. Martindale

33. To help prevent errors, which drugs should not be placed next to each other
   a. hydroxyzine and hydralazine.
   b. Bactroban® ointment and hydrocortisone cream.
   c. timolol ophthalmic and Alphagan® ophthalmic.
   d. Crestor® and Dilantin®.

34. Companies that specialize in returns of expired and discontinued drugs to the manufacturer are known as
   a. reverse distributors
   b. pharmacy benefit managers
   c. mail order pharmacy
   d. mass-merchandiser pharmacy

35. Of the following, which one deals with the issue of safety caps on prescription bottles?
   a. The Controlled Substance Act
   b. The Poison Prevention Act
   c. Hazardous Substance Act
   d. Federal Food and Cosmetic Act

36. Most drugs are kept at room temperature between
   a. 33°–45°F
   b. 33°–45°C
   c. 59°–86°C
   d. 59°–86°F

37. The appearance of crystals in mannitol injection would indicate that the product
   a. was exposed to cold.
   b. has settled during shipment.
   c. contains impurities and should be returned.
   d. was formulated using sterile saline.

38. The rules for coordination of benefits ensure that the benefit coverage for a claim does not exceed _____ of the total cost.
   a. 25%
   b. 33%
   c. 50%
   d. 100%

39. Dextrose 25% 1,000 ml is ordered. You have only dextrose 70% solution available. How much of the dextrose 70% solution and sterile water will you use to fill this order?
   a. 250 ml dextrose 70% and 750 ml sterile water
   b. 357 ml dextrose 70% and 643 ml sterile water
   c. 424 ml dextrose 70% and 576 ml sterile water
   d. none of the above

40. The Occupational, Safety & Health Administration (OSHA) requires pharmacies to have Material Safety Data Sheets (MSDS) for
   a. all drugs in the pharmacy inventory.
   b. all materials stored in the pharmacy refrigerator.
   c. each hazardous chemical used in the pharmacy.
   d. all controlled substances in the pharmacy inventory.

41. Of the following group names, which one would be used for cough?
   a. anthelmintics
   b. antitussives
   c. antihistamines
   d. anticholinergics

42. Tobrex® ophthalmic ung refers to
   a. an ointment used for the eye.
   b. a solution used for the eye.
   c. a topical ointment for external use only.
   d. an ointment used for the ear.

43. Suspending or thickening agents are added to suspensions to thicken the suspending medium and the sedimentation rate. Which of the following is not a suspending agent?
    a. carboxymethylcellulose
    b. tragacanth
    c. acacia
    d. bentonite

44. Oral polio virus vaccine (Poliovax®) should be stored in a temperature not to exceed 46 degrees Fahrenheit. What is this temperature in Centigrade?

    Use this formula: Centigrade = 5/9 (F° - 32°)
    a. 6°C
    b. 8°C
    c. 10°C
    d. 12°C

45. You receive a prescription for amoxicillin 75 mg QID for 10 days. How many ml of amoxicillin 250 mg/5ml do you need to fill this prescription to last the full 10 days?
    a. 20 ml
    b. 40 ml
    c. 60 ml
    d. 100 ml

46. Medicare Part D covers
    a. prescription drugs.
    b. doctors' services.
    c. inpatient hospital expenses.
    d. hospice expenses.

47. You receive a prescription for sertraline (Zoloft®) qd x 30 days. What is sertraline?
    a. antihypertensive
    b. anticonvulsant
    c. antidepressant
    d. antianginal

48. All aseptic manipulations in the laminar flow hood should be performed at least
    a. four inches within the hood.
    b. six inches within the hood.
    c. eight inches within the hood.
    d. twelve inches within the hood.

49. Which auxiliary label would be used for a prescription for tetracycline 250 mg capsules?
    a. May Cause Drowsiness
    b. Avoid Aspirin
    c. Avoid Dairy Products and Antacids
    d. Take with Food

50. Generic drugs are usually in tier
    a. 1.
    b. 2.
    c. 3.
    d. 4.

51. Which of the following is a Schedule II Controlled Substance?
    a. diazepam
    b. meperidine
    c. pentazocine
    d. propoxyphene

52. If the manufacturer's expiration date for a drug is 12/10, the drug is considered acceptable to dispense until which date?
    a. 12/01/10
    b. 12/31/10
    c. 11/30/10
    d. 1/01/10

53. HMOs, POSs, and PPOs are examples of
    a. MAC
    b. co-insurance
    c. managed care programs
    d. co-pays

54. The laminar flow hood should be left operating continuously. If it is turned off, it should not be used until it has been running for at least
    a. ten minutes.
    b. thirty minutes.
    c. forty-five minutes.
    d. sixty minutes.

55. Which auxiliary label would you use for this particular sig: ii gtts AU bid?
    a. take with meals
    b. for the ear
    c. avoid sunlight
    d. for the eye

56. A dose is written for 5 mg/kg every eight hours for one day. The adult to take this medication weighs 145 pounds. How much drug will be needed to fill this order?
    a. 765 mg
    b. 844 mg
    c. 989 mg
    d. 1,254 mg

57. How much medication would be needed for the following order?

    prednisone 10 mg, one qid x 4 days, one tid x 2 days, one bid x 1 day, then stop
    a. 16
    b. 20
    c. 24
    d. 26

58. Benzethidine is in DEA Schedule I, meaning that benzethidine
    a. has a currently accepted medical use in the United States with severe restrictions.
    b. can only be handled by the pharmacist.
    c. has no currently accepted medical use in the world.
    d. has no currently accepted medical use in the United States.

59. In which controlled substance schedule is Tylenol® No. 2 classified?
    a. Schedule I
    b. Schedule II
    c. Schedule III
    d. Schedule IV

60. Where would a pharmacy technician look for nationally recognized AWPs and NDCs for FDA-approved drugs?
    a. AHFS
    b. "Orange Book"
    c. Red Book
    d. Remington's

61. The first line of defense against infection/contamination of an IV product is
    a. antibiotics.
    b. antiseptics.
    c. disinfectants.
    d. handwashing.

62. HIPAA requires that
    a. all Medicaid patients are offered counseling by a pharmacist.
    b. all patients receive counseling by a pharmacist.
    c. all patients are offered counseling by a pharmacist.
    d. privacy rules are observed for PHI.

63. Which of the following medications must be administered in a glass IV container?
    a. aminophylline
    b. dopamine
    c. nitroglycerin
    d. potassium

64. The two parts of the syringe that should not be touched are
    a. the tip and needle.
    b. the collar and barrel.
    c. the tip and plunger.
    d. the collar and plunger.

65. The sale of what medication is restricted by the Combat Methamphetamine Epidemic Act (CMEA)?
    a. Claritin®
    b. Claritin-D 24®
    c. Chlor-Trimeton®
    d. Robitussin DM®

66. The first five digits of the National Drug Code (NDC) number identifies the
    a. product.
    b. manufacturer.
    c. units.
    d. type of packaging.

67. The "Orange Book" provides information about
    a. current pricing.
    b. drug product stability.
    c. generic equivalents.
    d. investigational drugs.

68. The common name for the FDA's Approved Drug Products with Therapeutic Equivalent Evaluations is the
    a. "Green Book."
    b. "Orange Book."
    c. "Red Book."
    d. "Blue Book."

69. What should the last digit be of this DEA number?
    AB431762 __
    a. one
    b. three
    c. five
    d. seven

70. Aminosyn® is an amino acid often used in TPN orders to provide protein for cellular repair and growth. A physician writes an order for Aminosyn® 2.5% 500 ml. You have only Aminosyn® 8.5% 500 ml. How do you prepare this order using a sterile evacuated container?
    a. Add 320 ml of Aminosyn® 8.5% and qs with sterile water to 500 ml.
    b. Add 147 ml of Aminosyn® 8.5% and qs with sterile water to 500 ml.
    c. Add 124 ml of Aminosyn® 8.5% and qs with sterile water to 500 ml.
    d. Add 74 ml of Aminosyn® 8.5% and qs with sterile water to 500 ml.

71. A company that provides access to the Internet is a/an
    a. URL
    b. ISP
    c. search engine
    d. browser

72. Hard copies of order reports
    a. are kept for an established amount of time for business and legal reasons.
    b. are only needed if there is a computer failure.
    c. are only needed if there is a power failure.
    d. are no longer needed since everything is computerized

73. The type of formulary that allows the pharmacy to obtain all medications that are prescribed is a(an)
    a. international formulary.
    b. closed formulary.
    c. wholesaler formulary.
    d. open formulary.

74. Zantac®, Tagamet®, and Pepcid® are H2 blockers that are now available over-the-counter (OTC). What are these drugs used for?
    a. used as an antihistamine to alleviate runny nose
    b. used as a decongestant to unclog nasal passages
    c. used to inhibit stomach acid secretion
    d. used as an antacid in that it neutralizes stomach acid

75. A _____ is an inventory system in which the item is deducted from inventory as it is sold or dispensed.
    a. reorder point system
    b. point-of-sale system
    c. turnover system
    d. automated system

76. Of the following drug recalls, which one is the most important in that all parties involved in the dispensing of a prescription (doctor, pharmacy, and patient) must be notified due to the drugs potential for serious harm?
    a. Class I Recall
    b. Class II Recall
    c. Class III Recall
    d. Class IV Recall

77. The pharmacist should be alerted if a patient is allergic to codeine and prescribed
    a. alprazolam.
    b. Robitussin AC®.
    c. methylphenidate.
    d. phenobarbital.

78. A prescription for amoxicillin 250 mg #30 has a usual and customary price of $8.49. The acquisition cost of amoxicillin 250 mg #30 is $2.02. What is the gross profit?
    a. $2.02
    b. $6.47
    c. 50%
    d. 1/3

79. A senior citizen is paying for a prescription for penicillin VK 250 mg #30. The usual and customary price is $8.49. However this patient qualifies for a 10% discount. How much will the patient pay?
    a. $8.49
    b. $6.99
    c. $8.39
    d. $7.64

80. A medication used to reduce a fever is called an
    a. antipyretic.
    b. antitussive.
    c. antiemetic.
    d. anthelmintic.

81. A prescription is written for Septra® Suspension 240 ml 1 teaspoonful h.s. + 1 refill. The insurance plan has a 34-day supply limitation. How many ml can be dispensed using the insurance plan guidelines?
    a. 120 ml
    b. 170 ml
    c. 240 ml
    d. 360 ml

82. A prescription is written for Humulin® N U-100 insulin 10 ml, 40 units daily. What is the days supply?
    a. 25
    b. 34
    c. 21
    d. 28

83. A prescription is written for Tetracycline HCl suspension 125 mg/5 ml compounded from capsules and a mixture of Ora-Plus® 50% and Ora-Sweet® 50%. How many capsules of Tetracycline 250 mg are needed to prepare 50 ml of this suspension?
    a. 5
    b. 10
    c. 15
    d. 20

84. How many units of insulin does a 1/3 ml insulin syringe hold?
   a. 0.3
   b. 25
   c. 30
   d. 50

85. Nurses track medication administration on a(an)
   a. STAT
   b. MAR
   c. IVP
   d. IVPB

86. When entering a new prescription into the pharmacy computer, the technician must enter the following information:
   a. the prescription number
   b. the directions for use
   c. the DEA number of the wholesaler
   d. the date the bottle was opened

87. Alprozolam is a
   a. narcotic.
   b. barbiturate.
   c. benzodiazepine.
   d. stimulant.

88. A prescription for Duragesic® patches should be filed under which DEA schedule?
   a. Schedule I
   b. Schedule II
   c. Schedule III
   d. Schedule IV

89. Which of the following medications is an antidiarrheal?
   a. propranolol
   b. famotidine
   c. methylphenidate
   d. loperamide

90. If a medication is to be taken a.c., it should be taken
   a. in the morning.
   b. around the clock.
   c. after meals.
   d. before meals.

THE EXAM FOR THE CERTIFICATION OF PHARMACY TECHNICIANS (ExCPT)

PRACTICE EXAM

The following multiple choice questions are in the *choose the best answer* format of the national Exam for the Certification of Pharmacy Technicians (ExCPT) offered by the Institute for the Certification of Pharmacy Technicians (ICPT). There are four possible answers with only one answer being the most correct. Many of these questions can be answered through a careful review of this workbook. However, others require knowledge gained from practice as a technician. Answers for all questions can be found on page 264.

Since the time limit for taking the ExCPT is two hours, you may want to test your ability to answer the questions under a time limit, or you may simple wish to time yourself to see how long it takes you. There are 110 questions here, the same number as on the ExCPT exam. If you wish to have a similar experience, you can allow yourself two hours to answer these questions.

For more information on the Exam for the Certification of Pharmacy Technicians, see the preface of this Workbook.

Answers are on page 264.

1. Which of the following may be performed only by a pharmacist?
   a. accepting a call from a wholesaler about an order
   b. accepting a return call from a prescriber's office clarifying a prescription
   c. calling a prescriber on behalf of a patient to request refills
   d. calling an insurance company to verify a patient's eligibility

2. All of the following duties may be performed by a pharmacy technician EXCEPT
   a. requesting PHI from a patient such as date of birth, address, allergy, and insurance information.
   b. selecting an OTC product for a patient.
   c. inputting and updating patient information in the computer.
   d. placing the medicaiton in a vial and attaching the prescription label to it.

3. A patient brings in two new prescriptions from two different doctors. One prescription is for ibuprofen 800 mg, 1 tablet po t.i.d. and another prescription is for Anaprox DS®, 1 tablet b.i.d. What should the technician do?
   a. Tell the patient to decide which prescription s/he wants to fill.
   b. Tell the patient that s/he must get generic for both prescriptions.
   c. Alert the pharmacist of a possible therapeutic duplication.
   d. Fill both prescriptions as written.

4. A list of the goods or items a business will use in its normal operation is called a (an)
   a. open formulary.
   b. closed formulary.
   c. inventory.
   d. protocol.

5. Checking order reports to ensure the order contains no errors is done
   a. by computer.
   b. manually.
   c. by the wholesaler.
   d. by the corporate office.

6. In receiving an order, it is important to be alert for drugs that have been incorrectly picked, received damaged, are outdated, or missing, so orders are reconciled
   a. item by item.
   b. once per month.
   c. once per year.
   d every two years.

7. A small volume intravenous bag specifically used to deliver medication is called an
   a. LVP.
   b. IVPB.
   c. vial.
   d. ampule.

8. According to federal law, the prescriber must provide his/her DEA number for which of the following prescriptions?
   a. Ultram®
   b. Xanax®
   c. Elavil®
   d. Prozac®

9. Accutane® is associated with
   a. iPLEDGE.
   b. RevAssist.
   c. STEPS.
   d. TOUCH.

10. MSDS sheets provide
   a. protocols for evacuation of the pharmacy
   b. safety codes from OSHA
   c. ordering numbers from the wholesaler
   d. information about hazardous substances

11. An antibiotic is prescribed 15 mg/kg twice a day by IV. What is the daily dose in mg for a child weighing 66 pounds?
    a. 225 mg
    b. 450 mg
    c. 675 mg
    d. 900 mg

12. Outdated drugs can be
    a. sent to reverse distributors.
    b. shipped to the DEA.
    c. shipped to the state board of pharmacy.
    d. stocked with medications that are to be dispensed.

13. An example of a major drug-drug interaction is
    a. warfarin-aspirin.
    b. hydrocodone-codeine.
    c. guaifenesin-pseudoephedrine.
    d. hydrochlorothiazide-triamterene.

14. The patient's _____ is necessary for billing a prescription.
    a. birth date
    b. medication history
    c. allergy information
    d. disease information

15. As you are putting away an order from a wholesaler, you notice one bottle is missing a label. The pharmacist tells you that the medication cannot be dispensed and must be returned to the wholesaler or destroyed. The drug cannot be dispensed because it is
    a. adulterated.
    b. misbranded.
    c. exempt.
    d. recycled.

16. Companies that administer drug benefit programs are called
    a. HMOs.
    b. PBMs.
    c. MACs.
    d. PPOs.

17. Copy 2 of DEA Form 222 is
    a. retained by the pharmacy.
    b. retained by the wholesaler.
    c. retained by the manufacturer.
    d. forwarded to the DEA.

18. Proper disposal or destruction of non-returnable medications includes
    a placement in regular trash.
    b. flushing down a sink or water system.
    c. using a company that meets EPA regulations.
    d. selling the medications at a discount.

19. Each tablet of Claritin D® 12 hour contains 120 mg of pseudoephedrine sulfate. What is the maximum number of tablets that could be sold in a single transaction if the maximum amount per transaction of pseudoephedrine is 3.6 g?
    a. 15
    b. 20
    c. 30
    d. 36

20. Exempt narcotics are in DEA schedule
    a. II.
    b. III.
    c. IV.
    d. V.

21. Exempt narcotics are regulated for how many dosage units can be sold without a prescription in a _____ hour period.
    a. 24
    b. 48
    c. 72
    d. 168

22. Federal law requires pharmacies to keep _____ of the DEA Form 222.
    a. Copy 1
    b. Copy 2
    c. Copy 3
    d. Copy 4

23. For aseptic technique, all work should be performed at least _____ inches inside the laminar flow hood.
    a. 2
    b. 4
    c. 6
    d. 8

24. All of the following are used to store medications EXCEPT
    a. automated dispensing machines.
    b. carousels.
    c. Pyxis machines.
    d. shoe boxes.

25. Counseling as required by OBRA is provided by
    a. physicians.
    b. physician assistants.
    c. certified pharmacy technicians.
    d. pharmacists.

26. All of the following pharmacy personnel must be formally trained on HIPAA EXCEPT
    a. pharmacy technicians
    b. pharmacists
    c. pharmacy clerks
    d. none of the above

27. For the following prescription, how much drug is taken each day?
    Amoxicillin 250 mg/5 ml 150 ml, Sig: 2 drams t.i.d.
    a. 15 ml
    b. 30 ml
    c. 45 ml
    d. 50 ml

28. HIPAA is a federal law that protects a patient's PHI when it is
    a. written.
    b. electronically transferred.
    c. spoken.
    d. all of the above.

29. The directions on a prescription read ii gtt q8h ou. The directions on the label should read:
    a. Instill one drop in the right ear every eight (8) hours.
    b. Inhale two puffs orally every eight (8) hours.
    c. Instill two drops in each eye every eight (8) hours.
    d. Take two drops by mouth every eight (8) hours.

30. How many cases of 8 dram vials should be ordered to last two weeks if there are 500 vials per case and the pharmacy uses 120 vials per day on average?
    a. 2
    b. 4
    c. 6
    d. 8

31. The common abbreviation ss means
    a. safety service
    b. left ear.
    c. left eye.
    d. one-half.

32. Which abbreviation is on The Joint Commissions "Do Not Use List"?
    a. qd
    b. prn
    c. ac
    d. mg

33. How many grams of sucrose are needed to prepare 4 ounces of a 20% solution?
    a. 6
    b. 12
    c. 24
    d. 36

34. How many milliliters of magnesium sulfate 4 mEq/ml are needed to add 10 mEq of magnesium sulfate to an IV bag?
    a. 2
    b. 2.5
    c. 4
    d. 10

35. Aseptic techniques are methods used to maintain
    a. pH
    b. temperature
    c. osmolarity
    d. sterility

36. How much hydrocortisone powder is needed to compound 60 g of hydrocortisone cream 2%?
    a. 1.2 mg
    b. 1,200 mg
    c. 0.06 g
    d. 6 g

37. Good interpersonal skills include
    a. making eye contact.
    b. calling the patient by name.
    c. listening carefully.
    d. all of the above.

38. How much should be withdrawn from a vial if the strength of the medication is 0.5 mg/ml and a dose of 250 micrograms is needed?
    a. 0.25 ml
    b. 0.5 ml
    c. 1 ml
    d. 5 ml

39. How should a prescription for BenzaClin® be stored after it has been mixed?
    a. refrigerator
    b. freezer
    c. room temperature
    d. in a warm and moist environment as defined by USP

40. Which DAW code should be used for a prescription written for Cymbalta 20 mg if DAW was not written on the prescription?
    a. 0
    b. 1
    c. 2
    d. 3

41. If a medication is to be taken p.c., when should it be taken?
    a. after meals
    b. in the evening
    c. before meals
    d. in the morning

42. Which DAW code should be used for a prescription written for Norvasc 5 mg if the patient requested brand name and DAW was not written on the prescription?
    a. 0
    b. 1
    c. 2
    d. 3

43. If the dose of liquid amoxicillin for a child is one and one-half teaspoonsful three times a day for 10 days, what is the volume needed to fill the prescription?
    a. 100 ml
    b. 150 ml
    c. 200 ml
    d. 225 ml

44. Information about generic equivalents can be found in the
    a. *Red Book.*
    b. "Orange Book."
    c. Blue Book.
    d. Green Book.

45. Tall man letters are used
    a. to distinguish look-alike, soundalike drug names.
    b. to promote brand products.
    c. for growth hormones.
    d. for fast movers.

46. MedWatch Form 3500 is for reporting adverse reactions to
    a. vaccines.
    b. drugs.
    c. veterinary products.
    d. produce.

47. Normal saline solution is
    a. hypotonic.
    b. isotonic.
    c. hypertonic.
    d. hyperosmotic.

48. OSHA required notices for hazardous substances that provide hazard, handling, clean-up, and first aid information are called
    a. MAC.
    b. MSDS.
    c. MEC.
    d. HCFA-1500.

49. When a technician receives a rejected claim "NDC Not Covered," this probably means
    a. the insurance plan has a closed formulary.
    b. the insurance plan has an open formulary.
    c. the birth date submitted does not match the birth date on file.
    d. the patient has single coverage.

50. Plan B® has dual marketing status and can be sold without a prescription to individuals
    a. 16 years and older.
    b. 17 years and older.
    c. 18 years and older.
    d. 21 years and older.

51. Premarin® cream has been prescribed 0.5 g pv twice a week. The medication should be administered
    a. vaginally.
    b. rectally.
    c. on the stomach.
    d. on the forearms.

52. Lidoderm® is an example of an
    a. analgesic.
    b. anti-anxiety.
    c. anesthetic.
    d. antidepressant.

53. What is the % concentration if 268 g of sugar is in 400 ml of aqueous solution?
    a. 33%
    b. 50%
    c. 67%
    d. 75%

54. Sublingual nitroglycerin is used for
    a. hyperlipidemia.
    b. angina.
    c. hypertension.
    d. coagulation.

55. The term for a drug that reduces fever is
    a. analgesic.
    b. antipyretic.
    c. anti-inflammatory.
    d. antidepressant.

56. When a technician receive a rejected claim "Invalid Person Code," this probably means
    a. the patient is on Medicare.
    b the patient has a mail order program.
    c. the person code entered does not match the birth date and/or sex in the insurer's computer.
    d. the patient is on Medicaid.

57. When a technician receives a rejected claim "Unable to Connect," this probably means
    a. the insurer has an incorrect birth date for the patient.
    b. the patient's coverage has expired.
    c. the connection with the insurer's computer is temporarily unavailable due to computer problems.
    d. the insurer has a closed formulary.

58. The class of drugs to dissolve blood clots is
    a. thrombolytics.
    b. vasopressors.
    c. antianginals.
    d. antihypertensives

59. The CMEA sets _____ and _____ limits on the over-the-counter sale of pseudo-ephedrine.
    a. daily, weekly
    b. weekly, monthly
    c. daily, monthly
    d. monthly, yearly

60. The commission that surveys and accredits health-care organizations is the
    a. DPH.
    b. FDA.
    c. ASHP.
    d. TJC.

61. Nitroglycerin sublingual tablets should be dispensed
    a. in a glass container.
    b. in a plastic container.
    c. with a cotton plug.
    d. with a medicine dropper.

62. The Controlled Substances Act is enforced by the
    a. FDA.
    b. CPSC.
    c. DEA.
    d. Bureau of Alcohol, Tobacco and Firearms.

63. The directions state 2 gtt a.u. q12h. How is the drug to be administered?
    a. both ears
    b. right eye
    c. by mouth
    d. topically

64. The CPT odes for billing Medication Therapy Management services provided by pharmacists are
    a. MAC.
    b. PPO.
    c. ICD-9.
    d. 99605, 99606, and 99607.

65. Which of the following information is generally not required for online claim processing?
    a. birth date
    b. sex
    c. group number
    d. height

66. The following drugs are antidepressants EXCEPT
    a. citalopram.
    b. trazodone.
    c. venlafaxine.
    d. diazepam.

67. The following drugs are considered antihyperlipidemic drugs EXCEPT
    a. Pravachol®.
    b. Tricor®.
    c. Vytorin®.
    d. Aldactone®.

68. The following medications should be refrigerated EXCEPT
    a. Biaxin® suspension.
    b. Augmentin® suspension.
    c. Duricef® suspension.
    d. Thyrolar®.

69. The generic name for Neurontin® is
    a. gabapentin.
    b. etodolac.
    c. nabumetone.
    d. finasteride.

70. The government agency that regulates investigational medications is the
    a. FDA.
    b. DEA.
    c. CPSC.
    d. USP.

71. An example of a robotic dispensing machine is
    a Pyxis®.
    b. Parata Max®.
    c. Kirby Lester®.
    d. a carousel.

72. The middle set of digits of the NDC represents
    a. the manufacturer.
    b. product identification.
    c. package size.
    d. country of origin.

73. Patient Package Inserts (PPIs) are required to be dispensed with all new prescriptions and at least every 30 days with refill prescriptions for
    a. oral contraceptives.
    b. antibiotics.
    c. cough syrups.
    d. NSAIDs.

74. The pharmacist should be alerted if a patient is allergic to sulfa and prescribed
    a. Ceftin®.
    b. Keflex®.
    c. Eryc®.
    d. Bactrim®.

75. The *Red Book* provides information about
    a. pricing.
    b. stability.
    c. solubility.
    d. generic substitution.

76. Prescriptions for controlled substances from Schedules II, III, and IV must contain the following warning
    a. Take with food.
    b. May cause drowsiness.
    c. Caution: Federal law prohibits the transfer of this drug to any person other than the patient for whom it was prescribed.
    d. Take on an empty stomach.

77. The temperature of a refrigerator in a pharmacy should generally be
    a. 33–45°F.
    b. 40–42°F.
    c. 43–55°F.
    d. 50–52°F.

78. The type of formulary that allows the pharmacy to obtain only drugs listed on the formulary with no exceptions is a/an
    a. open formulary.
    b. closed formulary.
    c. third-party formulary.
    d. P&T list.

79. The type of medication order for medication to be administered only on an as needed basis is called a
    a. standing order.
    b. PRN order.
    c. STAT order.
    d. standard order.

80. The unique identifying number of a drug is called a/an
    a. NDC.
    b. PHI.
    c. NPI.
    d. DEA.

81. Theft or loss of controlled substances must be recorded on DEA Form
    a. 41.
    b. 106.
    c. 222.
    d. 224.

82. When compounds are prepared from solids dissolved in water, the beyond-use date should not be later than _____ when stored in the refrigerator.
   a. 5 days
   b. 7 days
   c. 10 days
   d. 14 days

83. The type of recall for drug products most likely to cause serious adverse effects or death is
   a. Class I.
   b. Class II.
   c. Class III.
   d. Class V.

84. Under HIPAA, who *cannot* have access to information about a patient's prescription?
   a. the patient
   b. the pharmacist & support staff
   c. the physician/prescriber and support staff
   d. the pharmaceutical companies or their representatives

85. Under the Combat Methamphetamine Epidemic Act, what is the maximum amount of pseudoephedrine that can be sold per month to an individual?
   a. 3.6 g
   b. 7.5 g
   c. 10 g
   d. 20 g

86. Warfarin is a common
   a. thrombolytic.
   b. anticoagulant.
   c. vasopressor.
   d. vasodilator.

87. What is the cost for 60 tablets of a drug if the cost for 100 tablets is $75.00?
   a. $39.30
   b. $43.66
   c. $45
   d. $48.46

88. Which type of mortar and pestle is recommended for mixing liquids and semisolids?
   a. wedgwood
   b. porcelin
   c. glass
   d. earthenware

89. When compounding parenterals, multi-dose vials
   a. can be reused within 24 hours if they are refrigerated.
   b. can be used within 48 hours if they are refrigerated.
   c. do not contain preservatives.
   d. contain preservatives.

90. What size insulin syringe is needed to deliver a dose of 60 units?
   a. 0.3 ml
   b. 0.5 ml
   c. 1 ml
   d. 2 ml

91. Irrigation solutions are administered
   a. through a filter needle.
   b. through a special administration set.
   c. orally.
   d. by pouring from a bottle.

92. Which class of drugs is used to treated elevated blood lipids?
   a. keratolytics
   b. anthelmintics
   c. antihyperlipidemics
   d. antihistamines

93. Which DAW code should be entered if a physician has ordered Coumadin DAW.?
   a. 0
   b. 1
   c. 2
   d. 3

94. Which drug does not require child resistant packaging according to the Poison Prevention Packaging Act?
   a. nitroglycerin sublingual tablets
   b. isosorbide dinitrate oral tablets
   c. nitroglycerin sustained release capsules
   d. isosorbide mononitrate oral tablets

95. If a laminar flow hood is turned off between aseptic processing sessions, how long should it run before it is used again?
   a. does not matter
   b. at least 15 minutes
   c. at least 30 minutes
   d. it should never be turned off

96. Which drug is an NSAID?
   a. bumetanide
   b. nabumetone
   c. doxazosin
   d. meclizine

97. Which information is not required by federal law on a prescription label?
   a. date
   b. patient's name
   c. prescriber's name
   d. national drug code

98. Which medication is ordered using DEA Form 222?
   a. alprazolam
   b. phenobarbital
   c. diazepam
   d. morphine sulfate

99. Which of the following drugs is a controlled substance?
   a. phenobarbital
   b. carbamazepine
   c. imipramine
   d. furosemide

100. Which of the following drugs is considered a diuretic?
   a. furosemide
   b. lovastatin
   c. hydroxyzine
   d. hydralazine

101. Which of the following drugs is considered an analgesic?
   a. tramadol
   b. phenelzine
   c. lidocaine
   d. diazepam

102. Which of the following drugs is NOT an antihistamine?
   a. diphenhydramine
   b. paroxetine
   c. desloratadine
   d. cetirizine

103. Which of the following medications does not require ordering with DEA Form 222?
   a. Percodan®
   b. Percocet®
   c. Codeine
   d. Stadol®

104. When using the laminar flow hood, a technician should work inside the hood at least
   a. two inches.
   b. four inches.
   c. six inches.
   d. eight inches.

105. While preparing a prescription, a bottle of finasteride is spilled on the floor and some tablets are broken. Who should stay away from the spill area?
    a. males with BPH
    b. females in menopause
    c. females who are or may become pregnant
    d. males with hypertension

106. Who is authorized to sign a DEA Form 222 order form?
    a. pharmacy technicians
    b. licensed pharmacists
    c. individuals with power of attorney
    d. pharmacy managers

107. You are preparing a prescription for Patanol®. Where in the pharmacy should you look for the drug?
    a. ophthalmics and otics
    b. tablets and capsules
    c. creams and ointments
    d. refrigerator

108. You are putting away an order from a wholesaler and notice the packages in one order crate are floating in water. The pharmacist tells you that the medications in that crate cannot be dispensed and must be destroyed or returned to the wholesaler. These drugs cannot be dispensed because they are
    a. adulterated.
    b. misbranded.
    c. exempt.
    d. recycled.

109. Which route of administration is least likely to give a systemic effect?
    a. oral
    b. sublingual
    c. rectal
    d. intradermal

110. Zostavax® should be stored at 5°F or colder. What temperature is this in degrees C?
    a. 0°
    b. -5°
    c. -10°
    d. -15°

ExCPT Practice Exam

Use this space to make notes of what you may still need to study after having scored your exam.

CALCULATIONS PRACTICE EXAM

The following 50 multiple choice problems provide you with extra practice with pharmacy calculations before taking a national certification exam. There are four possible answers for each problem, with only one answer being the most correct. Similar to the questions in the certification exams, many of the problems in the Calculations Practice Exam can be solved using techniques that are included in this workbook; however, others require knowledge gained from practice as a technician. Answers for all questions can be found on page 264.

Pharmacy calculations must be carefully done with 100% accuracy. Therefore, you should practice doing calculations using a systematic approach for problem solving and always double-check your work.

Answers are on page 264.

1. You are filling a prescription that reads: Amoxicillin 125 mg/5 ml, Sig 1 tsp t.i.d. Dispense 150 ml. How many milliliters should the patient take each day?
   a. 5 ml
   b. 10 ml
   c. 15 ml
   d. 20 ml

2. You are filling a prescription that reads: EES® 200, Sig 1 tsp t.i.d. Dispense 150 ml. How many days should this prescription last?
   a. 5 days
   b. 7 days
   c. 10 days
   d. 14 days

3. A compounded prescription calls for 600 g of white petrolatum. How many 1 lb. jars should you obtain so there is enough to prepare this prescription?
   a. 1 jar
   b. 2 jars
   c. 3 jars
   d. 4 jars

4. Each tablet of Tylenol® #3 has 30 mg of codeine. How many grains of codeine are in each tablet of Tylenol® #3?
   a. 1/2 grain
   b. 1 grain
   c. 2 grains
   d. 3 grains

5. One form of influenza vaccine, the Live Attenuated Intranasal Vaccine, must be stored at -15°C. What is this temperature in degrees F?
   a. 5°F
   b. -5°F
   c. 27°F
   d. -27°F

6. The lead pharmacy technician must reorder billing forms when 80% of the case has been used. A full case of billing forms contains 20 packages of forms. How many packages of forms should be remaining in the case when it's time to reorder?
   a. 16 packages
   b. 12 packages
   c. 8 packages
   d. 4 packages

7. In reconstituting a liquid antibiotic, 90 ml of distilled water should be used. If 1/3 of the water should be added first to moisten the powder, how much water should be added to moisten the powder?
   a. 45 ml
   b. 60 ml
   c. 15 ml
   d. 30 ml

8. How many capsules of clindamycin hydrochloride should be used to prepare 30 ml of the following preparation, if each capsule contains 150 mg of clindamycin hydrochloride?

   clindamycin hydrochloride   600 mg
      70% isopropyl alcohol   qs ad 60 ml
   a. 4 capsules
   b. 2 capsules
   c. 10 capsules
   d. 20 capsules

9. A prescription is written for ibuprofen 10% cream. How much ibuprofen is needed to make 20 g of the cream?
   a. 400 mg
   b. 200 mg
   c. 2 g
   d. 4 g

CALCULATIONS PRACTICE EXAM

10. You are entering a prescription for an albuterol inhaler that delivers 90 mcg per actuation. If each container delivers 200 actuations and each dose is two actuations, how many mg are delivered in each dose?
    a. 180 mg
    b. 90 mg
    c. 0.18 mg
    d. 0.09 mg

11. What is the days supply for a Z-Pak® that contains six azithromycin 250 mg tablets, with directions of 500 mg on the first day, followed by 250 mg once daily until gone?
    a. 3
    b. 5
    c. 4
    d. 6

12. What is the day's supply for metronidazole vaginal gel 70 g, Sig 5 g twice daily?
    a. 5 days
    b. 7 days
    c. 10 days
    d. 14 days

13. What is the days supply for Humulin® N insulin 20 ml, if the dose is 40 U daily?
    a. 100 days
    b. 30 days
    c. 60 days
    d. 50 days

14. How much change should be given to a patient who gives you $50 to pay for 3 prescriptions if the patient's prescription plan has a $10 co-pay?
    a. $20
    b. $10
    c. $40
    d. $30

15. What is the gross profit for a prescription if the selling price is $73.14, the acquisition cost is $52.10, and the AWP is $65.12?
    a. $21.04
    b. $8.02
    c. $13.02
    d. $73.14

16. A prescription has been written for Prevacid® 30 mg #100, Sig i cap qd, 2 refills; however, the patient's insurance benefit has a 34-day supply limit. If the original prescription is filled for 34 capsules, how many refills of 34 would be available?
    a. 6 refills of 34
    b. 8 refills of 34
    c. 5 refills of 34
    d. 7 refills of 34

17. You are preparing a prescription for Synthroid® 0.1 mg tablets. How many micrograms are in each tablet?
    a. 0.1 mg
    b. 0.1 mcg
    c. 100 mg
    d. 100 mcg

18. You are entering a prescription for timolol 0.25% ophthalmic solution 5 ml, Sig i gtt o.u. twice daily. How many days should this bottle last if the dropper delivers 20 drops of timolol 0.25% ophthalmic solution per ml?
    a. 10 days
    b. 50 days
    c. 12.5 days
    d. 25 days

19. The dose of a drug is 250 micrograms per kg of body weight. What dose should be given to a child that weighs 55 lbs?
    a. 6.25 micrograms
    b. 6.25 mg
    c. 12.5 mg
    d. 12.5 micrograms

20. A physician has ordered 15 ml of Brand X antacid suspension to be taken four times daily. How many days will a 12 oz. bottle last?
a. 6 days
b. 12 days
c. 3 days
d. 10 days

21. How many mcg of digoxin are in 0.4 ml of digoxin solution if the strength of the digoxin solution is 50 mcg per ml?
a. 20 mcg
b. 125 mcg
c. 0.02 mcg
d. 12.5 mcg

22. You are filling a prescription for gentamicin 80 mg. How much gentamicin solution should be measured from a 2 ml vial of gentamicin 40 mg/ml?
a. 2 ml
b. 1 ml
c. 0.8 ml
d. 1.6 ml

23. 45 units of Humulin® R insulin are to be added to a TPN bag. How much Humulin R (U-100) is needed?
a. 45 microliters
b. 0.45 ml
c. 4.5 ml
d. 0.45 microliters

24. How much potassium chloride solution (2 mEq/ml) should be added to a 1 liter IV bag if 25 mEq of potassium chloride is needed?
a. 25 ml
b. 0.25 ml
c. 12.5 ml
d. 50 ml

25. How much sodium chloride is in 25 ml of normal saline?
a. 225 g
b. 225 mcg
c. 225 mg
d. 2.25 g

26. A drug is in a vial that contains 500 mg of the drug in 2 ml of solution. What is the percent strength of this drug?
a. 2.5%
b. 25%
c. 10%
d. 5%

27. You have dissolved 20 g of drug in 500 ml of solution. What is the percent strength of the resulting solution?
a. 0.4%
b. 4%
c. 0.2%
d. 2%

28. How many capsules are needed to prepare 30 ml of 1% clindamycin hydrochloride solution if each capsule contains 150 mg of clindamycin hydrochloride?
a. 4 capsules
b. 3 capsules
c. 1 capsule
d. 2 capsules

29. How much 1% lidocaine is needed to fill an order for 30 mg of lidocaine?
a. 0.3 ml
b. 3 ml
c. 3 microliters
d. 0.03 ml

30. What is the percent strength of a 1:100 solution?
a. 10%
b. 1%
c. 0.01%
d. 0.1%

CALCULATIONS PRACTICE EXAM

31. How much gentian violet is needed to prepare 100 ml of a 1:10,000 solution of gentian violet?
    a. 0.01 mg
    b. 10 g
    c. 10 mg
    d. 10 mcg

32. How much vancomycin should be given per dose for a child that weighs 32 lbs if the dose is 10 mg/kg q6h IV?
    a. 582 mg
    b. 145 mg
    c. 0.69 mg
    d. 704 mg

33. A patient is to receive 100 mg/kg/day of ampicillin. What is the total daily dose for a patient that weighs 40 lbs?
    a. 182 mg
    b. 1.8 g
    c. 18.2 g
    d. 0.182 g

34. If 250 mg of penicillin VK is equivalent to 400,000 Units of penicillin, how many Units of penicillin are in 1 mg of penicillin VK?
    a. 1,600 U
    b. 1,600 MU
    c. 16 MU
    d. 1.6 U

35. A nomogram has been used to determine a patient's BSA is 1.95. If the dose of a drug is 40 mg/sq meter, how much drug should be administered per dose?
    a. 780 mg
    b. 7.8 g
    c. 78 mg
    d. 7.8 mg

36. A 500 ml IV bag is administered over 4 hours. What is the infusion rate?
    a. 125 ml/min
    b. 100 ml/min
    c. 100 ml/hr
    d. 125 ml/hr

37. A 500 ml IV bag is infused at a rate of 100 ml/hr. How long will this bag last?
    a. 2.5 hours
    b. 2 hours
    c. 10 hours
    d. 5 hours

38. An IV has been running at 80 ml/hr for 5 hours and 20 minutes. How much solution has the patient received?
    a. 427 ml
    b. 40 ml
    c. 400 ml
    d. 43 ml

39. An IV is set to deliver 30 drops/min. What is the infusion rate in ml/hr if there are 15 drops/ml?
    a. 30 ml/hr
    b. 40 ml/hr
    c. 120 ml/hr
    d. 270 ml/hr

40. How many ml of a 20% solution should be added to 50 ml of a 40% solution to obtain a 25% solution?
    a. 50 ml
    b. 100 ml
    c. 150 ml
    d. 200 ml

41. How many teaspoons equal 20 ml?
    a. 5
    b. 6
    c. 4
    d. 2

42. If a prescription reads: Aspirin 5 gr, dispense 100 tablets, 1 tablet q 4-6h prn headache, what is the dose in milligrams?
    a. 650
    b. 750
    c. 100
    d. 325

43. How many gallons of Coca Cola™ fountain syrup are needed to package 150 bottles of 120 ml per bottle?
    a. 3
    b. 4
    c. 5
    d. 6

44. If a prescription reads: Amoxicillin 250 mg/5 ml, dispense 150 ml, 375 mg t.i.d. x 5d, what is the dose in household units?
    a. 1 teaspoonful
    b. 1 tablespoonful
    c. 1.5 teaspoonful
    d. 1.5 tablespoonful

45. How many ml are in 2 liters of normal saline?
    a. 200
    b. 2,000
    c. 0.2
    d. 0.002

46. How many ml of KCl 2 mEq/ml are needed if the dose is 30 mEq?
    a. 5
    b. 10
    c. 15
    d. 30

47. How many ml of 25% dextrose are needed to prepare 500 ml of 40% dextrose if you are to prepare 40% dextrose from 25% dextrose and 60% dextrose?
    a. 214 ml
    b. 286 ml
    c. 200 ml
    d. 300 ml

48. If 1 liter is infused over 8 hours, what is the rate of infusion in ml/hr?
    a. 62.5
    b. 100
    c. 125
    d. 250

49. A patient weighs 121 pounds. What is the patient's weight in kg?
    a. 37
    b. 45
    c. 55
    d. 68

50. How many grams of sodium bicarbonate are needed to make 400 ml of a 1:1,000 w/v solution?
    a. 0.2
    b. 0.4
    c. 0.8
    d. 1

ANSWERS TO PRACTICE EXAMS

PTCE PRACTICE EXAM

#	Ans	#	Ans	#	Ans
1.	b	31.	a	61.	d
2.	d	32.	c	62.	d
3.	a	33.	a	63.	c
4.	c	34.	a	64.	a
5.	a	35.	b	65.	b
6.	c	36.	d	66.	b
7.	d	37.	a	67.	c
8.	c	38.	d	68.	b
9.	b	39.	b	69.	c
10.	c	40.	c	70.	b
11.	c	41.	b	71.	b
12.	d	42.	a	72.	a
13.	d	43.	c	73.	d
14.	b	44.	b	74.	c
15.	c	45.	c	75.	b
16.	a	46.	a	76.	a
17.	d	47.	c	77.	b
18.	c	48.	b	78.	b
19.	a	49.	c	79.	d
20.	a	50.	a	80.	a
21.	a	51.	b	81.	b
22.	d	52.	b	82.	a
23.	c	53.	c	83.	a
24.	b	54.	b	84.	c
25.	a	55.	b	85.	b
26.	a	56.	c	86.	b
27.	c	57.	c	87.	c
28.	c	58.	d	88.	b
29.	c	59.	c	89.	d
30.	c	60.	c	90.	d

ExCPT PRACTICE EXAM

#	Ans	#	Ans	#	Ans
1.	d	38.	b	75.	a
2.	b	39.	c	76.	c
3.	c	40.	a	77.	b
4.	c	41.	a	78.	b
5.	b	42.	c	79.	b
6.	a	43.	d	80.	a
7.	b	44.	b	81.	b
8.	b	45.	a	82.	d
9.	a	46.	b	83.	a
10.	d	47.	b	84.	d
11.	d	48.	b	85.	b
12.	a	49.	a	86.	b
13.	a	50.	b	87.	c
14.	a	51.	a	88.	c
15.	b	52.	c	89.	d
16.	b	53.	c	90.	c
17.	d	54.	b	91.	d
18.	c	55.	b	92.	c
19.	c	56.	c	93.	b
20.	d	57.	c	94.	a
21.	b	58.	a	95.	d
22.	c	59.	c	96.	b
23.	c	60.	d	97.	d
24.	d	61.	a	98.	d
25.	d	62.	c	99.	a
26.	d	63.	a	100.	a
27.	b	64.	d	101.	a
28.	d	65.	d	102.	b
29.	c	66.	d	103.	d
30.	b	67.	d	104.	a
31.	d	68.	a	105.	c
32.	a	69.	a	106.	c
33.	c	70.	a	107.	a
34.	b	71.	b	108.	a
35.	d	72.	b	109.	d
36.	b	73.	a	110.	d
37.	d	74.	d		

CALCULATIONS PRACTICE EXAM

#	Ans	#	Ans
1.	c	26.	b
2.	c	27.	b
3.	b	28.	d
4.	a	29.	b
5.	a	30.	b
6.	d	31.	c
7.	d	32.	b
8.	b	33.	b
9.	c	34.	a
10.	c	35.	c
11.	b	36.	d
12.	b	37.	d
13.	d	38.	a
14.	a	39.	c
15.	a	40.	c
16.	d	41.	c
17.	d	42.	d
18.	d	43.	c
19.	b	44.	c
20.	a	45.	b
21.	a	46.	c
22.	a	47.	b
23.	b	48.	c
24.	c	49.	c
25.	c	50.	b

ANSWERS TO CHAPTER EXERCISES AND PROBLEMS

CHAPTER 1

p.4
1. cocaine
2. salicylic acid
3. quinine
4. human genome
5. panacea
6. pharmacology
7. penicillin
8. MTM services
9. antitoxin
10. antibiotic
11. hormones
12. pharmacognosy
13. Medicare Modernization Act
14. formularies
15. synthetic

p.5
1. F
2. T
3. T
4. F
5. T
6. T
7. F
8. F
9. T
10. F

p.6
1. c
2. d
3. b
4. a
5. c
6. d
7. b
8. a
9. b
10. c

CHAPTER 2

p.15
1. scope of practice
2. personal inventory
3. confidentiality
4. patient welfare
5. PTCE
6. certification
7. technicians
8. professionals
9. pharmacist
10. performance review
11. ASHP
12. ExCPT
13. continuing education
14. HIPAA

p.16
1. T
2. F
3. F
4. T
5. T
6. F
7. F
8. T
9. T
10. F

p.17
1. b
2. d
3. c
4. a
5. b
6. d
7. c
8. b
9. c
10. c

CHAPTER 3

p.23
1. DEA number
2. injunction
3. placebo
4. adverse effect
5. legend drug
6. negligence
7. pediatric
8. product labeling
9. dual marketing status
10. liability
11. recall
12. Controlled Substances Act
13. NDC
14. OTC drugs

p.24
1. F
2. T
3. T
4. T
5. T
6. F
7. T
8. T
9. F
10. T

p.25
1. Schedule II
2. Schedule III
3. Class III recall
4. Schedule V
5. Class II recall
6. Schedule I
7. Schedule IV
8. Class I recall

p.26
1. tight, light resistant
2. Qualitest Pharmaceuticals
3. Endocet®
4. oxycodone and acetaminophen
5. tablets
6. oxycodone hydrochloride and acetaminophen
7. C-II
8. room temperature
9. 06/2014

p.27
1. d
2. a
3. d
4. b
5. a
6. b
7. d
8. c

ANSWERS TO CHAPTER EXERCISES AND PROBLEMS

9. d
10. a

CHAPTER 4

p. 35

1. hypertension
2. fibromyalgia
3. encephalitis
4. euthyroid
5. cardiomyopathy
6. parathyroid
7. arthritis
8. hyperglycemia
9. aphagia
10. dyspepsia
11. colitis
12. hepatitis
13. hernia
14. dysuria
15. subcutaneous
16. transdermal
17. hematoma
18. hemophilia
19. lymphoma
20. epidermis
21. tendinitis
22. neuralgia
23. patchyderm
24. endometriosis
25. vasectomy
26. prostatolith
27. bronchitis
28. pulmonary
29. cystitis
30. lordosis
31. blepharitis

p.36

1. a
2. b
3. c
4. d
5. c
6. d
7. b
8. c
9. c

10. b
11. c
12. a
13. b

CHAPTER 5

p.41

1. of each
2. before meals
3. right ear
4. morning
5. left ear
6. each ear
7. water
8. body surface area
9. twice a day
10. with
11. capsules
12. per gastric button
13. dilute
14. dispense
15. per nasogastric tube
16. dextrose 5% in water
17. elixir
18. fluid
19. gram
20. drop
21. hour
22. at bedtime
23. intramuscular
24. intravenous
25. intravenous push
26. no refill
27. intravenous piggyback
28. liter
29. left
30. liquid
31. microgram
32. milliequivalent
33. milligram
34. milliliter
35. no refill
36. normal saline
37. right eye
38. left eye
39. each eye
40. after meals

41. by nebulizer
42. by mouth
43. as needed
44. every
45. every 4 hours
46. every 6 hours
47. four times a day
48. a sufficient quantity
49. add sufficient quantity to make
50. without
51. subcutaneously
52. one-half
53. write, label
54. immediately
55. suppository
56. syrup
57. three times a day
58. tablets
59. tablespoon
60. topically
61. teaspoon
62. ointment
63. as directed

p.44
Prozac® Prescription

1. Prozac®
2. 20 mg
3. capsules
4. by mouth
5. one capsule every day
6. 2
7. no

Triamcinolone Prescription

1. 0.1%
2. twice daily

p.45
Protonix® Prescription

1. 30
2. 1

Atrovent® HFA/Flovent® HFA Prescription

1. Each inhaler would last 33 days if two puffs per

ANSWERS TO CHAPTER EXERCISES AND PROBLEMS

dose are used or 22 days if three puffs per dose are used. We would normally enter 22 days for the days supply on a prescription of this type.
2. 30 days

p.46
Synthroid® Prescription
1. DAW

Miacalcin® Prescription
1. Miacalcin® is a nasal spray. The directions read "one inhalation every day" and the patient should administer the medication to alternate nostrils, meaning that the patient should not use the same nostril two days in a row.

p.47
Metrogel® Prescription
1. A 70 gram tube should be dispensed
2. "per vagina"

Premarin®/Provera® Prescription
1. Since the patient takes the medication for 21 days and off for 7 days, the medication will last 28 days.
2. Since the patient takes the medication for only 5 days in a 28-day cycle, this medication will also last 28 days.

p.48
Ortho Novum® 777 Prescription
1. 7 (1 original fill plus 6 refills)

Bactrim® DS Prescription
1. sulfa allergy

p.49
Cefadroxil Prescription
1. Take one teaspoonful twice daily for 10 days.

Amoxicillin, Biaxin®, and Aciphex® Prescription
1. 28
2. 14
3. 14

p.50
1. pneumonia, dehydration
2. penicillin allergy
3. every four hours by mouth
4. 2200 and 600 orders
5. 500 mg by mouth, every 12 hours
6. by mouth, each day

p.51
1. Lopressor® 50 mg, Hydrochlorothiazide 25 mg, and Sonata® 5 mg
2. one at bedtime as needed

p.52
Mary Smith Physician Order
1. docusate sodium 100 mg
2. Metamucil®

Andrew Smith Physician Order
1. This medication should be administered as soon as possible.
2. intramuscular injection

p.53
Steve Smith Physician Order
1. 100 cc per hour
2. hydrochlorothizide 25 mg and Diovan® 80 mg

Barbara Smith Physician Order
1. glyburide 5 mg and

Ambien® 5 mg
2. Ambien® 5 mg

p.54
1. Schedule II drugs
2. extemporaneous compounding
3. HIPAA
4. prescription origin code
5. auxiliary label
6. medication order
7. look-alikes
8. Rx
9. DAW
10. PHI
11. unit dose labels
12. DUR
13. NPI
14. DEA number

p.55
1. T
2. T
3. F
4. T
5. F
6. T
7. T
8. F
9. F
10. F

p.56
1. c
2. b
3. a
4. b
5. b
6. a
7. c
8. c
9. c
10. c
11. c
12. a
13. b
14. a
15. c

267

ANSWERS TO CHAPTER EXERCISES AND PROBLEMS

CHAPTER 6

p.60
1. 0.625
2. 0.002
3. 0.2
4. 0.67
5. 0.12
6. 0.385
7. 0.015
8. 70%
9. 75%
10. 150%
11. 25%
12. 4%
13. 80%
14. 2.5%
15. LXVII
16. XXIX
17. XLI
18. CVIII
19. VI
20. XCVIII
21. IX
22. 19
23. 103
24. 1900
25. 1 ½
26. 20
27. 54

p.61
1. 30
2. 21
3. 3.5
4. 600 mg
5. 300 ml

p.64-65
6. 20 ml
7. 200 ml
8. 7.2 ml
9. 1 ml/min
10. 1.4
11. 180 ml
12. 357 ml of 70% dextrose and 643 ml of sterile water
13. 286 ml 70% dextrose and 714 ml sterile water

14. 250 ml 50% dextrose and 250 ml sterile water

p. 66
1. Aminosyn® 500 ml
2. dextrose 400 ml
3. KCl 12 ml
4. MVI 5 ml
5. NaCl 5.45 ml
6. sterile water 77.55 ml

CHAPTER 7

p.71
1. F
2. T
3. F
4. T
5. F
6. T
7. T
8. T
9. T
10. T

p.72
1. local effect
2. systemic effect
3. buffer system
4. bulk powders
5. buccal
6. hydrates
7. enteric coated
8. water soluble
9. sublingual
10. pH
11. parenteral
12. necrosis
13. ophthalmic
14. intradermal injections
15. intravenous sites
16. hemorrhoid
17. suspensions
18. lacrimal canalicula
19. transcorneal transport
20. emulsion
21. intramuscular injection

22. syringeability
23. aqueous
24. alveoli
25. wheal
26. lacrimal gland
27. disintegration
28. colloids
29. Z-tract injection
30. nasal mucosa
31. atomizer
32. nasal inhaler
33. injectability
34. metered dose inhalers
35. percutaneous absorption
36. dissolution
37. syrups
38. sterile
39. Toxic Shock Syndrome
40. diluent
41. IUD

p.74
1. intraocular
2. intranasal
3. sublingual or oral
4. inhalation
5. peroral
6. intravenous
7. vaginal
8. subcutaneous
9. intramuscular

p. 75, Routes of Administration
1. intradermal
2. subcutaneous
3. intravenous
4. intramuscular

Intramuscular Administration Sites
1. a
2. d
3. b
4. e

ANSWERS TO CHAPTER EXERCISES AND PROBLEMS

5.   c

p.76
1.   c
2.   a
3.   b
4.   c
5.   c
6.   b
7.   b
8.   a
9.   a
10. c
11. a
12. d
13. a
14. d

CHAPTER 8

p.83
1.   F
2.   T
3.   T
4.   T
5.   T
6.   F
7.   F
8.   F
9.   F
10. T
11. F
12. T

p.88
1.   extemporaneous compounding
2.   USP–NF Chapter <795>
3.   USP–NF Chapter <797>
4.   calibrate
5.   volumetric
6.   compounding record
7.   meniscus
8.   trituration
9.   levigation
10. geometric dilution
11. sieves
12. spatulation

13. formulation record
14. aliquot
15. syrup
16. sensitivity
17. flocculating agents
18. thickening agent
19. USP–NF grade
20. ointment
21. emulsifier
22. emulsion
23. nonaqueous solutions
24. cream
25. hydrophilic emulsifier
26. lipophilic emulsifier
27. primary emulsion
28. mucilage
29. aqueous solutions
30. immiscible
31. pipets

p.90
1.   a
2.   b
3.   a
4.   c
5.   b
6.   d
7.   b
8.   b
9.   a
10. a
11. a
12. d
13. a
14. b
15. b
16. c

CHAPTER 9

p.95
1.   F
2.   T
3.   T
4.   F
5.   T
6.   F

p.102
1.   aseptic techniques
2.   pyrogens
3.   Flashball
4.   isotonic
5.   hypertonic
6.   hypotonic
7.   flow rate
8.   heparin lock
9.   piggybacks
10. clean rooms
11. admixture
12. buffer capacity
13. diluent
14. anhydrous
15. bevel
16. gauge
17. lumen
18. coring
19. membrane filter
20. depth filter
21. final filter
22. laminar flow
23. HEPA filter
24. biological safety cabinets
25. irrigation solution
26. shaft
27. sharps
28. ions
29. osmotic pressure
30. valence
31. osmosis
32. peritoneal dialysis solution
33. TPN solution
34. zone of turbulence
35. dialysis

p.104
1.   b
2.   c
3.   a
4.   c
5.   b
6.   d
7.   b
8.   c
9.   a
10. b

ANSWERS TO CHAPTER EXERCISES AND PROBLEMS

11. d
12. a
13. c
14. b
15. c
16. c

CHAPTER 10

p.112
1. biopharmaceutics
2. elimination
3. receptor
4. absorption
5. agonists
6. antagonists
7. complexation
8. onset of action
9. duration of action
10. disposition
11. passive diffusion
12. active transport
13. hydrophobic
14. hydrophilic
15. lipoidal
16. gastric emptying time
17. ionized
18. protein binding
19. metabolite
20. enzyme
21. enzyme induction
22. enzyme inhibition
23. first pass metabolism
24. enterohepatic cycling
25. nephron
26. unionized
27. bioavailability
28. bioequivalency
29. pharmaceutical equivalents
30. pharmaceutical alternatives
31. therapeutic equivalents

p.114
1. T
2. T
3. T
4. F
5. F
6. T
7. T
8. F
9. F
10. T
11. F

p.114
1. b
2. a
3. c
4. b
5. a
6. a
7. c
8. d
9. b
10. d
11. a
12. c
13. a
14. c

CHAPTER 11

p.118
1. hypersensitivity
2. anaphylactic shock
3. idiosyncrasy
4. hepatotoxicity
5. nephrotoxicity
6. carcinogenicity
7. teratogenicity
8. potentiation
9. pharmacogenomics
10. enzyme inhibition
11. displacement
12. obstructive jaundice
13. antidote
14. hypothyroidism
15. hyperthyroidism
16. complexation
17. cirrhosis
18. adverse drug reaction

p.119
1. F

2. T
3. T
4. T
5. T
6. T
7. T
8. T
9. T
10. T

p.120
1. d
2. b
3. c
4. b
5. b
6. d
7. a
8. d
9. a
10. b
11. a
12. b
13. b

CHAPTER 12

p.124
1. primary literature
2. tertiary literature
3. *Red Book*
4. Material Safety Data Sheets (MSDS)
5. secondary literature
6. HIPAA
7. *Drug Facts and Comparisons (DFC)*
8. *Physician's Desk Reference (PDR)*
9. *Handbook on Injectable Drugs*
10. *King's Guide to Parenteral Admixtures*
11. Martindale
12. "Orange Book"
13. Internet Service Provider
14. URL

ANSWERS TO CHAPTER EXERCISES AND PROBLEMS

p.125
1. T
2. T
3. T
4. F
5. F
6. T
7. T
8. T
9. F
10. T
11. T

p.126
1. c
2. b
3. d
4. d
5. c
6. a
7. d
8. d
9. c
10. a
11. b
12. a
13. c
14. d

CHAPTER 13

p.130
1. open formulary
2. closed formulary
3. turnover
4. stock bottles
5. perpetual inventory
6. inventory
7. reorder points
8. MSDS
9. therapeutic equivalent
10. purchase order number
11. automated dispensing system
12. unit-dose
13. point-of-use stations

p.131
1. T
2. F
3. T
4. F
5. T
6. F
7. T
8. F
9. F
10. T

p.132
1. b
2. d
3. b
4. a
5. d
6. b
7. a
8. c
9. d
10. b

CHAPTER 14

p.136
1. pharmacy benefit managers
2. online adjudication
3. co-insurance
4. co-pay
5. dual co-pay
6. maximum allowable cost
7. U&C or UCR
8. HMO
9. POS
10. PPO
11. deductible
12. prescription drug benefit cards
13. CPT code
14. Medicare
15. Medicaid
16. CMS 1500 form
17. workers' compensation
18. patient assistance programs

19. coordination of benefits

p.137
1. F
2. T
3. T
4. T
5. T
6. T
7. F
8. T

p.138
1. b
2. a
3. c
4. a
5. d
6. a
7. d
8. c
9. b
10. a

CHAPTER 15

p.145
1. pharmacist immunization programs
2. interpersonal skills
3. walk-in clinics
4. transaction windows
5. prescription counter
6. pharmacist's judgement
7. patient profile
8. signature log
9. markup
10. safety caps
11. counting tray
12. shelf stickers
13. disease state management programs
14. auxiliary labels
15. unit price

p.146
1. T
2. T

ANSWERS TO CHAPTER EXERCISES AND PROBLEMS

3. T
4. F
5. F
6. T
7. T
8. T
9. T
10. F
11. T

p.147
1. b
2. a
3. c
4. c
5. a
6. a
7. c
8. c
9. b
10. a

CHAPTER 16

p.157-158
1. reconstitute
2. CPOE
3. electronic medical record
4. unit dose
5. standing order
6. PRN order
7. STAT order
8. medication administration record (MAR)
9. code cart
10. central pharmacy
11. inpatient pharmacy
12. pharmacy satellite
13. nurse's station
14. clean rooms
15. outpatient pharmacy
16. policy and procedure manual
17. unit inspection

p.158
1. F
2. F
3. T
4. T
5. F
6. T
7. T

p.159
1. b
2. b
3. d
4. a
5. d
6. a
7. d
8. c
9. c
10. b
11. b
12. b

CHAPTER 17

p.161
1. F
2. T
3. F
4. T
5. F
6. F
7. T
8. T

p.162
1. d
2. d
3. d
4. a
5. a
6. c
7. d
8. c
9. a
10. b

CHAPTER 18

p.172
1. Respiratory Agent
2. Psychotropic Agent
3. Cardiovascular Agent
4. Anti-infective
5. Anti-infective
6. Cardiovascular Agent
7. Cardiovascular Agent
8. Anti-infective
9. Musculoskeletal Agent
10. Cardiovascular Agent
11. Anti-infective
12. Respiratory Agent
13. Anti-infective
14. Psychotropic agent
15. Anti-infective
16. Cardiovascular Agent
17. Dermatological Agent
18. Cardiovascular Agent
19. Gastrointestinal Agent
20. Cardiovascular Agent
21. Psychotropic Agent
22. Anti-infective Agent
23. Respiratory Agent
24. Cardiovascular Agent
25. Antidiabetic
26. Cardiovascular Agent
27. Dermatological Agent
28. Analgesic
29. Antidiabetic Agent
30. Gastrointestinal Agent
31. Anti-infective Agent
32. Cardiovascular Agent
33. Gastrointestinal Agent
34. Cardiovascular Agent
35. Cardiovascular Agent
36. Cardiovascular Agent
37. Gastrointestinal Agent
38. Gastrointestinal Agent
39. Electrolytic Agent
40. Anesthetic
41. Psychotropic Agent
42. Dermatological Agent
43. Electrolytic Agent
44. Antineoplastic
45. Analgesic
46. Gastrointestinal Agent

ANSWERS TO CHAPTER EXERCISES AND PROBLEMS

47. Anti-infective
48. Cardiovascular Agent

p.174
Analgesics
1. g
2. a
3. b
4. c
5. f
6. d
7. e

Anti-infectives
1. d
2. c
3. b
4. h
5. g
6. a
7. e
8. f

Cardiovascular Agents
1. a
2. e
3. f
4. b
5. h
6. d
7. c
8. g

p.175
Dermatologicals
1. f
2. h
3. g
4. a
5. c
6. b
7. d
8. e

Gastrointestinal Agents
1. c
2. d
3. g

4. a
5. e
6. h
7. f
8. b

p.176
Hormones & Modifiers: Adrenal corticosteroids
1. a
2. b
3. c
4. d

Hormones & Modifiers: Oral antidiabetics
1. e
2. c
3. b
4. d
5. a

Musculoskeletal Agents
1. b
2. c
3. f
4. d
5. e
6. a

Neurological Agents
1. g
2. e
3. b
4. c
5. a
6. h
7. d
8. f

p.177
Psychotropic Agents
1. a
2. f
3. e
4. g
5. b
6. h

7. d
8. c

Respiratory Agents
1. b
2. d
3. f
4. e
5. c
6. g
7. a

p.178
1. T
2. F
3. F
4. T
5. F
6. T
7. F
8. F
9. T
10. F

1. c
2. d
3. a
4. b
5. b
6. a
7. c
8. c
9. a
10. b
11. a
12. b
13. a
14. c
15. a

KEY CONCEPTS INDEX

Following is an index to the topics found in the Key Concepts sections of this workbook.

absorption 107
abstracting services 122
ACE inhibitors 168
acetaminophen 166
additive effects 117
ADME 107
admixture preparation 161
admixtures 92
age 116
age limitations 135
agonists 106
AHFS Drug Information 122
allergic reactions 117
Alzheimer's disease 169
amber bottle 142
American Drug Index 123
analgesia 166
ancillary areas 148
androgens 169
anemia 169
anion 168
antacids 168
antagonists 106
anthelmintic 167
antianginals 167
antiarrhythmics 167
antibiotic (antimicrobial) 166
anticoagulants 168
antidiarrheals 168
antiemetics 168
antifungal 167
antihistamines 170
antihyperlipidemics 167
antihypertensives 167
antimycobacterial 167
antineoplastic 167
antiprotozoal 167
antipyretic 166
antitussives 170
antiviral 166
aqueous pores 107
aqueous solution 79
arrhythmia 167
aseptic techniques 93
asthma 170
automated filling & dispensing machine/
    system 128, 142, 161
automation 149

auxiliary labels 39, 142
average life span 2
bactericidal 167
bacteriostatic 167
beta blockers 168
biological safety cabinets 93
bioavailability 108
bioequivalency 108
bipolar disorder 170
blind tests 19
blocker 166
blood concentration 106
bronchodilators 170
calcium channel blockers 168
capsules 80
cardiac cycle 167
cardiovascular system 28
cart fill 149
cation 168
central pharmacy 148
certification 9
class A torsion balances 78
chain pharmacy 140
chemotherapy 149
chyme 168
clinical tests 19
close interaction with patients 140
closed formulary 128, 150
co-insurance 134
co-pay 134
cocaine 2
code cart 151
combining vowel 28
common adverse reactions 117
community pharmacy 140
compounding area 141
compression molding 80
computer maintenance 128
computerization 3
computerized physician order entry (CPOE) 150
conjunctivitis 170
consultant pharmacist 161
control classifications 20
Controlled Substances Act (CSA) 18
controlled substance labels 39
controlled substance shipping 129
controlled substances 20, 151
conversions 59

KEY CONCEPTS INDEX

coordination of benefits 135
corticosteroids 169
cost control 3
counseling 140
counting tray 142
DEA number/formula 20
decongestants 170
deductible 134
delivery technician 148
depression 170
dermal formulations 70
dermatological 168
diabetes mellitus 169
diastolic pressure 167
digitalis 2
directions for use 38
discounts 67
disease state management programs 141
disease states 116
dispense as written (DAW) 135
displacement 117
disposition 107
dissociation 168
distribution 107
distributive pharmacist 161
diuretics 168
dose-response curve 106
droppers 79
drug classes/classifications 29, 166
drug-diet interactions 117
drug-drug interactions 117
Drug Enforcement Administration 18
Drug Facts and Comparisons (DFC) 122
Durham-Humphrey Amendment 18
ear 29
electrolytes 168
electrocardiogram (EKG or ECG) 167
electronic or analytical balances 78
electronic medical records 150
elimination 107
embolism 167
emergency kits 161
emphysema 170
employment opportunities 8
emulsifiers 80
emulsion 79
endocrine system 28, 169
enterohepatic cycling 108

enzyme(s) 108, 168
enzyme induction 108, 117
enzyme inhibition 108, 117
epilepsy 170
errors 8
estrogen 169
excretion 108
extemporaneous compounding 78
extracellular fluids 168
eyes 29
federal regulations 140
female reproductive system 29
fibrin 169
filing 141
Fillmaster® 142
filters 93
final check by pharmacist 142
first-pass metabolism 108
flocculating agents 79
flow rate 63, 93
Food and Drug Act of 1906 18
Food and Drug Administration 18
Food, Drug, and Cosmetic (FDC) Act 18
food store pharmacies 140
formulary 149
formulations 68
freshness 129
front counter 148
fusion molding 80
gastric emptying 107
gastrointestinal (GI) tract 28
gastrointestinal action 68
generics 19
genetics 19, 116
geometric dilution 79
germ theory 2
glaucoma 170
glomerular filtration 108
glucagon 169
good customer service 141
gout 169
graduated cylinders 78
half-life 107
Handbook on Injectable Drugs 123
Health Insurance Portability and
        Accountability Act (HIPAA) 9, 19, 39
hematological agents 169
hemostatic drugs 169

KEY CONCEPTS INDEX

herbal medicine 2
HMO (health maintenance organization) 134
home care 160
home infusion 160
homeostasis 166
hormones 169
Human Genome Project 3
human variability 116
hydrophilic drugs 107
hydrophobic drugs 107
hyperthyroidism 169
hypnotics 170
hypothyroidism 169
independent pharmacies 140
infusion 69
infusion pumps 160
inhalation formulations 70
institutional settings 39
insulin 3, 169
integumentary system 28, 168
Internet 123
interpersonal skills 140
interstitial fluid 168
intracellular fluids 168
intradermal injections 70
intramuscular injections 69
intranasal formulations 70
intravenous formulations 69
intravenous sites 69
inventory 128
inventory control 149
investigational drug service 149
ions 168
IV admixtures 151
IV/clean room 149
IV emulsions 69
IV fat emulsions 92
job responsibilities 8
judgment questions 38
Kefauver-Harris Amendments 18
King's Guide to Parenteral Admixtures 123
label 38
labels and product labeling 19
laminar flow hood 93
laxatives 169
levigation 79
liability 20
local and systemic effects 68

local anesthetics 166
long-term care 161
lymphatic system 28
lymphocyte 167
mail order pharmacy 160
maintenance medications 135
maintenance therapy 160
male reproductive system 29
markup 67, 142
Martindale 122
mass merchandiser pharmacies 140
Material Safety Data Sheets (MSDSs) 122, 129
math skills 9
maximum allowable cost (MAC) 134
Medicaid 135
Medicare 135
medication administration record 150
medication order form 150
medication orders 39
medicine droppers 93
medullary paralysis 166
MedWatch 20
meniscus 79
Merck Index 122
metabolism 108
metabolite 108
metastasis 167
migraine headaches 170
milliequivalent 63
mimetic 166
minimum effective concentration (MEC) 106
minimum toxic concentration (MTC) 106
mobile device 123
monitoring drug therapy 149
mortar and pestle 79
muscular system 28
mydriatics 170
myocardium 167
narcotic analgesics 166
narcotics/controlled substances 149
National Drug Code (NDC) number 19
needle sizes 93
negligence 20
neoplasm 167
nervous system 29
neurotransmitter 166
new drugs 19
nonaqueous solutions 79

KEY CONCEPTS INDEX

non-formulary 150
NSAIDs 166
nuclear pharmacy 161
nurse's station 148
objective of drug therapy 106
oil-in-water (o/w) 80
ointments and creams 80
Omnibus Budget Reconciliation Act (OBRA) 18
online adjudication 135
online billing 38, 141
online drugstores 160
online ordering 129
open formulary 128
ophthalmic agents 170
ophthalmic formulations 70, 179
opiate-type analgesics 166
oral administration 68
oral formulations 68
"Orange Book" 123
order processing 149
osteoarthritis 169
OTC products 142
outpatient pharmacy 149
parenteral administration 69
parenteral solutions 92
Parkinson's disease 169
passive diffusion 107
patent protection 19
patient care units 148
patient education 161
patient identification number 135
patient profile 141
patient-specific trays 150
pediatric doses 62
penicillin 3
percents and solutions 62
peristalsis 168
peritoneal dialysis solutions 93
perpetual inventory 128
pharmaceutical alternatives 108
pharmaceutical equivalents 108
pharmacist check 38
pharmacist counseling 8
pharmacist education and training 3
pharmacist review 160
pharmacist supervision 148
pharmacist's judgement 141
pharmacogenetics 116

pharmacology 2
pharmacy benefit manager (PBM) 134
pharmacy technician supervisor 149
Physician's Desk Reference (PDR) 122
piggybacks 93
placebos 19
point-of-sale (POS) system 128
point-of-service (POS) 135
point-of-use stations 129
Poison Prevention Packaging Act 18
policy and procedures manual 151
polio vaccine 2
polyethylene glycols (PEGs) 80
prefix 28
preferred provider organization (PPO) 135
pregnancy 116
prepacking 150
preparation 38
prescription 38
prescription bins or shelves 141
prescription counter 141
prescription drug benefit cards 134
prescription drug labels 19
prescription intake 141
prescription origin code 38
prescription verification 38
primary literature 122
PRN order 150
progesterone 169
properties 92
protected health information (PHI) 39
protein binding 107
pumps 93
quality assurance 78, 149
quality control 79
quinine 2
ratio and proportion 58
recalls 20
receptors 106
reconstitute 142
rectal administration 69
Red Book 123
refills 135, 141
regulation 160
rejected claims 135
remission 167
reorder points 128
respiratory system 29

KEY CONCEPTS INDEX

retail math 67
rheumatoid arthritis 169
risks of approved drugs 20
Roman numerals 60
root word 28
route of administration 68
safety caps 141
salicylates 166
satellite pharmacy 148
Schedule II substances 128
scanning a hard copy prescription 141
scope of practice 8
search engine 123
secondary literature 122
sedatives 170
selective action 107
sensitivity 78
separation and removal of trash 142
serum glucose 169
sharps container 151
shelf stickers 142
signature log 142
site of action 106
skeletal system 29
small volumes 93
solvents 93
specialized jobs 8
spoilage 128
staff development 149
standards 9
standing order 150
STAT order 150
state regulations 20, 122, 141
stems 166
stock bottles 129
stool softeners 169
storage 129, 141
subcutaneous injections 69
sublingual administration 69
suffix 28
supervision 8
suppository bases 80
surgical anesthesia 166
suspensions 79
synergism 117
synthetic drugs 2
syringes 79, 93
syrup 79

system backup 128
systolic pressure 167
teamwork 9
teratogenicity 117
terminology 9, 28
tertiary literature 122
testosterone 169
therapeutic alternative 108
therapeutic equivalent 108
therapeutic interchange 150
therapeutic window 107
thickening agents 79
third-party programs 134
thrombolytics 168
thrombus 167
TJC 151
total parenteral nutrition solutions 66, 92
transaction windows 141
trituration 79
trustworthiness 8
turnover 128
unit dose 150
unit dose labels 151
unit price 142
United States Pharmacopeia (USP) 78
urinary reabsorption 117
urinary tract 29
URL (uniform resource locator) 123
USAN 166
usual and customary (U&C) 134
vaccine 168
vaginal administration 70
vasodilators 168
vasopressors 167
vial 141
virustatic 167
volumetric glassware 78
water-in-oil (w/o) 80
weighing papers or boats 78
weight 116
wholesalers 128
workers' compensation 135